AN INTRODUCTION TO
CHEMICAL
THERMODYNAMICS

AN INTRODUCTION TO
CHEMICAL
THERMODYNAMICS

BY

E. F. CALDIN

M.A., D.Phil.

SENIOR LECTURER IN CHEMISTRY
UNIVERSITY OF LEEDS

OXFORD
AT THE CLARENDON PRESS
1958

Oxford University Press, Amen House, London E.C.4

GLASGOW NEW YORK TORONTO MELBOURNE WELLINGTON
BOMBAY CALCUTTA MADRAS KARACHI KUALA LUMPUR
CAPE TOWN IBADAN NAIROBI ACCRA

PRINTED IN GREAT BRITAIN

PREFACE

THIS book is intended as a first course in thermodynamics for university students of chemistry. It is based on lectures given in the second year of the chemistry course at the University of Leeds. My aim has been to write a book which a student can work through for himself. Many cross-references have therefore been provided, occasional repetitions have been permitted, and no special knowledge of mathematics has been assumed. Selected references are given to experimental papers, fuller treatments of thermodynamic theory, and reviews of chemical topics to which thermodynamics is relevant. The analytical table of contents may suggest the plan of the book and help to keep it in view.

Anyone who teaches chemical thermodynamics must seek to outline, in due proportion, the fundamental laws and functions, the principles of their applications in chemistry, and the experimental results, with at least a glance at their interpretation in molecular terms. Methods, conclusions, and results must be epitomized, and the way must be pointed forward. Everyone has his own way of mingling these elements; that is the justification of a variety of textbooks. The blend to be found within these covers is that of an experimentalist whose approach to thermodynamics was first influenced by the books of Lewis and Randall and of Butler, and later by those of Guggenheim and of Zemansky. I wish to acknowledge my debt to these authors, whose works between them made almost inevitable the design of an introduction such as this, intended to precede the study of such books as Guggenheim's *Thermodynamics* or Denbigh's *Principles of Chemical Equilibrium*. As regards the scope of the book, it should be said that electrolyte solutions have been treated relatively briefly, in view of the excellent books available on electrochemistry, and that surfaces are barely mentioned. The treatment of gases is largely concerned with the behaviour of the hypothetical perfect gas, since this is a good approximation for real gases; while in the treatment of solutions activities are introduced from the start, since they are necessary in handling all but the simplest problems.

It is a pleasure to thank those who have contributed to this book: my wife, who typed the manuscript and helped me in every way; the officers of the Clarendon Press; those who have allowed me to reproduce figures and tables; and the colleagues and friends who have patiently read and commented on the text, in whole or in part—Messrs. C. R. Allen, R. P. Bell, J. W. Belton, A. S. Carson, E. Collinson, P. Gray, R. M. Noyes, and G. S. Rushbrooke. They have saved me from committing a good many errors, though it would be too much to hope that none remain. I must acknowledge also the help of several generations of undergraduates, whose critical attention has been a constant stimulus.

E. F. C.

June 1957

ACKNOWLEDGEMENTS

GRATEFUL acknowledgements are due to the authors, editors, and publishers concerned for permission to reproduce certain figures and tables. References are given in the text. The figures are those numbered 4 *a*, 4 *b*, 4 *c*, 6 *c*, 15, 16, 17, 19, 20, 21, 24, 38 *a*, 38 *b*, 38 *c*, 40, 41, 44, 45, 52, 53, 54, 61 *a*, 61 *b*, 67, 70, 73, 74 *a*, 74 *b*, 76, 77, 78, 79, and 80. The tables are those numbered 9, 10, 11, 13, 18, 20, 21, 22, 23, 24, 25, 27, 30, 32, 35, 36, 37, 38, 40, 41, 44, 46, 47, and 48.

CONTENTS

TABLE OF SYMBOLS

ENGLISH ALPHABET

A	Helmholtz free energy, usually per mole	a	area
B	second virial coefficient		
B	coefficient for regular solutions		
C_P	heat capacity at constant pressure	c	molar concentration
C_V	heat capacity at constant volume		
C_S, C_L, C_G	heat capacity at constant pressure of solid, liquid, or gas		
C_i	internal heat capacity of gas at constant pressure		
C	capacity factor		
D	dielectric constant	d	differential operator
		$đ$	inexact differential
		∂	partial differential operator
E	internal energy	e	electronic charge; base of Napierian logarithms
$\mathbf{E}$	electromotive force		
F	faraday	f	(solutions): activity coefficient
F	number of degrees of freedom	f	partition function
G	Gibbs free energy, usually per mole		
H	heat content (enthalpy), usually per mole	h	Planck's constant
$H^0_{G(T)}$	(gases): heat content of gas at 1 atm and $T°$ K, usually per mole		
H_1	(mixtures): partial molar heat content of species 1 in mixture		
H^0_1	(mixtures): molar heat content of pure species 1		
$\mathbf{H}$	magnetic field strength		
I	(solutions): ionic strength	i	vapour-pressure constant
I	intensity factor		
$\mathbf{I}$	intensity of magnetization		
J	integration constant for van 't Hoff's isochore		

K	equilibrium constant	k	constant; Boltzmann's constant
K_p	equilibrium constant in terms of pressure		
L	latent heat (general)	l	length
L_e	latent heat of evaporation of liquid		
L_f	latent heat of fusion of solid		
L_s	latent heat of sublimation of solid		
M	molecular weight	m	molality (molal concentration)
N^0	Avogadro's number	n	number of moles
P	pressure	p_i	(gas mixtures): partial pressure of species i
P^e	pressure at equilibrium, e.g. vapour pressure of liquid or solid	p_1, p_2	(solutions): partial vapour pressures of solvent and solute over solution
P^*	fugacity	p_1^0, p_2^0	(solutions): vapour pressures of pure constituents of a solution
P	number of phases		
Q	quantity of electricity	q	heat absorbed by system
R	gas constant		
S	entropy, usually per mole	s	solubility
S^0	(gases): standard entropy (at unit pressure)		
$S^0_{G(T)}$	(gases): standard entropy of gas at 1 atm and T° K, usually per mole		
$S_{S(T)}$	entropy of solid at T° K		
$S_{S(0)}$	entropy of solid at 0° K		
S_1	(mixtures): partial molar entropy of species 1 in mixture		
S_1^0	(mixtures): molar entropy of pure species 1		
T	temperature on thermodynamic scale	t	temperature on an empirical scale; tension in wire or fibre
T_e	temperature of evaporation (boiling-point of liquid)		
T_f	temperature of fusion (melting-point)		
T_s	temperature of sublimation of solid; temperature of saturation of solution		
V	volume	v	velocity
V_i, V_s	(gas): volumes at ice-point and steam-point		

V_i (mixtures): partial molar volume of species i in mixture

V_i^0 (mixtures): molar volume of pure species i

W number of complexions

w work

x_i mole fraction of species i in mixture

GREEK ALPHABET

γ surface tension

ϵ energy of a molecule

η efficiency of heat engine

θ temperature on absolute perfect-gas scale

μ chemical potential

π osmotic pressure

τ tension

ϕ volume fraction

Φ gravitational potential

SUPERSCRIPTS

0: (a) For gases: indicates standard state (unit pressure); e.g. S^0 = entropy at 1 atm. Exceptionally, $(PV)^0$ = value of PV in the limit at low pressure $= RT$.

(b) For solutions: indicates standard state, usually pure liquid in the case of the solvent; e.g. μ_1^0 = chemical potential in the pure liquid; H_1^0 = heat content of pure liquid; p_1^0 = vapour pressure of pure liquid.

e: equilibrium; e.g. P^e = vapour pressure, p_A^e = partial pressure of species A in gas mixture in chemical equilibrium.

E: excess; e.g. ΔH_m^E = excess heat of mixing (of solutions).

id: ideal; e.g. p_1^{id} = vapour pressure of solvent over an ideal solution.

α, β: phases; e.g. S^α = entropy in phase α.

SUBSCRIPTS

i, j, 1, 2, etc. Chemical species; e.g. n_1 = number of moles of species 1; S_i = partial molar entropy of species i. i refers to any one species; j refers to all species except i.

T: temperature on absolute scale; e.g. $S_{G(T)}$ = entropy of gas at temperature T° K.

0: absolute zero of temperature; e.g. $H_{G(0)}$ = heat content of gas at 0° K.

G, L, S: gas, liquid, solid; e.g. $S_{S(T)}$ = entropy of solid at T° K.

m: change of property on mixing; e.g. ΔS_m = entropy increase on mixing.

e, f, s: evaporation, fusion, sublimation; e.g. L_f = heat of fusion, ΔS_e = entropy of evaporation. (ΔH_f, exceptionally, represents heat of formation.)

INTRODUCTION
THE SCOPE OF THERMODYNAMICS

THERMODYNAMICS is a branch of physical science and there-fore deals with matter from the point of view of measurement. In this chapter we shall try to give a preliminary idea of the kinds of measurement that it is concerned with. We shall return to most of the general statements made here, for they will be exemplified in succeeding chapters. Indeed they cannot be properly understood apart from their applications; but it is convenient to group them together at the start.

Thermodynamics is concerned with macroscopic objects, not with individual molecules. Thermodynamics is concerned with matter on the macroscopic scale; that is, with matter in bulk, not with individual atoms or molecules. It starts with measure-ments on objects such as we find in ordinary experimental work—that is to say, measurements of pressure, volume, tem-perature, electromotive force, and so on—and is content with the description of a system in these macroscopic terms. It leaves as a further problem their explanation in terms of atoms and molecules. As far as pure thermodynamics is concerned, it does not matter whether there are atoms and molecules or not, so long as we can measure macroscopic properties.

This, however, is true also for other branches of physical science. Mechanics, for instance, is concerned with properties of macroscopic systems—the positions of a body at various times—and with the laws that relate them. Mechanics differs from thermodynamics in that it deals with those properties that are concerned with the relations of a body to other bodies, whereas thermodynamics is concerned with the internal state of the body. Thermodynamic properties are those macroscopic measurable quantities that have a bearing on the internal state of a system. A 'thermodynamic' system is any macroscopic system regarded from this point of view.

If we are attempting to explain the thermodynamic properties of a system in terms of molecules and their interactions, the

B

system may be described from this different point of view as a 'statistical assembly'. Thermodynamics does not itself deal with molecular interpretations; that is the task of statistical mechanics, which is concerned with averaging, so to say, the behaviour of individual molecules, and deducing the macroscopic behaviour of a system composed of many molecules. Simple kinetic theory provides examples of this procedure. Pressure, for instance, which is a macroscopic and directly measurable quantity, may be interpreted as the average rate of change of momentum due to the impacts of molecules on unit area of wall; and temperature may be correlated with the average kinetic energy of translation of the molecules. In some ways it would obviously be desirable to develop systematically both the thermodynamical descriptions and their statistical interpretations in a single book. However, the starting-point and methods of statistical mechanics are so different from those of thermodynamics that this is hardly practicable. In this book we shall therefore quote, without their full derivation, statistical interpretations of certain thermodynamic conclusions; for their exposition in detail the reader will be referred to the excellent monographs available.†

Macroscopic systems, then, are regarded as made up of molecules, and their properties as depending on averages of molecular properties. This affects the scope of thermodynamics. A system composed of relatively few molecules—a hundred, say—would be expected to show considerable random deviations from those averages; under given conditions it could not be said to have a definite pressure or a definite temperature. But thermodynamics is built upon the possibility of measuring stable and reproducible values of such quantities. Thermodynamics therefore does not concern itself with systems whose mass is comparable with that of a single molecule, but only with systems

† Of these we may mention, as introductory, Rushbrooke, *Introduction to Statistical Mechanics* (Oxford, 1949), Guggenheim, *Boltzmann's Distribution Law* (North Holland Publishing Company, 1955), and Mayer and Mayer, *Statistical Mechanics* (Wiley, 1940); and as advanced works, Tolman, *The Principles of Statistical Mechanics* (Oxford, 1938), and Fowler and Guggenheim, *Statistical Thermodynamics* (Cambridge, 1939).

where the number of molecules is so large that random variations are small enough to be normally undetectable. (Such systems may be very small by experimental standards; a microgram of hydrogen contains more than 10^{17} molecules and is undeniably a thermodynamic system.) For the same reason, thermodynamics ignores those rare phenomena where even large systems exhibit fluctuations. For instance, the turbidity observed in gases near the critical point is believed to be due to local fluctuations of pressure, and so is not suitable for consideration by the methods of thermodynamics.

Thermodynamics, then, is based on the measurement of macroscopic properties. It proceeds on the assumption that such measurements can in principle be made with any desired degree of accuracy. In the mathematical formulation of thermodynamics, this is reflected in the use of infinitesimal quantities. It is assumed that it is meaningful to speak of an infinitesimal change of pressure (dP), of volume (dV), and so on, even though the fluctuations due to molecular motions set a limit to the accuracy with which pressure or volume can be measured, so that the smallest difference of pressure or volume that can be observed is not infinitesimal but finite. It is obviously convenient to suppose that we can consider infinitesimal changes, because then we can use ordinary differential and integral calculus; but since such changes are in principle inaccessible, the procedure stands in need of justification. The solution of the puzzle is that when we speak of an infinitesimal change we refer to an ideal mathematical limit—the limit of small changes —and not to an experimentally realizable situation. This procedure is justified *a posteriori*, in that thermodynamic theory is found in practice to be applicable to experimental facts; the error resulting from fluctuations is too small, compared with the errors of observations, to be noticed.

Thermodynamics is concerned with the states of systems, not with rates of change. The state of a macroscopic system is defined by the values of the pressure, volume, temperature, magnetic susceptibility, electrical capacity, surface area, and so on, that characterize it. It is the *state* that concerns thermodynamics—

not the processes by which the system was brought into that state, nor the rates at which those processes occurred. Chemical kinetics, which studies the rates of chemical changes, contains elements that are not to be found in thermodynamics, though it may also borrow from thermodynamic methods.† Thermodynamics is concerned not with rates, but with states. This is one reason why in thermodynamics we are so much concerned with equilibria. Thermodynamics is also concerned with the results of changes from one state to another, but, as we shall see, it contrives to handle changes by the same methods as it handles equilibria, in virtue of the theoretical device of 'reversible changes'. These are changes in which the situation never differs from the equilibrium condition by more than an infinitesimal amount. Such a process, involving as it does situations which are ideal limits not experimentally realizable, is only conceivable in theory, but may be approached in practice as closely as our experimental arrangements allow.

Thermodynamics is concerned with exchanges of heat, work, and material. Thermodynamics is concerned with equilibria and with changes in which different bodies exchange (i) heat, (ii) work, or (iii) material. Heat is here distinguished from other forms of energy because, as we shall see, it is thermodynamically unique.

Thermodynamic cycles and thermodynamic functions. There are two general methods in thermodynamics. One is the use of cycles, in which the exchanges of heat, mechanical work, electrical work, and so on, are considered directly. We shall consider a few examples of this procedure. But the method is cumbrous, since one has to invent a special cycle for each phenomenon; gaseous equilibria, osmotic pressure, boiling-point, vapour pressure, and so on, must each be treated individually. The second method is the use of thermodynamic functions, such as the internal energy, heat content, entropy, and free energy, which are defined in later sections. This method

† Cf., for example, Hinshelwood, *Kinetics of Chemical Change* (Oxford, 1940); Glasstone, Laidler, and Eyring, *Theory of Rate Processes* (McGraw-Hill, 1941); Fowler and Guggenheim, *Statistical Thermodynamics* (1939), chap. 12.

is a very powerful one, and we shall use it in all the systematic work in this book. The thermodynamic functions are variables defined in such a way that they have a fixed value for a given state of a system, independent of the way in which it came to be in that state. From the values of these thermodynamic functions can be deduced the work and heat changes in a given phenomenon. Heat and work, as it turns out, are not quantities fixed by the initial and final states of the changing system, but depend also on the way in which the change is carried out. For this reason they are not the most prominent quantities in modern thermodynamic theory. The centre of interest has shifted to the more manageable thermodynamic functions—which, however, are ultimately measured in terms of heat and work, the quantities that are directly accessible to measurement.

Of these thermodynamic functions, a preliminary statistical picture or molecular interpretation is easily available for two: the internal energy and the entropy. We can picture changes in the internal energy of a system as due to changes in the sum of the energies of the molecules of the system—their kinetic energy, whether translational, vibrational, or rotational, and their potential energy, whether due to electrical, gravitational, magnetic, or other forces. We can picture the entropy as related to the internal order or disorder of the system—the regularity or randomness of the arrangement of its particles in space and of the distribution of energy among them. If the system is so orderly that it can be put together in only one way, the entropy may be taken as zero. If it is in a state that can be reached in W ways, W being greater the more random the arrangement, then the entropy S is given by statistical theory as $S = k \ln W$, where k is the gas constant R divided by the number N^0 of molecules in a mole.† Thus S increases with the 'degree of randomness' of the system. The other thermodynamic functions are less easy to visualize in molecular terms, but are all related to the internal energy and entropy by definition.

† Cf. section 4.44.

Three kinds of inquiry may be included under the title 'thermodynamics'. (i) The first concerns the fundamentals, which apply to all material systems. It includes the first and second laws of thermodynamics, with the evidence for them, and the general relations based on them, such as the conditions of equilibrium. We shall be concerned with such topics in Chapters II and IV, for example. (ii) The second consists of deductions from these fundamentals, for special kinds of system —gases, for instance, or liquids in equilibrium with their vapours, or galvanic cells. It is a deductive study, based on the first and second laws. It leads to such expressions as that which states the variation of vapour pressure with temperature, in terms of the latent heat of evaporation. We shall be concerned with such matters in most parts of this book. (iii) The third kind of inquiry consists of the application of this scheme to particular substances. This depends upon measurements of their individual properties—for instance one might determine the vapour-pressure curve for water, and use it in calculating the latent heat of evaporation. Often one is interested in special classes of substances—imperfect gases, for example, or crystalline solids, or ideal solutions. We shall be concerned with such applications in most parts of this book, since it is through them that thermodynamics, after its deductive investigations, comes back to experiment again.

I

TEMPERATURE AND HEAT

BECAUSE, as we have mentioned, heat is in some ways a unique form of energy, a special preliminary note on heat and temperature is called for.† Elementary experience with calorimeters and thermometers leads to the distinction between *temperature* and *quantity of heat*. The quantity of heat involved in a given change is proportional, other things being equal, to the mass of material undergoing the change, while the temperature changes are independent of the mass. Temperature is said to be *intensive*, while quantity of heat is *extensive*. Temperature is essentially the variable that determines the direction of flow of heat, in a purely thermal change. If two bodies are capable of exchanging heat—whether by conduction, by radiation, or by some indirect means—heat passes from the body at the higher temperature to that at the lower temperature. Temperature is the intensive variable that determines the direction of flow of heat. Correspondingly, heat may be described as that which is transferred to or from one system in thermal contact with another by virtue of a difference of temperature only.

It should be noted that though we commonly speak in this way of a 'flow of heat', this is really a phrase left over from an earlier phase of science. What we actually observe experimentally are changes—such as fusion, evaporation, or chemical reaction—resulting from thermal contact between systems at different temperatures. These changes are conventionally said to be due to the transfer of something. In the late eighteenth century this was thought to be some kind of fluid, called 'caloric'. Further experiments showed that mass was not transferred, and the fluid theory was abandoned; but the conventional metaphor that something is transferred has remained, and sometimes proves helpful to the investigator.

† Cf. Zemansky, *Heat and Thermodynamics* (McGraw-Hill, 1943), chap. 4.

The conceptions of temperature and heat presuppose, in a sense, the conceptions of thermal contact and thermal insulation. A solid body, for instance, has a steady temperature if it is thermally insulated, by an asbestos jacket, a Dewar vessel, or the like. It can exchange heat with other bodies only if it is in thermal contact with them through a conducting or 'diathermic' wall—for instance a thin metallic plate. We can only measure temperatures and exchanges of heat because we can experimentally realize good approximations to perfect thermal contact and thermal insulation.

Instead of bringing two bodies into direct thermal contact in order to compare their temperatures, it is obviously convenient to use a thermoscope, which will indicate qualitatively which of the bodies is at the higher temperature. (We have not yet introduced the notion of a scale of temperature, and therefore speak of thermoscopes rather than of thermometers.) Experience shows that if two bodies have equal temperatures when compared with a third body acting as a thermoscope, they have equal temperatures when compared directly with each other. This is the justification for using thermoscopes (or in practice thermometers); temperatures could not be compared by means of thermoscopes if this principle could not be relied upon. It is not self-evident, but a conclusion from experience, that self-consistent temperature observations can be made in this way. The principle concerned has come to be regarded by recent authors as of such fundamental importance that it is now known as the *zeroth law of thermodynamics*. It may be formally stated as: 'Two systems, each in thermal equilibrium with a third, will be found to be in thermal equilibrium with each other.'

To indicate equality or inequality of temperature, various systems are satisfactory—for instance, mercury-in-glass thermometers, gas thermometers, platinum resistance thermometers, and thermocouples. Difficulties begin to arise when we seek to use these not as thermoscopes but as thermometers; that is, when we try to define a *temperature scale*. We do not find perfect agreement between scales defined in different ways. For

instance, the temperature change might be defined as proportional to the change in the volume of a mass of mercury, to the
change in the pressure of a mass of hydrogen kept at constant
volume, to the change in the resistance of a platinum wire, or
to the change in the e.m.f. of a thermocouple with one junction
kept in ice. If these scales were made to agree at the melting-
point of ice (defined as 0°) and the boiling-point of water (defined as 100°), then the various scales would differ at intermediate temperatures by several tenths of a degree, that is by
several hundred times the experimental errors. Empirical scales
of temperature thus depend on the particular properties of
the system used as thermometer. However, the discrepancies
are very much less if we confine our attention to gas thermometers; for instance, the constant-volume hydrogen thermometer and the constant-volume air thermometer agree to
within about a hundredth of a degree over the above range.
Gas thermometers are therefore chosen as experimental thermometric standards. We shall consider them further below (section
3.32).

Quantities of heat can be compared, and can therefore be
measured in terms of a standard, by several methods. Without
a thermometer, they can in principle be compared in terms of
the amounts of ice (for example) that they will melt. With any
thermometer, they can be compared in terms of the different
amounts of some given material that they will raise through a
given temperature interval. The '15° calorie' was formerly used;
this is defined as the amount of heat that will raise 1 g of water
through the temperature-interval designated as $14 \cdot 5°$ to $15 \cdot 5°$ C,
so that if a given quantity of heat will raise the temperature
of x g of water from $14 \cdot 5°$ to $15 \cdot 5°$ C, it is equal to x '15° calories'.
With a good empirical temperature scale such as the hydrogen
scale, amounts of heat can also be compared in terms of temperature changes.

These descriptions of heat and temperature will be adequate
to start with. Later (section 2.23) we shall show that heat can
be defined in terms of mechanical quantities alone and that
the empirical temperature scales are superseded by a 'thermo-

dynamic' scale independent of the special properties of any particular system (section 4.43). At present it is enough to note that heat changes can be measured in various empirical ways, which do not necessarily require a temperature scale; and that temperature is the intensive variable that determines the direction of flow of heat in purely thermal changes.

It will be convenient to define here the terms *adiabatic* and *isothermal*. A change in a system is said to be adiabatic, or to be carried out adiabatically, if the system is thermally insulated, so that no heat passes to or from the surroundings; the temperature may alter. An isothermal change is one in which the temperature of the system remains constant throughout; this may require heat to be supplied by the surroundings, as for instance in the melting of ice, or absorbed by them, as when an exothermic reaction is carried out in a thermostat. That changes can be carried out in these two ways is in accord with the distinction of temperature and heat.

ENERGY, THE FIRST LAW OF THERMO-DYNAMICS, AND THE THERMODYNAMIC FUNCTIONS ASSOCIATED WITH IT

THE definition of energy depends upon the experimental facts about the interconvertibility of heat, mechanical work, electrical work, and other kinds of work. When one of these disappears, another takes its place; for instance, when mechanical work is applied to a dynamo, electrical work can be obtained, and this in turn can be made to produce heat in a resistance. The experimental evidence shows that when such interconversions occur there are *fixed ratios* of heat to mechanical work, heat to electrical work, and so on, which are independent of the particular arrangement used to effect the conversion. Further, these ratios are self-consistent, in the sense that if we start, for example, with mechanical work and convert it all into heat, we get the same amount of heat whether we convert it directly as in Joule's classic experiments, or convert it first into electrical energy which is then used to heat a wire. This implies that, by a suitable choice of units, heat and the various kinds of work can all be regarded as equivalent, and we can combine them into a single function, called the *energy*. This is the general conception of energy. The evidence for it is partly direct, from experiments such as those of Joule, and partly indirect in that no contradiction has ever arisen in the course of the manifold applications of the energy function to practical problems.

In thermodynamics we are usually interested in the internal state of a system, disregarding any motion it may possess as a whole. It will therefore be of great importance if we can define for any thermodynamic system an *internal energy function* that will summarize the effects of heat, work, and composition changes in which the system is concerned. The First Law of thermodynamics leads, as we shall see, to the definition of such a function. But we must first outline the experimental evidence.

2.1 The evidence on which the First Law is based

The *direct* evidence on which the First Law is based consists of experiments in which mechanical work is converted by various methods as completely as possible into heat, or electrical work into heat, or electrical work into mechanical work, and the ratio between the two quantities determined. Each of these ratios is found to be constant, and the several ratios bear a special relation to one another. Accurate work has been done on the three ratios mentioned.

The ratio of mechanical work to heat. The early work on this ratio was done by Joule in the years 1840–78, and was historically one of the main sources of the concept of energy, which was expressed clearly by Helmholtz in 1848. Joule used a number of methods of converting work to heat—churning water with paddles, forcing water through capillaries, compressing air, and working a dynamo connected to a resistance—and the results all agreed within about 1 per cent. Among later and more precise measurements, two are noteworthy. Rowlands (1879) used Joule's method of converting mechanical work to heat by churning water; a large calorimeter containing water was suspended by a wire, and the water in it was agitated by perforated paddle-wheels turned by a steam-engine. The rate of supply of work was measured by the torque; the rate of production of heat was given by the rate of temperature rise. Laby and Hercus (1927)† used a continuous-flow method, adapting the principle of the electromagnetic brake. The calorimeter was stationary and consisted of copper tubes through which a uniform flow of water was maintained. It was set between the poles of an electromagnet which was mounted on bearings and could be rotated round the calorimeter. Eddy currents were thus induced in the copper, and ultimately dissipated with evolution of heat. The rate of production of heat was deter-

---

† Laby and Hercus, *Phil. Trans. Roy. Soc.* A, 1927, **227**, 63; *Proc. Phys. Soc.*, 1935, **47**, 1003.

mined by measuring the temperatures of the ingoing and out-
flowing water; the mechanical power supplied was determined
by measuring the torque and the angular velocity, with a correction for friction in the bearings. Heat loss from the copper
tubes was minimized by surrounding them with a vacuum
jacket. In these experiments the unit of heat employed was the
empirically defined '15° calorie' (now superseded, p. 15), the
amount of heat which will raise the temperature of one gramme
of water from 14·5° to 15·5° C; and the unit of work was the
joule, 10^7 ergs, defined in terms of the standard metre, gramme,
and second. In each of these two precise investigations the
ratio of work to heat was constant within narrow limits, and
the final results for the ratio were respectively 4·188±0·008 and
4·1853±0·0008 joule/calorie. It is evident from these figures
that within the limits of experimental error the ratio is constant
and independent of the experimental arrangement used for
converting the work into heat.

The ratio of mechanical work to electrical work. The constancy
of the ratio of mechanical to electrical work is assumed in the
definition of the electrical potential difference between two
points as the work done in transferring unit charge from one
point to the other, and is indirectly verified by the self-con-
sistency of electrical measurements based on this definition.
It is also verified directly in work on the absolute determination
of potential differences with the aid of a sensitive current
balance; here electrical quantities are directly compared with
mechanical ones.†

The ratio of electrical work to heat. Of the many determinations that have been made, the following may be mentioned.
Callender and Barnes (1899) used a continuous-flow method;
a uniform stream of water was passed through a tube, insulated

† The ratio of mechanical to electrical work is measured by determining
resistances and currents in terms of mechanical units. Thus absolute resistances and currents in terms of mechanical units. Thus absolute resistances were measured with an uncertainty of 2 in 10^5 by Curtis, Curtis,
and Critchfield, *Bur. Stand. J. Res.*, 1939, **22**, 485, and by Vigoureux, *Coll.
Res. Nat. Phys. Lab.*, 1938, **24**, 173; and absolute currents with about the same
accuracy by Curtis, Moon, and Sparks, *Bur. Stand. J. Res.*, 1938, **21**, 375, by
Hartshorn and Astbury, *Phil. Trans. Roy. Soc.* A, 1937, **236**, 423, and by
Vigoureux, *Coll. Res. Nat. Phys. Lab.*, 1938, **24**, 277.

by a vacuum jacket, over a resistance wire carrying a constant current. The initial and final temperatures of the water were measured with platinum resistance thermometers. A steady rise of temperature was reached. This, with the rate of flow, gave the rate of heat evolution, which was compared with the electrical power consumed, calculated from the observed current and potential difference. An advantage of this constant-flow method is that, since a steady state is reached, there are no corrections for the heat used in warming up the apparatus. Heat losses can be dealt with by carrying out two runs in which the currents differ and the rates of flow are adjusted to give the same temperature rise; the rates of heat loss are then the same in each run and can be eliminated from the equations.

Heat losses can, however, be estimated with some accuracy if the system is not more than a few degrees hotter than its surroundings, and an alternative method has therefore been preferred by later workers. Jaeger and Steinwehr (1921) used the simple procedure of passing an electric current through a coil surrounded by thoroughly stirred water, and observing the rise in temperature. The same method was chosen for the very accurate measurements of Osborne, Stimson, and Ginnings (1939),† which were made because new determinations of electrical standards had been completed,‡ and because the platinum thermometers used as thermometric standards could be more accurately calibrated than in earlier work. What these workers actually determined was the heat capacity of water, in electrical units, at various temperatures; the value at 15° gave the ratio of the unit of electrical work to the 15° calorie. To compute the ratio of mechanical work to heat from this, they used the ratio of electrical to mechanical work, whose determination has already been noted.‡ The result was $4 \cdot 1858 \pm 0 \cdot 0004$ joule/calorie.

The relation between the several ratios. The figure just given is seen to agree with the value determined directly, within the

† Osborne, Stimson, and Ginnings, *Bur. Stand. J. Res.*, 1939, **23**, 197.

‡ See note † on p. 13.

estimated experimental errors.† The significance of this is that the several ratios which we are considering are not only constant from one experiment to another, and independent of the experimental arrangement, but are self-consistent in the sense that (mechanical work)/(heat) is equal to (electrical work)/(heat) multiplied by (mechanical work)/(electrical work). All three characteristics are essential for the concept of energy towards which we are working. It would not be enough to show that the separate changes take place at constant ratios, if the ratios could not be combined self-consistently. At one time, for instance, Callender and Barnes, taking an inaccurate value for the 'absolute' potential difference of the Weston cell which they used as standard, obtained a value for the ratio of mechanical work to heat that differed significantly from the directly determined value; if the discrepancy had not been cleared up by the redetermination of the potential difference, the conception of energy could not have been exact.

Units. Since electrical work is now more accurately measurable than either heat or mechanical work, it is convenient to define the units of mechanical work and of heat in terms of it, so that all three can be expressed in absolute joules (based on the standard metre, kilogram, and second). This convention was recommended in 1948 by the International Union of Physics. The calorie, however, remains a popular unit. Evidently its value is a matter of definition, and when it is used in the most accurate work the factor adopted when converting from joules to calories should be stated. The value 1 calorie ≡ 4·1840 absolute joules ≡ 4·18331 international joules‡ is adopted as the 'thermochemical calorie' in the standard tables of *Selected values of chemical thermodynamic properties.*§ The heat capacity of

† For a review of the accurate determinations, see Birge, 'The General Physical Constants', in *Reports on the Progress of Physics*, 1941, **8**, 112.

‡ The international joule differs slightly from the absolute joule because it was defined in 1908 on the basis of values for reproducible standards of potential difference and resistance—the e.m.f. of a Weston cell and the resistance of a column of mercury—that have since been found to be slightly in error.

§ Rossini *et al.* (ed.), *Selected Values of Chemical Thermodynamic Properties* (Circular of the National Bureau of Standards, Washington, No. 500, 1952). For a summary of the fundamental constants, see Rossini *et al.*, *J. Amer. Chem. Soc.*, 1952, **74**, 2699.

water in calories per degree is evidently a derived quantity, when the above definitions are adopted; it is nearly 1 calorie per degree at 15° C.

The *indirect evidence* about the ratios between heat and the various kinds of work is that in thermodynamics it is a fundamental assumption that the ratios are constant, independent of the method of conversion, and self-consistent, and that thermodynamics is applicable in practice without anomalous results. As far as the various forms of work are concerned, there is a special piece of indirect evidence in that a perpetual motion of the first kind has never been realized; that is, it has never been found possible to produce an unending supply of work by a method that leaves no change in any system. This implies that the rates of exchange are constant and independent of the method of interconversion. For, suppose for instance that the ratio of mechanical to electrical work depends on the method of interconversion; let one unit of mechanical work give a units of electrical work when converted by process A, and b units when converted by process B. If we transform one unit of mechanical work into electrical by process A, and back again into mechanical by reversing process B, we shall obtain a/b units of mechanical work, so that if $a > b$ we shall on balance have gained work. No such process has ever been discovered.

In a complete account of this subject we should consider also the *interconversion of mass and energy*, which is manifested in nuclear reactions. But this phenomenon has only a limited importance in chemical thermodynamics at present and a bare mention of it must suffice.

The uniqueness of heat. Experiments on the interconversion of heat, mechanical work, and so on, yield one other very important result that may be mentioned here in passing. In these exchanges heat is found to be thermodynamically unique, in that whereas mechanical and other forms of work can all be converted entirely into heat, the converse is not possible—heat cannot be converted completely into work. The best that can be done is to use a *heat-engine*. In a heat-engine, a fixed amount of some substance undergoes a cycle of changes in which heat

is supplied to it, some of the heat is converted into work, and
the rest of the heat is rejected, at a lower temperature than
that at which it was supplied. A typical heat-engine cycle,
approximating to the cycle used in a turbine or Diesel engine,
is represented in fig. 1.

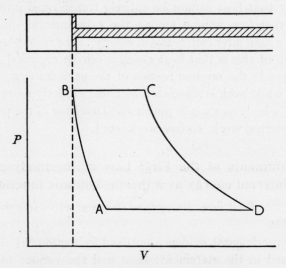

Fig. 1. Constant-pressure heat-engine cycle.

A definite amount of air (the 'working substance') may be
supposed to be contained in a cylinder in which its volume and
pressure can be altered, and heat supplied or withdrawn by
contact with suitable heat reservoirs. The changes of pressure
(P) and volume (V) are shown on the P–V diagram. The air,
whose initial pressure and volume are represented by the point
A, is compressed adiabatically (AB). Heat is added, while the
gas is expanded so as to keep the pressure constant (BC). The
gas is then expanded adiabatically until its pressure has fallen
to the initial value (CD). To bring the gas back to its initial
condition, heat is withdrawn, while the pressure is kept constant
by decreasing the volume. At the stage represented by D, the
gas is still hot, but no more useful work can be extracted from
it, if the lowest available temperature is that represented by A;
to complete the cycle, and bring the gas to this lowest tempera-

ture, heat must be withdrawn by cooling, not by turning into work. We shall later work out the ratio of heat supplied to work generated in such an engine (section 3.54, p. 114); this ratio is found to depend on the temperature-range in which it works. At present the important point is that we find experimentally that heat cannot be entirely transformed into work, and is therefore unique among the experimental quantities which we shall later call 'forms of energy'. The molecular interpretation of this is that heat changes can be regarded as due to changes in the random motion of the particles composing a system, while work is associated with more orderly movements, either of a body as a whole (mechanical work) or of the particles in it (electrical work, surface work, etc.).

2.2. Statements of the First Law of thermodynamics. The internal energy as a thermodynamic function

2.21. *The First Law: Energy and its conservation in an isolated system*

The experimental evidence outlined in section 2.1 may be generalized in the statement: Heat and the various forms of work are mutually interconvertible, at constant and self-consistent ratios, which are independent of the details of the process employed for the conversion.

The various statements usually given for the First Law can all be deduced from this. For instance, one direct statement, which differs from the foregoing only in taking for granted the truth of the statement as regards the interconversion of the various forms of work, is† 'When equal quantities of work are produced by any means from purely thermal sources, or spent in purely thermal effects, equal quantities of heat are put out of existence, or are generated'. Most authors, however, have expressed the law in the form of a statement about 'energy' and its conservation. Because of the quantitative equivalence of heat and the forms of work, these quantities have been regarded as 'forms of energy', and the First Law then becomes

† J. R. Partington, *Textbook of Thermodynamics* (Constable, 1913), p. 31.

a statement of the *conservation of energy in an isolated system*, such as 'When a quantity of energy in one form disappears, an equivalent amount of energy in another makes its appearance'; or 'The algebraic sum of the changes in energy (all measured in the same units) is zero in any isolated system'. These are legitimate reformulations of the generalization derived from the experimental evidence, requiring in addition only that we agree on the verbal definition of the phrase 'change in energy', using it to mean the sum of any changes in heat and work in a given isolated system.

2.22. *The internal energy E as a thermodynamic function, for a closed system*

The energy, so defined, of an isolated system is thus constant. The really important conclusion that we can reach, however, is concerned with systems that are *not* isolated. Suppose we have a given thermodynamic system, which does not exchange material with its surroundings (a 'closed system'), but which can absorb heat from its immediate surroundings, and on which work can be done by agencies forming part of its immediate surroundings. As an example we can think of a gas in a metal cylinder closed by a piston, or a galvanic cell or accumulator, or a calorimeter in which ice is melted or a reaction made to occur. The system is thus not isolated as regards heat and work exchanges, though we are keeping it isolated as regards material, by preventing exchange of material with the surroundings. Suppose the system is initially in some state A, characterized by a certain mass, volume, pressure, temperature, surface, electrical condition, magnetic condition, gravitational situation, and so on; and that it passes to a state B in which some or all of these variables have different values. This change will in general have been accompanied by an exchange of heat with the surroundings, and by the performance of work on or by the surroundings, whether mechanical work (against the atmosphere, for instance) or electrical work or some other kind of work. Each of these heat and work quantities will be related to the two states A and B and, in addition, to the details of the processes employed in bringing the system from state A to state B. For instance, referring to fig. 1, if we take the gaseous system there represented from state A to state B by the adiabatic process represented by AB, there is no heat change; but if we use the three processes represented by the path ADCB, there is a heat change, given by the difference of the heats absorbed in process AD and rejected in process CB. Another

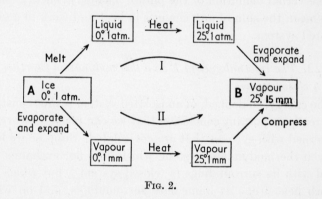

FIG. 2.

example of alternative paths, for which the heats and works differ, between two states of a system is illustrated in fig. 2, which shows two possible paths for converting ice at 0° C and 1 atmosphere pressure to water vapour at 25° C and 15 mm of mercury.

Consider now the *difference* between the heat q absorbed by the system (negative if it loses heat) and the work w done by the system (negative if work is done *on* the system). This quantity $(q-w)$ is an energy quantity, on the definition just given (p. 19) of the word 'energy'; it is the quantity of energy that has been gained by the system. Let us call this the gain of internal energy—the increase in the amount of energy associated with the internal state of the system, whether due to thermal motion of molecules, mechanical potential energy, electrical or any other form of energy. (A corresponding quantity must, by the First Law, have been lost by the immediate surroundings of the system.) Representing the internal energy by E, we may write for the increase in internal energy:

$$\Delta E = q - w. \tag{1}$$

We shall now show, using the First Law, that this quantity ΔE is characteristic of the initial and final states of the system, A and B, and does not depend on the path taken between A and B, that is, on the intermediate states through which the system passed in changing its state from A to B, nor on the time that it took to do so.

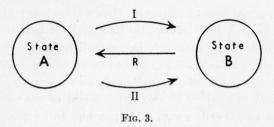

FIG. 3.

First let us consider the energy change when the cycle is completed by the system passing from state A to state B and then back again to A. Over the whole cycle, the sum of the quantities of heat absorbed by the system must be equal to the sum of the works done by it: $\sum q = \sum w$. Otherwise it would be possible, by carrying out the cycle repeatedly, to produce or destroy unlimited amounts of heat without destroying or producing any work, and vice versa; this would be contrary to the principle of the equivalence of heat and work, stated above as part of the First Law. Thus for the completed cycle, we can deduce from the First Law that $\sum q - \sum w = 0$, so that (using equation 1) the internal energy change is zero.

Now let us return to the energy change of the system when it passes from state A to state B, and the question whether ΔE depends on the path or not. Suppose that there are at least two possible paths, I and II; and also that (as is generally true) the reverse change from B to A can be effected by some path R (this might, but need not, be the reverse of I or II). This is represented in fig. 3. Suppose now that we take the system twice through the cycle A–B–A, using the different paths I and

II from A to B but returning each time by the same path R
from B to A:

$$(1) \quad A \xrightarrow{\text{I}} B \xrightarrow{\text{R}} A,$$

$$(2) \quad A \xrightarrow{\text{II}} B \xrightarrow{\text{R}} A.$$

As we have just shown, the internal energy change in the
system at the end of each cycle will, by the First Law, be zero.
But the processes by which the system is taken by path R from
B to A can be made identical for the two cycles, and must then
result in equal energy changes. Hence the energy changes in
passing from A to B must also be equal for paths I and II.
This deduction can evidently be generalized, and we reach the
conclusion: *The internal energy change of a system in passing
from one state to another depends only on the two states and not
on the path*. Clearly it is also independent of the rates of the
processes concerned, which have not had to be considered in
the above derivation.

We can therefore advance from the conception of an energy
change, as a quantity associated with *processes*, to a conception
of energy as a *property characteristic of the state of a system*.
The difference of the heat absorbed and the work done by the
system in a given change is characteristic not of the processes
by which the change was effected, but of the initial and final
states. We can therefore write:

$$\Delta E_{A \to B} \quad = \quad E_B \quad - \quad E_A$$

| (Increase in energy of system after passing from state A to state B) | (Energy of system in state B) | (Energy of system in state A) |

And we can attribute to each state of a thermodynamic system
a characteristic value of a function E, called the *internal energy*,
which is independent of the way in which the system was
brought into that state. In the equation above, E_A and E_B are
the internal energies of the system in the two states, each
characteristic of the state of the system alone and not of its
history, just as ΔE is a quantity dependent on the two states
alone and not on the path between them. Incidentally it is

evident from the definition that we can only measure ΔE, which is equal to $q-w$ (cf. equation 1); we cannot measure the individual values E_A and E_B. It is often convenient in thermodynamic algebra to use E and not ΔE, but the value of E must always be regarded as relative to the value in some standard state—for instance, the energy of a chemical compound may be expressed relative to that of the elements at 25° C.

We have reached, then, a preliminary definition of the internal energy function E; it is defined, for changes in a system that can exchange heat and work, but not material, with its surroundings, by the equations:

$$E_B - E_A = \Delta E_{A \to B} = q - w. \tag{2 a}$$

For an infinitesimal change, we write similarly:

$$dE = đq - đw, \tag{2 b}$$

where the symbol $đ$ represents an 'inexact differential', and is used because heat and work, unlike ΔE, are not independent of the path (cf. below, section 2.4, p. 32).

If we write equation 2 a in the form

$$\Delta E - q + w = 0 \tag{2 c}$$

we see that the internal energy has been so defined that the sum of the three energy terms is constant. Thus by the definition of E the equation expressing the principle of conservation of energy (section 2.21) has been *extended to systems that are not isolated*.

These equations (2 a, 2 b, and 2 c) may be regarded as the mathematical equivalent of the First Law; they rest on the experimental basis outlined in section 2.1, plus the definition of internal energy. More important, they express the consequence of the First Law that is relevant to thermodynamics—the dependence of the internal energy function of a system on the state of the system alone.

Since the quantities q and w for a given change are both found experimentally to be proportional (other things being equal) to the amount of matter that undergoes the change, the function E is also proportional to the mass of the system; E

is thus an *extensive* function. The direct experimental evidence for this is that the heat changes used in determining E (sections 2.63, 2.72) are always proportional to the mass of material; the internal energy change per unit mass is constant within experimental error. The indirect evidence comes from the success of thermodynamics, which assumes that E varies directly with the mass of a given system, in interpreting experimental data.

The internal energy is the first of the functions that we shall call *thermodynamic functions*. Much of the work of fundamental thermodynamics consists in defining thermodynamic functions. These are extensive quantities, dependent solely on the state of the system; they permit us to express the heat and work in a given change. Some other variables such as the pressure, temperature, and volume resemble thermodynamic functions in being characteristic of the state of the system and not of its history; but if the system undergoes a change we cannot calculate the corresponding heat and work solely from the values of such variables in the initial and final states. The heat and work themselves differ from thermodynamic functions in that they are not characteristic solely of the initial and final states of the system, but of the path as well. We have already seen that this is true of heat (p. 20); it is easy to show that it is true also of work. For instance, the mechanical work done against the external pressure in any change, such as the expansion of a gas, is $\int P \, dV$, which evidently depends on the way in which P varies with V during the change, since it is given by the area under the curve of P against V. The *difference* of the heat and work $(q-w)$ is, however, characteristic only of the two states, if there is no transfer of material; it can be used as a thermodynamic function, changes of which can be related once for all to changes in the state of the system with temperature, pressure, electric field, and any other relevant variables.

A simple statistical interpretation can be given of the fact that ΔE is characteristic of the initial and final states of a system and not of the path between. ΔE may be regarded as the sum of changes in the energies associated with the translation, vibration, and rotation of individual particles, and with their interactions. These are all fixed by the state of the system, whatever its history. Hence the sum of their changes, ΔE, is dependent only on the states of the system and not on its particular history. We can also see in molecular terms why ΔE is an extensive quantity, because the sum of the individual energies in an assembly will be proportional to the number of particles and so to the mass of the system.

2.23. *Alternative approach to the internal energy function for a closed system; mechanical definition of quantity of heat*

The formulation given in section 2.21 of the First Law and in section 2.22 of the derivation from it of the internal energy function follows more or less the order of the historical development of theory, based on the empirical facts about heat and work. It may, however, be criticized on the ground that it uses a concept of heat which, although experimentally satisfactory in the sense that experimentalists know how to use it and obtain self-consistent results, is not rigorously defined in terms of mechanical quantities. This criticism is overcome in a formulation due to Born, of which the following is a sketch which the interested reader may follow up.†

The approach is quite different from the foregoing in that it begins with postulates and makes contact with experiment only at a relatively late stage. First we define the term thermal insulation. Since we are seeking a definition of heat we must not beg the question by presupposing that we already have one at this stage. A thermally-insulated system, or one surrounded by an insulating wall, is therefore defined as one whose equilibrium is not disturbed by any external process so long as no part of the wall is moved and so long as no long-range forces (such as magnetic or electric forces) are involved. This definition implies that a thermally-insulated system is unaffected by any changes except work done on it, and so agrees with the

† M. Born, *Natural Philosophy of Cause and Chance* (Oxford, 1949), chap. 5; *Phys. Z.*, 1921, **22**, 218. A full and clear account of the whole approach is given by Zemansky, *Heat and Thermodynamics* (McGraw-Hill, 1943), chaps. 1–5; it is also used by Guggenheim, *Thermodynamics* (1957), chap. 1.

notion we have used hitherto; from the present point of view its advantage is that it is a definition in mechanical terms alone. We next state the first principle of thermodynamics in the form: *If a thermally-insulated system is brought from one state to another by applying external work, the amount of this work is always the same, independent of the type of work and of the path of the system from the initial to the final state.* It follows at once that for adiabatic changes from state A to state B, if $-w$ is the work done on the system (we use the minus sign because we are reckoning work done *by* the system as positive):

$$-w = E_B - E_A,$$

where E_A and E_B depend only on the states A and B and not on the path between them. Thus we have reached a definition of an internal energy function that holds so long as all changes in the system are carried out adiabatically. For these changes, $\Delta E + w = 0$. In a process which is not adiabatic, $\Delta E + w$ is not zero; it is called the *heat absorbed* by the system. We may formulate a *thermodynamic definition of the quantity of heat absorbed* for a given change of a closed system; it is the energy transferred by means other than sources of work, equal to the difference between the internal energy change and the work done on the system. This could be determined if this work were measured and if ΔE were also found by measuring the work in experiments in which the same changes were effected adiabatically. By definition, then,

$$\Delta E = q - w.$$

We have thus reached the same equation as that obtained in section 2.22 from the First Law. We have, however, introduced a purely mechanical definition of heat, and in this respect the derivation is perhaps more satisfactory.

We have not, however, as yet given any experimental basis for it. The treatment so far depends on a principle concerning adiabatic changes and a definition of heat. The principle that in an adiabatic change the work required depends only on the initial and final states is not a generalization from experimental results, for accurate measurements of adiabatic work along different paths between the same states have never been made. It is a theoretical postulate, which must be supported experimentally by the agreement of its consequences with experiment. As we shall see, deductions from the conclusions that $\Delta E = q - w$ in general and $\Delta E = -w$ for adiabatic changes in particular are found to agree with experiment, and the postulate is as well supported by experiment as any in physical science.

It is probably largely a matter of taste whether one adopts the treatment outlined in this section, using postulates and appealing to the agreement of their consequences with experiment at a much later stage, or that of sections 2.21 and 2.22, which keeps as close as possible to experiment so that the evidence for every step can be cited. The former approach appeals more to mathematical physicists, the latter to experimental chemists. Both have their virtues, and both depend for experimental support on the facts mentioned in section 2.1.

2.24. *Direct determination of ΔE by heat changes when no work is done*

The magnitude of ΔE can be directly determined for certain changes in a closed system, because it may be shown to be equal to the heat absorbed by such a system in a change carried out in such a way that no work is done.

The general equation for the effect on the internal energy of some change in a closed system is (sections 2.22, 2.23):

$$\Delta E = q - w.$$

If no work is done by the system on its surroundings, or vice versa—that is, if there is no volume change leading to the performance of work against the atmosphere, no change of surface area leading to work against surface tension, no transfer of electric charge leading to electrical work, no magnetization or demagnetization, and so on—then $w = 0$, and

$$\Delta E = q.$$

To show that this equation is a special case corresponding to zero work, and therefore to constant volume (V), area (a), electric charge, and so on, we may write it in the alternative form

$$\Delta E = (q)_{w=0} = (q)_{V,a,\ldots}.$$

In chemical thermodynamics we are often concerned with closed systems that can perform work only against the atmosphere—chemical reactions, for example, other than those taking place in galvanic cells—and for these the internal energy change when $w = 0$ may be written as

$$\Delta E = (q)_V.$$

That is, the change in internal energy can be measured as the heat absorbed when such a system undergoes its change at constant volume, when no work is done. In particular, the value of ΔE for a chemical reaction can be determined by measuring the *heat of reaction at constant volume*; this can be done for reactions involving gases, for instance, by conducting the reaction in a bomb-calorimeter (p. 42). By convention, this heat of reaction is defined as the heat *evolved* in reaction, and is therefore equal to $-\Delta E$; this difference of sign must be borne in mind in thermochemical calculations.

2.25. *The internal energy for an open system*

Our definition of the internal energy for a closed system (one which does not exchange material with its surroundings) gives (equation 2 b, p. 23):

$$dE = dq - dw.$$

We now wish to extend this to cover open systems, those that do exchange material with their surroundings—for instance a pure liquid boiling and losing material to the vapour phase, or a solution being diluted with solvent, or a chemical reactant to which another is being added. Suppose a system consisting of a single pure substance undergoes an infinitesimal change in which it not only absorbs heat dq and does work dw on its surroundings, but acquires an increment of the same substance. Let this increment be dn_1, measured in some convenient unit, usually the gram-molecular weight or mole, corresponding to the accepted chemical formula. We have mentioned that for closed systems E is proportional to the mass of the system, other things being equal, and the simplest way of extending equation 2 b to open systems is to define the change of internal energy for the above change as

$$dE = dq - dw + \mu_1 dn_1, \tag{3}$$

where μ_1 is some proportionality constant.

This is in accord with experimental fact, for so long as we are simply adding increments of some pure substance (water, for instance) to a large mass of the same substance, we can arrange for the heat change to be zero (by making the temperatures equal) and for the work to be zero (by performing the operation *in vacuo* to eliminate work against atmospheric pressure), and in that case equation 3 reduces to $dE = \mu_1 dn$, which expresses the direct proportionality of E to the mass of the system when there are no changes in other factors affecting E.

Suppose now, however, that the system acquires an increment of some different substance; then in general there will be a heat change, as for instance when sulphuric acid is added to water, and the change in E cannot be represented as due solely to changes in the amount n_2 of the second substance. In this general case, to cover changes in E due to all possible changes of composition, we write:

$$dE = dq - dw + \mu_1 dn_1 + \mu_2 dn_2 + \mu_3 dn_3 ...,$$

or

$$\boxed{dE = dq - dw + \sum \mu \, dn}, \tag{4}$$

where dn_1, dn_2, dn_3,... represent increments of various chemical species, and the μ's are corresponding proportionality constants (which of course remain to be determined empirically, and may vary with the n's). It is hardly possible to give a direct experimental justification of the assumption that lies behind this definition, namely that E as so defined is a thermodynamic function, determined by the state of the system. The justification is to be found in the agreement of its consequences with experiment, to be shown in succeeding sections.

Equation 4 is of fundamental importance in the thermodynamics of open systems. The equation is the mathematical formulation of the fact that such a system can change its energy for three reasons:

(i) *Gain or loss of heat* by exchange with its surroundings. If no work is done ($đw = 0$) and if the system is closed ($dn = 0$), equation 4 gives $dE = đq$, so that for a finite change of this kind $\Delta E = q$.

(ii) *Performance of work* of some kind, on or by the surroundings. If there is no heat change ($đq = 0$) and if the system is closed ($dn = 0$), equation 4 gives $dE = -đw$, so that for a finite change $\Delta E = -w$.

(iii) *Gain or loss of material* by exchange with the surroundings. If $đq = đw = 0$, equation 4 gives $dE = \sum \mu \, dn$.

To avoid confusion over the different signs in the equation $dE = đq - đw + \sum \mu \, dn$, it may be noted that they all assume an 'acquisitive' sign convention. Heat *gained* and material *gained* are reckoned as positive contributions, while work *done* by the system is reckoned as negative.

Fundamental thermodynamics is largely concerned with relating such changes of heat and work in various circumstances to thermodynamic functions. The applications of thermodynamic functions consist largely in relating such changes to variables such as pressure, temperature, electrical potential, and the other quantities that define the state of a thermodynamic system.

2.3. Intensity and capacity factors in energy terms

The fields of application of thermodynamics. It is an important fact that the change of energy due to each of the terms on the right of equation 4 (p. 29) can be expressed as the product of a *capacity factor*, which is an extensive variable, proportional to the mass of the system, and a *potential* or *intensity factor*, which is independent of the mass. For instance, if a specimen of gas occupies a volume V of gas at pressure P, and increases in volume by an infinitesimal amount dV (by pushing out a piston for example), the work done by the gas on its surroundings is $P \, dV$. In this product, P is an intensity factor, independent of the quantity of gas and unaltered if we subdivide the gas; while V is a capacity factor, being extensive, proportional (other things being equal) to the mass of gas. The table below shows how the other possible terms in the energy-function can similarly be analysed into intensity and capacity factors.

TABLE 1

Intensity and capacity factors and applications of thermodynamics

Internal energy term		Intensity factor	Capacity factor	Relevant to
Heat change, dq	$T\,dS$	Temperature	Entropy	All changes except adiabatic changes
Transfer of material	$\mu\,dn$	Chemical potential	Number of moles	Chemical thermodynamics
Work dw { Mechanical— pressure	$P\,dV$	Pressure	Volume	All changes where work is done against pressure, e.g. that of the atmosphere
Mechanical— surface tension	$\gamma\,da$	Surface tension	Area	Surface phenomena, adsorption, etc.†
Mechanical— tension in fibre	$\tau\,dl$	Tension	Length	Elastic phenomena‡
Electrical	$\mathbf{E}\,d\mathbf{Q}$	Potential difference	Quantity of electricity	Condensers, dielectrics§
Magnetic	$\mathbf{H}\,d\mathbf{I}$	Field strength	Intensity of magnetization	Magnetic phenomena‖
Gravitational	$\Phi\,dm$	Gravitational potential	Mass	Centrifugal and gravitational effects††

† On the thermodynamics of surface phenomena, cf., for example, Adam, *The physics and chemistry of surfaces* (3rd edn., Oxford, 1941).

‡ On the thermodynamics of elastic phenomena, cf. section 5.16.

§ On the thermodynamics of charging of condensers, and dielectrics, cf., for example, Guggenheim, *Thermodynamics* (North Holland Publishing Co., 1957), chap. 11.

‖ On the thermodynamics of magnetization, etc., cf. Guggenheim, *Thermodynamics* (1957), chap. 12; Stoner, *Phil. Mag.*, 1935, **19**, 565.

†† On the thermodynamics of gravitational fields, cf. Guggenheim, *Thermodynamics* (1957), chap. 10; and for experimental applications to galvanic cells, cf. McInnes, *Principles of Electrochemistry* (Reinhold, 1939), chap. 9.

The representation of a heat change as the product of a temperature and entropy change, $T\,dS$, will be explained later (section 4.44, p. 140), as will the term 'chemical potential' used to denote μ (section 2.71, p. 51). Various kinds of work are set out separately, since each of them gives rise to a special branch of thermodynamics. This book is mainly concerned with the branch in which the only work that need be considered is that done mechanically against an external pressure, and given by $\int P\,dV$; but we shall indicate in the appropriate places how modifications can be made in the theory of surface phenomena, elasticity, and other thermodynamic fields.

The intensity factors determine the direction of spontaneous change (section 4.1); thus temperature differences determine the direction of spontaneous flow of heat, electrical potential differences determine the direction of spontaneous flow of electricity, and so on.

The capacity factors are proportional to the mass of the system undergoing the change; hence values for the heat content change ΔH, the internal energy change ΔE, and so on, must refer to a definite amount of a system. The values normally given refer to a change involving one mole, such as the vaporization of one mole of liquid, or the formation of one mole of a compound. This usage is so general that in future we shall take ΔH, ΔE, etc., to refer to one mole, except where the context makes it obvious that the amount is unspecified.

2.4. Mathematical representation of thermodynamic changes

The deductive part of thermodynamics necessarily makes much use of algebraic representations of thermodynamic functions and their changes. The essentials may be shortly stated.†

If we are considering the variations of any thermodynamic function, denoted by X, due to changes in one variable, such as pressure, we express the dependence of X on P by a partial differential coefficient, writing subscripts to show what quanti-

† For fuller treatment see, for example, Margenau and Murphy, *The Mathematics of Physics and Chemistry* (van Nostrand, 1947), chap. 1.

ties are being held constant. Thus if the temperature and volume are kept constant, we express the change of X due to a change of P by the equation $dX = (\partial X/\partial P)_{T,V}\, dP$ for an infinitesimal change, and by $\Delta X = \int (\partial X/\partial P)_{T,V}\, dP$ for a finite change.

If we have to consider changes in X due to simultaneous changes in two variables—say pressure and temperature—which together fix the state of the system, so that X is a single-valued function of them, we use a general theorem which is proved in the Appendix (p. 407), and write for the change in X due to simultaneous variation of P and T:

$$dX = \left(\frac{\partial X}{\partial P}\right)_T dP + \left(\frac{\partial X}{\partial T}\right)_P dT.$$

Thus dX depends on the separate terms $(\partial X/\partial P)_T$ and $(\partial X/\partial T)_P$, in each of which one of the independent variables is kept constant while the other varies. Similar equations would express the dependence of X on three or more quantities varying simultaneously. This is called 'differentiating generally' with respect to the relevant variables.

The quantity dX in the above expression is called the *complete differential* of X (or the exact, perfect, or total differential). A complete differential is one obtained by differentiating a function generally with respect to all the independent variables upon which the function depends. It has the property that its definite integral has a unique value. Thus the expression $dX = (2xy^5\, dx + 5x^2y^4\, dy)$ is a complete or exact differential, because it can be integrated at once to

$$X_2 - X_1 = \left[x^2 y^5\right]_{x_1, y_1}^{x_2, y_2} = (x_2^2\, y_2^5 - x_1^2\, y_1^5),$$

an expression which is unique and depends only on the initial and final values of x and y. Thus if dX is an exact differential, the function X has a property corresponding to the important property of a thermodynamic function, that its changes depend only on the initial and final states of a system, and not on the process or path by which it was reached. Similarly the integral of dX about a closed path is zero, just as the sum of the changes in a thermodynamic function in a completed cycle is zero. We can thus express the essential properties of the thermodynamic functions, such as E and H, by saying that dE is, unlike dq or dw, an exact differential.

Another general result needed in using partial differentials is that if a thermodynamic function varies simultaneously with two variables (such as pressure and temperature) which together determine its value, the order of differentiation does not matter. For if X is any continuous single-valued function of x and y,

$$\frac{d}{dy}\left(\frac{\partial X}{\partial x}\right)_y = \frac{\partial^2 X}{\partial y \partial x} = \frac{\partial^2 X}{\partial x \partial y} = \frac{d}{dx}\left(\frac{\partial X}{\partial y}\right)_x.$$

If the variable x itself depends on another, z, the rule for changing the variable is

$$\left(\frac{\partial X}{\partial x}\right)_y = \left(\frac{\partial X}{\partial z}\right)_y \left(\frac{\partial z}{\partial x}\right)_y.$$

2.5. A second thermodynamic function based on the First Law: the heat content

The First Law permits us to use, besides the internal energy E, which is especially useful in dealing with changes at constant volume (section 2.24), another thermodynamic function which is especially useful in dealing with changes at constant pressure.

As in the preceding section, we consider any change in a closed thermodynamic system that can exchange heat with its surroundings and can do work on them of one kind only, namely work due to change of volume against a constant external pressure such as that of the atmosphere. This is a situation that is very common in practice, because it is much more convenient to work at constant pressure than at constant volume, especially when dealing with solids and liquids, which would need enormous pressures to keep their volumes constant during a temperature rise of say 10 deg. Examples of closed systems undergoing such changes are liquids freezing under their own vapour pressure, galvanic cells working at atmospheric pressure, and reactions proceeding at atmospheric pressure.

We now consider the heat absorbed in such a change in a

closed system at constant pressure. If the initial volume of the system in state A is V_A and the final volume in state B is V_B, the work done by the system on the surrounding atmosphere is

$$w = P(V_B - V_A). \tag{1}$$

Our general expression for the change of internal energy during a change in a closed system (section 2.22) gives

$$E_B - E_A = q - w. \tag{2}$$

Substituting for w from equation 1, and writing q as $(q)_P$ to show that it is the work absorbed in exchange at constant pressure, we obtain on rearranging:

$$(q)_P = (E_B + PV_B) - (E_A + PV_A). \tag{3}$$

The heat change at constant pressure, $(q)_P$, therefore measures directly the change in the quantity $(E + PV)$ on passing from state A to state B. Since $(q)_P$ can be measured for many interesting changes, it will evidently be convenient to define a function

$$H \equiv E + PV \tag{4}$$

so that for all changes that occur at constant pressure, the change in H is given by

$$H_B - H_A = (E_B - E_A) + P(V_B - V_A), \tag{5}$$

or $$\Delta H = \Delta E + P \Delta V. \tag{6}$$

Comparing equations 5 and 3, we find

$$H_B - H_A = \Delta H = (q)_P. \tag{7}$$

Thus the change in H due to any change at constant pressure in such a system is directly measurable, being equal to the heat absorbed by the system. The function H is, moreover, a true thermodynamic function. It is extensive; it is determined only by the state of the system, since E, P, and V are all characteristic of that state and not of the way in which it was reached; and it is related to heat and work changes. It therefore fulfils all the conditions for a thermodynamic function. It is known as the *heat content*, or sometimes the *heat function*,[†] or the *enthalpy*. ΔH has of course a definite value for any change,

† Cf. Guggenheim, *Thermodynamics* (1957), p. 26.

since H is a thermodynamic function; but it is only for changes at constant pressure that $\Delta H = q$.

For a change at constant pressure, $\Delta H = \Delta E + P \Delta V$, and we can think of ΔH as the result of modifying ΔE by a correction for work done on the surrounding atmosphere. For reactions involving only solids and liquids, the difference is negligible. When gases or vapours are concerned, the term $P \Delta V$ may be an appreciable fraction of ΔH. For instance, if in such a change a system produces one mole of gas at $0°$ C and one atmosphere pressure (defined as 1013250 dyne cm^{-2}), then $P \Delta V = 22 \cdot 4$ litre-atmospheres, or about $22 \cdot 6 \times 10^9$ ergs, or 500 calories. If the change in question is a chemical reaction, such as the decomposition of calcium carbonate by heat, this value of $P \Delta V$ may amount only to a few per cent. of ΔH; but if the change is the evaporation of a liquid, it may be an appreciable fraction of the latent heat.

The general relation between changes in H and changes in heat, work, and composition in an open system is evidently given by

$$dH = d(E + PV)$$
$$= dE + P\,dV + V\,dP.$$

Using equation 4 of section 2.25 (p. 29), which expresses dE generally in terms of heat, work, and composition, this becomes

$$dH = đq - đw + P\,dV + V\,dP + \sum \mu\,dn.$$

When the only work done is work against the atmosphere, $đw = P\,dV$, and so the equation simplifies to

$$dH = đq + V\,dP + \sum \mu\,dn.$$

For a closed system, where the n's are constant,

$$dH = đq + V\,dP.$$

And for a closed system at constant pressure ($dP = 0$), $dH = đq$, and $\Delta H = q$, as we have already seen.

2.6. Some properties of E and H in closed systems

2.61. *Additivity of heats of reaction*

Heats of reaction are commonly measured at constant pressure, and then give values of $-\Delta H$. (The difference of sign

arises because the heat of reaction is defined as heat *evolved*.)
A special consequence of the properties of ΔH as a thermodynamic function is that such heats of reaction are additive.
Since ΔH is independent of the path taken between two states,
the sum of the separate ΔH's for a reaction carried out in
stages must be equal to ΔH for the complete reaction. For
instance, for the following scheme of reactions,

$$A+B \xrightarrow{\Delta H} X+Y,$$

$$A+B \xrightarrow{\Delta H_1} C+D \xrightarrow{\Delta H_2} E+F \xrightarrow{\Delta H_3} X+Y,$$

we conclude that $\Delta H = \Delta H_1 + \Delta H_2 + \Delta H_3$. This deduction may
be experimentally verified. An instance where accurate data
are available is provided by the reactions

$$C_2H_4 + H_2 \rightarrow C_2H_6;$$
$$C_2H_6 + 3\tfrac{1}{2}O_2 \rightarrow 2CO_2 + 3H_2O;$$
$$C_2H_4 + 3O_2 \rightarrow 2CO_2 + 2H_2O;$$
$$H_2 + \tfrac{1}{2}O_2 \rightarrow H_2O.$$

The directly determined heat of hydrogenation of ethylene (cf.
section 2.63, p. 44) gives the value $32 \cdot 6 \pm 0 \cdot 1$ kcal/mole for
$-\Delta H$ at $25°$ C and one atmosphere. The difference of the
heats of combustion of C_2H_6 and of $C_2H_4 + H_2$ at the same
temperature is $32 \cdot 78 \pm 0 \cdot 13$ kcal/mole, which agrees within
experimental error.† Such results may be taken as confirma-
tion of the First Law, on which the definition of ΔH as a thermodynamic function depends.‡

By using the result that heats of reaction are additive, it is
often possible to determine indirectly heats of reaction that
would be inconvenient or impossible to determine directly.
Reactions between organic compounds, for instance, are often
slow, and commonly lead to by-products as well as the main
products. Combustion, however, is a rapid and complete reac-

† Rossini, *Bur. Stand. J. Res.*, 1936, **17**, 629.

‡ The result that heats of reaction are additive is often called 'Hess's law
of constant heat summation'; it was enunciated by Hess in 1840, before the
recognition of the general principle of conservation of energy, of which it is
a special case.

tion; thus for many organic reactions ΔH is best determined indirectly, by measuring the heats of combustion of reactants and products, and taking the difference. For instance, the heats of formation of a compound such as methane from the elements cannot be determined by calorimetric observations on the direct synthesis from carbon and hydrogen; but if we write the stoichiometric equations for combustion of the reactants and products, we can obtain from them by suitable addition and subtraction the equation for the synthesis of methane, and combining their measured heats of reaction in the same way gives us the unknown heat of reaction ΔH_f for the synthesis:

$$(1) \qquad C + 2H_2 \rightarrow CH_4: \qquad \Delta H_f \text{ (unknown)},$$

$$(2) \qquad C + O_2 \rightarrow CO_2: \qquad \Delta H_1 \text{ (measured)},$$

$$(3) \qquad H_2 + \tfrac{1}{2}O_2 \rightarrow H_2O: \qquad \Delta H_2 \text{ (measured)},$$

$$(4) \quad CH_4 + 2O_2 \rightarrow CO_2 + 2H_2O: \quad \Delta H_3 \text{ (measured)}.$$

Combining the stoichiometric equations,

$$(1) = (2) + 2 \times (3) - (4);$$

so that $\Delta H_f = \Delta H_1 + 2\Delta H_2 - \Delta H_3$, and ΔH_f is then known in terms of the experimentally accessible quantities. We shall return to the experimental determination of heats of reaction in section 2.63 (p. 40).

To specify completely the change to which a measured ΔH refers, we should give the stoichiometric equation, the state of each reactant and product, and also the temperature, thus:

$$C(\text{diamond}) + O_2(\text{gas}) \rightarrow CO_2(\text{gas});$$

$$\Delta H_{298°K} = -94·45 \pm 0·1 \text{ kcal/mole}.$$

The temperature given is of course the initial and final temperature. The temperature reached during the combustion is irrelevant to ΔH, which depends only on the initial and final states.

The same results apply, *mutatis mutandis*, to ΔE, which is likewise additive for a series of reactions; this is relevant to determinations of heats of reaction at constant volume (p. 42).

The quantities that can be measured experimentally are ΔH and ΔE, not H and E. It is often convenient in algebraic manipulation to use H rather than ΔH, and E rather than ΔE, but any equation that can be compared directly with experiment will be found to contain ΔH or ΔE, not H or E. It is sometimes convenient to define H or E as zero for some particular state of a system, by convention; for instance the heat contents of the elements at $25°$ C are taken as zero when citing values for the heat content of compounds formed from the elements. This is legitimate; the fact that we can only measure ΔH or ΔE implies that H or E can be put equal to zero in some particular state by an arbitrary convention. It does not imply any particular molecular interpretation.

2.62. *Summary of the equations relating E and H to heat, work, and changes in composition*

In the following tables are summarized the various relations between the thermodynamic functions E and H and the corresponding heat, work, and composition changes when a given change occurs in a system. As an example of a closed system we can think of a galvanic cell, such as a Daniell cell or an accumulator, which can exchange heat with its surroundings and also do work on them (both by supplying electric power, and by the small change in volume due to the chemical change occurring); or we can think of a chemical reaction occurring after the reactants have been brought together. As an example of an open system we can think of a solution to which solvent can be added; or of the vapour above a solution which can be boiled to increase the amount of vapour; or of the separate reactants in a chemical reaction, which when brought together will produce heat and work.

Changes in E: $dE = đq - đw + \sum \mu \, dn$

For a closed system, dn's $= 0$, hence

$$dE = đq - đw, \quad \text{and} \quad \Delta E = q - w.$$

For adiabatic change in a closed system, $đq = 0$, hence

$$dE = -đw \quad \text{and} \quad \Delta E = -w.$$

For adiabatic change where work $dw = P\,dV$ (e.g. compression of a gas), $dE = -P\,dV$ and $\Delta E = -\int P\,dV$; for constant P, $\Delta E = -P\,\Delta V$.

For change in closed system where no work is done on surroundings (e.g. reaction in a closed bomb), $dw = 0$, hence $dE = dq$, and $\Delta E = q$.

For adiabatic change where no work is done (e.g. free expansion of a gas into vacuum), $dw = dq = 0$, hence $dE = 0$.

For any complete cycle of changes in a closed system, $dE = 0$, hence $dq = dw$ and $q = w$.

Changes in H: $\quad dH = dq - dw + P\,dV + V\,dP + \sum \mu\,dn$

For a closed system, $dH = dq - dw + P\,dV + V\,dP$.

For any change in a closed system where $dw = P\,dV$,

$$dH = dq + V\,dP.$$

For such changes at constant pressure,

$$dH = dq \quad \text{and} \quad \Delta H = q.$$

For such changes carried out adiabatically, $dq = 0$, hence $dH = V\,dP$. If the pressure is constant, $dH = 0$.

For any complete cycle of changes in a closed system,

$$dq + V\,dP = 0.$$

2.63. *The measurement of changes in E and H in reactions, and some chemical applications*

The magnitude of the changes in E and H in reactions and in phase changes are of interest for a variety of important problems. Heats of reaction may be used in calculating free energies of reaction, which determine equilibrium constants, so that predictions may be made of the conditions under which a given reaction might be made to proceed (section 5.42); such data are of great importance in chemical engineering. Latent heats of fusion and evaporation are constantly needed in chemical calculations. Heats of reaction and evaporation are used in calculating quantities of great theoretical interest, such as bond energies. We have seen that heats of formation can be found from heats of reaction (p. 38). Now if, for example, to the heat of formation $(-\Delta H_f)$ of CH_4 from its elements in their standard states (solid carbon and diatomic hydrogen gas) we add the heat of sublimation of carbon (L_s) and the heat of atomization of hydrogen (D), we shall obtain the heat of formation of CH_4 from the elements in the state of gaseous atoms.† For methane at 25° C this heat of formation is

$$-\Delta H_f + L_s + 2D = -\Delta H_a$$
$$= -17 \cdot 89 + 171 \cdot 70 + 2 \times 104 \cdot 18 = 362 \cdot 17 \text{ kcal/mole.}‡$$

(At the absolute zero of temperature the value would be $-15 \cdot 98 + 170 \cdot 39 + 2 \times 103 \cdot 24 = 360 \cdot 89$ kcal/mole.) The heats of formation of a series of paraffin hydrocarbons, determined in this way, are found to agree with the supposition that the contributions from the several C–C and C–H bonds concerned are constant for each type of bond, and additive. This rule is also found to be a good approximation in inorganic chemistry. Tables of *bond energy terms* can therefore be constructed,§ as was done by Pauling.‖ Deviations from the rule of constant and additive contributions from the bonds in a molecule led Pauling to the formulation of a quantitative 'electronegativity scale' for the elements. Among organic compounds, such deviations occur when more than one valence-bond structure can be written for the molecule, and have been interpreted both by the resonance and the molecular-orbital

† In such calculations care must be taken with the signs. It is best to apply the principle that for a complete cycle $\sum \Delta E = 0$, and insert the various ΔE's, remembering that latent heats of evaporation, for example, are defined as heats *absorbed* and so have the same sign as the corresponding ΔE, while heats of reaction are given as heats *evolved* and are of opposite sign to the corresponding ΔE.

‡ There has been much controversy over the value of L_s, which is still not settled.

§ To eliminate the effects of thermal motion, such bond energy terms should in theory be computed from energy changes corrected to absolute zero (cf. p. 59); but this has not always been done, because a correction of the order of 1 kcal/mole is only a few per cent. of the whole. Sometimes, again, values of ΔH have been used instead of ΔE, the term $P \Delta V$ being neglected where an error of the order of 0·5 kcal is not important.

‖ The original tables were those of Pauling; cf. *Nature of the Chemical Bond* (Cornell, 2nd edn. 1941). For recent tables and discussion, see Cottrell, *The Strengths of Chemical Bonds* (Butterworth, 1954), pp. 272 seq.

theories of valence.† These are instances of the applicability of thermodynamics to important problems in general chemistry. Methods for determining ΔE and ΔH have accordingly been considerably developed. The following brief account is intended to suggest the principles of the methods used and to indicate where details and reviews can be found.

Determination of ΔE and ΔH for chemical reactions

Both ΔE and ΔH for a chemical reaction can in principle be determined by calorimetric measurements, since $\Delta E = (q)_V$ the heat absorbed when the reaction is conducted at constant volume (p. 28), and $\Delta H = (q)_P$ the heat absorbed when the reaction is conducted at constant pressure (p. 35). Calorimetric methods have been brought to high precision. Methods of the highest accuracy were first developed for combustion, on account of the wide application of this type of reaction.‡

For combustion of solids and liquids in oxygen, ΔE can be measured directly as q_V by using a bomb calorimeter (fig. 4a). The reactants are enclosed in a steel bomb which is filled with oxygen at about 30 atm pressure; a little water is present to collect soluble products. The bomb is immersed in water in a calorimeter surrounded with a suitable jacket. The reaction is initiated electrically and the rise in temperature of the water observed. The heat capacity of the whole system is determined electrically or by burning a standard substance such as benzoic acid. The experimental uncertainty in the most accurate work approaches ± 0.01 per cent., but in general is in the region of ± 0.1 per cent., rather greater than would be expected from the accuracy with which quantities of heat can be measured. The reason is that any by-products of the reaction have to be

---

† Cf., for example, Coulson, *Valence* (Oxford, 1952).

‡ For a review of calorimetric methods, see Sturtevant, in *Physical Methods of Organic Chemistry*, ed. Weissberger (New York, Interscience Pub., 2nd edn. 1949), vol. i, chap. 14; and for notes on later developments, see *Trans. Faraday Soc.*, 1956, **52**, 1152–5. For a collection of results see *Selected Values of Chemical Thermodynamic Properties*, ed. Rossini *et al.* (Circular of the U.S. National Bureau of Standards, No. 500, 1952). Other useful collections of thermochemical data are those of Quill (ed.), *The Chemistry and Metallurgy of Miscellaneous Materials: Thermodynamics* (McGraw-Hill, 1950), and Kelley, *Bull. U.S. Bur. Min.*, 476, 1949.

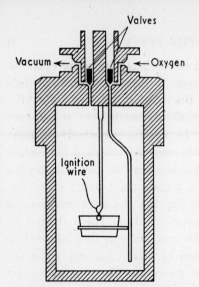

Fig. 4 (a). Bomb calorimeter of Prosen
and Rossini† (diagrammatic).

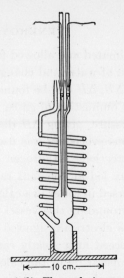

Fig. 4 (b). Flow calorimeter for
combustion of gases (Rossini).

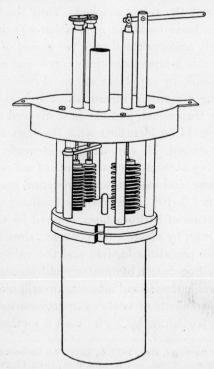

Fig. 4 (c). Vacuum calorimeter of Carson, Hartley, and Skinner for
reactions of organic compounds.

† Prosen and Rossini, *Bur. Stand. J. Res.*, 1941, **27**, 289.

estimated and allowed for, and corrections applied for evaporation of water and change of oxygen pressure. From the values of ΔE, ΔH can be found from the relation $\Delta H = \Delta E + P \Delta V$.

Combustion of gases is conveniently carried out at constant pressure, giving ΔH directly. In Rossini's method[†] an ingenious procedure was used which removed the need for cooling corrections. Hydrogen (or other combustible gas) and oxygen were led at constant rates into a glass combustion vessel immersed in water in a calorimeter (fig. 4 b), and out through a coil surrounding this vessel to absorption tubes. The hydrogen jet was electrically ignited and the reaction was then allowed to proceed at a steady rate for ten or fifteen minutes while the temperature of the calorimeter water was observed at regular intervals, using a platinum resistance thermometer accurate to $0 \cdot 00002°$ C. After an accurately measured time the reaction was stopped and the tubes weighed. Thus the temperature-time plot for a known amount of reaction was determined; it showed a nearly uniform rise during the period of reaction. In a second run this temperature-time curve was reproduced as exactly as possible by supplying electrical energy, the current and time being accurately measured. The heat-losses in the two runs were then equal, and the heat evolved chemically in the first run could be identified with the heat supplied electrically in the second. By eliminating systematic errors in this way, and making accurate measurements of temperature, time, electrical current, and mass, the experimental uncertainty was reduced to 1 or 2 in 10^4. However, the resulting values for the heats of formation of hydrocarbons, derived by the additivity rule, are uncertain by about $\pm 0 \cdot 5$ per cent., since in computing them the errors are also additive; and the values derived for the heats of hydrogenation of unsaturated hydrocarbons, which are of considerable theoretical interest, are still more uncertain.

Direct measurements of heats of hydrogenation were therefore made by Kistiakowsky,[‡] who used a method that some-

[†] Rossini, *Bur. Stand. J. Res.*, 1931, **6**, 1, 37. An improved reaction vessel is described by Prosen, Maron, and Rossini, ibid., 1949, **42**, 269.

[‡] Kistiakowsky, *J. Amer. Chem. Soc.*, 1935, **57**, 65.

what resembled Rossini's in principle but eliminated heat-losses
by carrying out the reaction adiabatically. The reaction vessel
containing the hydrogenation catalyst was surrounded by a
bath whose temperature was automatically kept nearly equal
to that of the reaction vessel. This was necessary because the
time of reaction was considerable and the thermal exchange
was slow, since the catalyst was necessarily porous and a poor
conductor. The reactants were passed over the catalyst at a
constant rate, and a steady rate of rise of temperature was
reached. This was measured, and the products estimated over
a known time; the same rate of temperature rise was then
reproduced electrically. The estimated uncertainty in the results was about 0·1 per cent. The principle of adiabatic calorimetry has been used in the more recent measurements of heats
of reaction in connexion with the determination of bond energies
(fig. 4 c).†

A classic thermodynamic method which has been widely
applied in the determination of ΔH for balanced chemical reactions, for which direct calorimetry is obviously difficult, is to
measure the *equilibrium constant* at a series of temperatures and
apply the relation (which we shall derive later in section 5.46,
p. 241): $d \ln K/d(1/T) = -\Delta H/R$. On plotting $\log K$ against
$1/T$, a nearly linear graph is obtained, whose slope gives ΔH.
This has been applied to determine, for example, the dissociation energies of the halogens,‡ and the heats of dissociation of
the double molecules of carboxylic acids formed by hydrogen
bonding.§ The variation with temperature of the *electromotive
force* of a galvanic cell can be used in a similar way to find ΔH
for the cell reaction (section 6.22, p. 258); this has led, for
instance, to the most accurate values of the heats of dissociation of weak acids in water.‖

Problems in chemical kinetics and also in valency calculations

---

† See, for example, Carson, Hartley, and Skinner, *Proc. Roy. Soc.* A, 1949,
195, 500.

‡ The most accurate work has been done on iodine, by Perlmann and
Rollefson, *J. Chem. Phys.*, 1941, **9**, 362; cf. p. 46.

§ Cf. Allen and Caldin, *Quart. Rev. Chem. Soc.*, 1953, **7**, 255.

‖ Everett and Wynne-Jones, *Trans. Faraday Soc.*, 1939, **35**, 1380.

sometimes require values not of the bond energy terms but of the energy required to break a particular bond in the molecule; this is called the *bond dissociation energy*. For a diatomic molecule, such as Cl_2 dissociating to two Cl atoms, this is evidently equal to the bond energy term; but it is different for a polyatomic molecule, even when all the bonds are alike, because the radicals formed will undergo electronic rearrangements leading to an appreciable change of energy. Thus for methane, ΔE for the reaction $CH_4 \rightarrow CH_3 + H$ is found by the methods described below to be 102 ± 1 kcal per mole, while one-quarter of the energy of formation of a mole of methane from atoms (p. 41) is $362 \cdot 17/4$ or about 90 kcal. (The sum of the energy changes for the successive removal of all four H atoms must of course be $362 \cdot 17$ kcal.) For the determination of bond dissociation energies, several non-thermodynamic methods have been used,† and may be briefly mentioned.

Spectroscopy gives values for simple diatomic molecules. Accurate values can be obtained for a few molecules (hydrogen, oxygen, halogens) from the convergence limit of the absorption spectrum, at which the bands due to quantized vibrations give place to a continuum. The limit corresponds to the energy at which the amplitude of the vibration becomes so great that the atoms separate. The products are usually one normal and one excited atom; but the energy of excitation can be allowed for, and the energy of formation of the two normal atoms obtained. This energy, multiplied by the Avogadro number, gives ΔE for the dissociation. Strictly, it gives the value of ΔE at absolute zero, because the observations give information about the molecule in its lowest energy state; corrections must therefore be applied (using the relations given below in section 2.72) before the values are comparable with those obtained by thermodynamic methods at ordinary temperatures. When this is done, good agreement is obtained; thus for iodine the spectroscopic and thermodynamic values are $35,547 \pm 20$ and $35,514 \pm 50$

† For reviews of these methods and of recent work on bond energies, see Cottrell, *The Strength of Chemical Bonds* (Butterworth, 1954), and Gaydon, *Dissociation Energies and the Spectra of Diatomic Molecules* (Chapman & Hall, 1949).

cal mole^{-1} respectively, at $0°$ K (p. 240). For many molecules, the absorption bands cannot be observed, or show no convergence; a value for the dissociation energy can still be obtained by extrapolation from the bands of the observed emission spectrum, but the result depends somewhat on the method of extrapolation, and on the number of bands that can be observed, so that the uncertainties in the result are much greater.† The *electron-impact method*‡ consists in bombarding the vapour with electrons accelerated by a measured potential, which is increased until the ions corresponding to the dissociation products appear in a mass-spectrograph; the experimental uncertainty is of the order of ± 1 kcal per mole. The study of *reaction kinetics* sometimes provides data of comparable accuracy. For a reversible reaction, the difference between the activation energies of the forward and back reactions is equal to the difference in heat content between products and reactants. A value has been obtained in this way for ΔH for the reaction $CH_4 \rightarrow CH_3 + H$, from the kinetics of the photochemical bromination of methane. This was found to be a chain reaction, in which successive steps could be identified as $CH_4 \rightarrow CH_3 + H$ and $CH_3 + H \rightarrow CH_4$, and the corresponding energies of activation determined.§ When the products are free radicals, the activation energy of recombination is generally small, and that of the forward unimolecular dissociation has often been taken as a measure of the bond dissociation energy concerned.‡ ||

Values of ΔE and ΔH for other types of change—changes of state, of concentration, adsorption, and so on—are continually used in chemical calculations.†† Direct calorimetric methods have been used for the measurement of *latent heats* of fusion and evaporation, and sensitive methods have been devised for *heats of dilution*, *heats of mixing*, and *heats of adsorption*. The ice-calorimeter, which is sensitive and has the advantage

† Cf. Herzberg, *Molecular Spectra and Molecular Structure: Diatomic Molecules* (Prentice Hall, 2nd edn. 1952), pp. 99 seq., 438 seq.

‡ See note † on p. 46.

§ Kistiakowsky and van Artsdalen, *J. Chem. Phys.*, 1944, **12**, 469.

|| Szwarc, *Quart. Rev. Chem. Soc.*, 1951, **5**, 22.

†† Experimental methods are reviewed by Sturtevant in *Physical Methods of Organic Chemistry*, ed. Weissberger (1949), vol. i, chap. 14.

of being isothermal, has been used to determine the heat of transition of monoclinic to rhombic sulphur, which is less than 100 calories per mole,[†] and to determine heats of adsorption, where the amounts adsorbed are minute;[‡] naphthalene (m.p. 80°) or diphenyl ether (m.p. 27°) may be used instead of ice.[§] Latent heats of evaporation can be determined also from the temperature-coefficient of vapour pressure (p. 273). Heats of dilution have been obtained from the e.m.f.s of concentration cells.[||] Some representative values of heat content changes and derived quantities are given in Tables 2, 3, and 4.

TABLE 2

Some representative values of ΔH observed for various changes

	Temp. °C	ΔH kcal/mole
Reactions (see also Table 3)		
$H_2 + \frac{1}{2}O_2 \rightarrow H_2O(g)$	25	$-57 \cdot 80$
$CH_4 + 2O_2 \rightarrow CO_2 + 2H_2O$	25	$-212 \cdot 8$
$C_{11}H_{24} + 17O_2 \rightarrow 11CO_2 + 12H_2O$	25	$-1784 \cdot 4$
$(HCO_2H)_2 \rightarrow 2HCO_2H$	100	14
$Cl_2 \rightarrow 2Cl$	25	$57 \cdot 9$
$H_2 \rightarrow 2H$	25	$104 \cdot 2$
Polymorphic change		
$S_\alpha \rightarrow S_\beta$	0	$0 \cdot 08$
Phase change		
Ice $\rightarrow$ water	0	$1 \cdot 43$
Benzene, solid $\rightarrow$ liquid	5	$2 \cdot 35$
Carbon dioxide, solid $\rightarrow$ vapour	$-78 \cdot 5$	$6 \cdot 03$
Water $\rightarrow$ steam	100	$9 \cdot 717$
Benzene, liquid $\rightarrow$ vapour	78	$7 \cdot 35$
n-Hexane, liquid $\rightarrow$ vapour	25	$7 \cdot 54$
Adsorption		
Ammonia on charcoal	25	-8
Oxygen on copper, initial amounts	0	-92
Dissolution		
Barium chloride in water	25	$2 \cdot 1$
Potassium hydroxide in water	25	$-13 \cdot 3$
Anthracene in m-xylene	25	$5 \cdot 6$

† Brønsted, *Z. phys. Chem.*, 1905, **55**, 371.
‡ Russell and Ghering, *J. Amer. Chem. Soc.*, 1935, **57**, 2544.
§ Coffin *et al.*, *Canad. J. Res.* B, 1950, **28**, 579; Giguère, ibid., 1955, **33**, 657.
|| Glasstone, *Ann. Rep. Chem. Soc.*, 1937, **34**, 92.

TABLE 3†

Bond dissociation energies: ΔE at $0°$ K

Reaction	D kcal/mole	Reaction	D kcal/mole
$H_2 \rightarrow 2H$	103·24	$Br_2 \rightarrow 2Br$	45·46
$HF \rightarrow H+F$	134	$I_2 \rightarrow 2I$	35·55
$HCl \rightarrow H+Cl$	102·2	$CO \rightarrow C+O$	224
$HBr \rightarrow H+Br$	86·5	$CO_2 \rightarrow CO+O$	127
$HI \rightarrow H+I$	70·5	$O_2 \rightarrow 2O$	117·2
$HO \rightarrow H+O$	103	$S_2 \rightarrow 2S$	102
$H_2O \rightarrow H+OH$	116	$N_2 \rightarrow 2N$	170·2
$H_2O_2 \rightarrow 2OH$	48	$NO_2 \rightarrow NO+O$	72
$CH_4 \rightarrow CH_3+H$	101	$NH_3 \rightarrow NH_2+H$	102
$C_6H_6 \rightarrow C_6H_5+H$	102	$KCl \rightarrow K+Cl$	101
$C_6H_5CH_3 \rightarrow C_6H_5CH_2+H$	89	$KBr \rightarrow K+Br$	91
$F_2 \rightarrow 2F$	36	$KI \rightarrow K+I$	77
$Cl_2 \rightarrow 2Cl$	57·07		

TABLE 4†

Bond energy terms, for $25°$ C

Bond	Bond energy term kcal/mole	Bond	Bond energy term kcal/mole
C—H	90·5	$C\equiv N$	160·6
C—C	66·2	N—O (nitrites)	44
C=C	112·9	N=O (nitrites)	126
$C\equiv C$	150·3	N—H (NH_3)	84·3
C—O	77·1	N—N (N_2H_4)	21
C=O (ketones)	162	N=N	64
C—Cl	73	$N\equiv N$ (N_2)	171·1
C—Br	60	O—H (H_2O)	116
C—I	44	O—O (H_2O_2)	35
C—N	55·5	O=O (O_2)	118·3
C=N	c. 112		

An interesting application of energy changes measured by several methods is the calculation of the *lattice energies* of alkali halides.‡ The energy of formation of solid potassium chloride, for example, from gaseous potassium and chlorine ions, can be calculated by applying to the following cycle (due to Born and

† Data from Cottrell, *The Strength of Chemical Bonds* (1954).

‡ See, for example, Syrkin and Diatkina, *Structure of Molecules* (Butterworth, 1950), pp. 316–18.

Haber) the principle that the sum of the internal energy changes in any completed cycle is zero:

$$KCl\ (cryst) \xrightarrow{\ U_{KCl}\ } K^+(gas) + Cl^-(gas)$$

$$\uparrow -Q_{KCl} \qquad\qquad -I_K \qquad\qquad +E_{Cl}$$

$$K\ (solid) + \tfrac{1}{2}Cl_2(gas) \xleftarrow[-\frac{1}{2}D_{Cl}]{\ -S_K\ } K(gas) + Cl(gas)$$

The result for the lattice energy U_{KCl} is:

$$U_{KCl} - I_K + E_{Cl} - L_K - \tfrac{1}{2}D_{Cl} - Q_{KCl} = 0.$$

Here I_K is the ionization potential of potassium, determined by spectroscopy or electron impact. E_{Cl} is the electron-affinity of chlorine, which may be calculated from thermionic effects when a hot tungsten filament is surrounded by chlorine at low pressure so that the equilibrium $Cl + e = Cl^-$ is set up.† L_K is the latent heat of sublimation of potassium, determined from the temperature-variation of the vapour pressure. D_{Cl} is the dissociation energy of chlorine, determined by spectroscopy or from the temperature-variation of the equilibrium constant for dissociation. Q_{KCl} is the heat of formation of potassium chloride from the elements in their standard states, and may be obtained from calorimetric observations. The result is $U_{KCl} = 167$ kcal/mole. This may be compared with the theoretical value 168 kcal/mole, calculated on the assumption that the lattice consists of ions situated in the positions given by X-ray analysis and exerting electrostatic forces on each other, with an empirical correction (determined from the compressibility) for short-range repulsive forces. The agreement, which is equally good for other alkali halides, supports the ionic picture of a salt crystal lattice. Calculated lattice energies are in fact often used, in conjunction with other thermochemical data, to find electron affinities, which are the most doubtful quantities in the above cycle. The lattice energy added to the heat of solution, which is relatively small, gives the heat of solvation of the ions. These may be

† For this method see, for example, Doty and Mayer, *J. Chem. Phys.*, 1944, **12**, 323.

compared with values calculated from theoretical views on the orientation of solvent molecules.[†]

2.7. The variation of E and H with composition, temperature, pressure, and volume

Typical of the subject-matter of thermodynamics are the changes in thermodynamic functions, manifested by observable heat and work changes, when a system passes from a state A, characterized by a certain pressure, volume, temperature, etc., to another state B characterized by different values of those variables. We are therefore much concerned with the variations of E, H, and other thermodynamic functions due to changes in the measurable quantities that define the state of a physical system. In chemical thermodynamics these may usually be taken as composition, pressure, volume, and temperature, though others have to be taken into account in dealing with paramagnetism, dielectrics, and so on (cf. section 2.3). We must therefore consider the partial derivations of E and H with respect to these quantities.

2.71. *Variation of E and H with composition; chemical potentials*

We have already concluded (p. 29) that when a certain mass, say n_1 moles, of a pure substance receives increments of the same substance, the energy change, assuming that no work or heat change contributes to it, is $dE = \mu_1 \, dn_1$. Under such conditions, therefore, the variation of E with n_1 is given by

$$\mu_1 = (\partial E / \partial n_1)_{w=0, q=0}.$$

If other substances, denoted by subscripts 2, 3, etc., are simultaneously added to the system—for instance, if to some water are added water, alcohol, and sulphuric acid—the energy change will depend on the increment of each substance added and also on the composition. Thus for the variation of E with n_1 alone we must now write

$$\mu_1 = (\partial E / \partial n_1)_{w=0, q=0, dn_2=0, dn_3=0\ldots}.$$

[†] O. K. Rice, *Electronic Structure and Chemical Bonding* (McGraw-Hill, 1940), chap. 19.

This could indeed be deduced directly from equation 4 of section 2.25,

$$dE = dq - dw + \sum \mu \, dn,$$

by putting $0 = dq = dw = dn_2 = dn_3 \dots$. We shall show later (section 4.61) that for the particular case of systems in equilibrium the relation may be more compactly written

$$\mu_1 = (\partial E / \partial n_1)_{S, V, n_j}.$$

Relations of μ to other thermodynamic functions will be derived later.

It will also emerge (section 4.7) that μ is one of the intensive variables that determine the direction of change. We shall find that just as the difference of temperature, other things being equal, between two parts of a system in thermal contact determines the direction of the flow of heat, and the difference of pressure on the two sides of a mercury manometer determines the direction of movement of the mercury, so the difference between the values of μ_i in two different phases of a system is related to the direction in which the species i tends to move as it finds its equilibrium distribution; at constant temperature and pressure, it uniquely determines the direction. For instance, if a liquid and its vapour are in contact and μ is greater in the liquid than in the vapour, liquid will evaporate, and equilibrium will only be reached if for some reason the values of μ in the two phases become equal. The same is true of dissolution, osmosis, or any other change involving variations of concentration. The direction of chemical change is also determined by the values of μ (section 4.63). Thus μ is an intensity factor, or potential, characteristic of a particular chemical species in a particular phase. It is called the *chemical potential*, though it is relevant to physical changes as well as to chemical ones. An absolute scale cannot be set up for chemical potentials; they must be measured relative to the value in some standard state. They will be used a great deal in problems where we have either more than one phase or more than one chemical species, as for instance in treating of vapour pressure, gas mixtures, and solutions.

2.72. *Variation of E and H with temperature*

The variation with temperature of E and H for a closed system can be related to the experimentally observed heat capacities at constant volume, C_V, and constant pressure, C_P, respectively. These are the amounts of heat absorbed per unit temperature rise in changes conducted at constant volume and constant pressure respectively; the values for one gram-molecular-weight of the system are called the molar heat capacities at constant volume and constant pressure. In this book we shall invariably use molar heat capacities.

Internal energy and C_V. Consider first the increase of the internal energy of a system with temperature, under conditions such that all the added heat goes to increase E. One can think, for example, of a closed vessel containing one mole of a pure gas. For a closed system, undergoing a change in which the volume is constant, so that the work done is zero (assuming that the only kind of work to be considered is $P-V$ work done against the atmosphere), the First Law of thermodynamics gives (p. 40) for an infinitesimal change† $(dE)_{V,n_i} = (dq)_{V,n_i}$. Dividing each side by the corresponding temperature rise dT, and remembering that $(dq/dT)_{V,n_i}$ is by definition equal to C_V at temperature T,‡ we find:

$$(\partial E/\partial T)_{V,n_i} = (dq/dT)_{V,n_i} = C_V. \tag{1}$$

This relates the observed heat capacity at constant volume to the temperature-variation of E. To find the effect on E of a finite change of temperature at constant volume, say from T_1 to T_2, we integrate this equation; representing the value of E at T_1 by $E_{(T_1)}$, and at T_2 by $E_{(T_2)}$, we obtain:

$$E_{(T_2)} - E_{(T_1)} = \int\limits_{T_1}^{T_2} C_V \, dT. \tag{2}$$

---

† The subscript V means that the volume is kept constant; the subscript n_i means that all the dn's are zero.

‡ Although we have not yet introduced the thermodynamic scale of temperature, we use here the symbol T which denotes temperatures on that scale, as all the relations here derived are true for the thermodynamic scale. We distinguish where necessary (as in section 3.4) between temperatures on the thermodynamic scale (T), on the perfect-gas scale (θ), and on empirical scales (t); where this is done, the context will make it obvious.

If C_V is nearly constant, the integral is approximately $C_V(T_2 - T_1)$. In general C_V varies with temperature; the integral can then be evaluated by plotting a graph of C_V against T and finding the area under the curve. Thus the change in E can be found from experiment if we know C_V over the temperature-range concerned. We can thus express E relative to the value at some standard temperature. For many substances C_V is known at temperatures down to near the absolute zero, which can be taken as standard. Then we may write for E at temperature T:

$$E_{(T)} = E_{(0)} + \int_0^T C_V \, dT, \qquad (3)$$

where $E_{(0)}$ is the value of E at absolute zero.

Heat content and C_P. Consider now a change in a closed system at constant pressure, instead of at constant volume. One can think of a gas enclosed by a manometric liquid, as in a Charles'-law experiment. If the temperature is raised, the gas expands and the heat absorbed goes partly to increase E and partly to do work as the gas expands against the atmospheric pressure. For an infinitesimal change, the First Law gives (p. 36):

$$dH = dq + V \, dP + \sum \mu \, dn,$$

so that for the present conditions $(dH)_{P,n_i} = (dq)_{P,n_i}$. Dividing by dT, and remembering that $(dq/dT)_{P,n_i}$ is by definition equal to C_P, we find

$$(\partial H / \partial T)_{P,n_i} = (dq/dT)_{P,n_i} = C_P. \qquad (4)$$

For a finite change of temperature at constant pressure, the change in H is given by

$$H_{(T_2)} - H_{(T_1)} = \int_{T_1}^{T_2} C_P \, dT. \qquad (5)$$

Thus the change in H, relative to the value at some standard temperature, can be found if we know C_P over the temperature range concerned; and if the range extends to near the absolute zero, we can use this as the standard temperature and write for H at temperature T:

$$H_{(T)} - H_{(0)} = \int_0^T C_P \, dT, \qquad (6)$$

where $H_{(0)}$ is the value of H at absolute zero. (If phase changes occur, the latent heats must be added in computing H; cf. p. 75.)

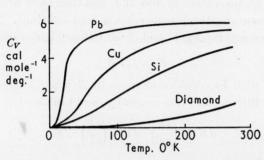

FIG. 5. Heat capacities of various elements plotted against temperature.

Some typical plots of C_V against temperature for solids are shown in fig. 5; plots of C_P for solids are similar in general shape. Some values of $(H - H_0)$ at various temperatures derived from a plot of this kind for aluminium are given in Table 5 (p. 62).

Since E and H reflect the energy locked up in molecular motions (translation, rotation, and vibration), molecular interpretations can be tested experimentally by comparison with the experimental values of C_V and C_P, which are thus of great interest. The quantum theory both of solids and of gases owes decisive support to the evidence of measurements of heat capacities to low temperatures. The application of the theory to gases is mentioned below (section 3.1); for the application to solids the reader is referred elsewhere.†

General relation between C_P and C_V from the First Law. A relation between C_P and C_V is of practical importance, as well as being an exercise in partial differentiation, because for solids

---

† e.g. Ubbelohde, *Modern Thermodynamics* (Oxford, 2nd edn. 1952), chap. 7; Fowler and Guggenheim, *Statistical Thermodynamics* (Cambridge, 1939), chap. 4; Guggenheim, *Thermodynamics* (1957), p. 138 seq.

it is easy to measure C_P, while C_V, which is of interest as a test of the quantum theory and of molecular models for solids, is not directly measurable. We investigate the relation between C_P and C_V by fixing attention on a closed system, whether solid, liquid, or gaseous, which undergoes no work changes except those due to changes of volume against atmospheric pressure. We consider the variation first of E and then of H with volume and temperature, the pressure being kept constant.

Since we are taking V and T as independent variables, we write:
$$E = f(T,V).$$

Since we wish to consider changes in E when V and T both vary, we differentiate this generally, and obtain:
$$dE = \left(\frac{\partial E}{\partial T}\right)_V dT + \left(\frac{\partial E}{\partial V}\right)_T dV.$$

Dividing by dT,
$$\frac{dE}{dT} = \left(\frac{\partial E}{\partial T}\right)_V + \left(\frac{\partial E}{\partial V}\right)_T \frac{dV}{dT} = C_V + \left(\frac{\partial E}{\partial V}\right)_T \frac{dV}{dT}.$$

To make it clear that we have supposed the pressure kept constant, we can write this in the form:
$$\left(\frac{\partial E}{\partial T}\right)_P = C_V + \left(\frac{\partial E}{\partial V}\right)_T \left(\frac{\partial V}{\partial T}\right)_P. \tag{7}$$

We can obtain an equation for the variation of H in the same change, from the definition of H in terms of E:
$$H \equiv E + PV$$

so that $dH = dE + P\,dV + V\,dP$

$$= dE + P\,dV \quad \text{when } P \text{ is constant.}$$

Dividing by dT and adding subscripts to show that P is constant,
$$\left(\frac{\partial H}{\partial T}\right)_P = C_P = \left(\frac{\partial E}{\partial T}\right)_P + P\left(\frac{\partial V}{\partial T}\right)_P. \tag{8}$$

Comparing equations 7 and 8, we find:
$$C_P - C_V = \left(\frac{\partial V}{\partial T}\right)_P \left[P + \left(\frac{\partial E}{\partial V}\right)_T\right]. \tag{9}$$

The value of $(C_P - C_V)$ thus depends on (i) the coefficient of expansion at constant pressure, which fixes $(\partial V/\partial T)_P$, and (ii) the quantity $(\partial E/\partial V)_T$, about which we have more to say below (sections 2.73, 3.2). This is as far as we can go with the aid of the First Law alone. With the Second Law we shall be able to derive a further relation (section 4.52, p. 159).

Variation with temperature of ΔE and ΔH (Kirchhoff's equations). We have so far considered the variation with temperature of E and H for a given system; we now turn to the variation with temperature of the *changes* in E and H associated with a chemical reaction, a phase change, or other process. A closed system in which a definite mass of material undergoes such a change exhibits definite changes of E and of H, characteristic of the change, but dependent also upon conditions such as temperature. Suppose that, when the change is carried out at constant volume at some temperature T_1, the change of internal energy per mole of material is $\Delta E_{(T_1)}$. We wish to know how ΔE will alter if we conduct the change at some other temperature T. If we split up ΔE into $(E_B - E_A)$, where A and B refer to the states of the system before and after the change, we find we can relate the changes in ΔE to heat capacities, since, using equation 1 (p. 53):

$$\left(\frac{\partial(\Delta E)}{\partial T}\right)_V = \left(\frac{\partial}{\partial T}(E_B - E_A)\right)_V = \left(\frac{\partial E_B}{\partial T}\right)_V - \left(\frac{\partial E_A}{\partial T}\right)_V$$

$$= (C_V)_B - (C_V)_A = \Delta C_V. \quad (10)$$

The temperature-coefficient of ΔE for changes at constant volume is thus determined by the difference of the heat capacities at constant volume of the system before and after the change, which we write as ΔC_V.

Similarly, consideration of a change at constant temperature and pressure, using equation 4 (p. 54), leads to the relations:

$$\left(\frac{\partial(\Delta H)}{\partial T}\right)_P = \left(\frac{\partial}{\partial T}(H_B - H_A)\right)_P = \left(\frac{\partial H_B}{\partial T}\right)_P - \left(\frac{\partial H_A}{\partial T}\right)_P$$

$$= (C_P)_B - (C_P)_A = \Delta C_P. \quad (11)$$

The temperature-coefficient of ΔH for changes at constant pressure is thus determined by the difference of the heat capacities at constant pressure of the system before and after the change.

Integration of equations 10 and 11, which are often known as Kirchhoff's equations, gives values for ΔE and ΔH at a given temperature (ΔE_T, ΔH_T) in terms of the values at some standard temperature T_1 and the heat capacities over the temperature range concerned. For changes at constant volume and temperature T, integration gives at once:

$$\Delta E_{(T)} = \Delta E_{(T_1)} + \int_{T_1}^{T} \Delta C_V \, dT. \tag{12}$$

For changes at constant pressure and temperature T, similarly,

$$\Delta H_{(T)} = \Delta H_{(T_1)} + \int_{T_1}^{T} \Delta C_P \, dT. \tag{13}$$

In general C_V and C_P vary with temperature and the integrals are evaluated graphically or analytically, though for short temperature ranges they can be taken as approximately $C_V(T-T_1)$ and $C_P(T-T_1)$.

As a numerical example of the use of these equations we may cite the transformation of monoclinic or β-sulphur to rhombic or α-sulphur. The heat of reaction for $S_\beta \rightarrow S_\alpha$ at 18° C was determined by Brønsted† and gives $-\Delta H = 77$ cal/mole. The heat capacities for S_α and S_β in the range 18° to 100° C differ by about 0·27 cal deg.$^{-1}$ mole^{-1}.‡ Hence the value of $-\Delta H$ at 95·4° C, the transition temperature, is $77+0·27$ (95·4—18) or about 98 cal/mole.

When the heat capacities have been determined down to near absolute zero, we can take T_1 as zero, and write

$$\Delta E_{(T)} = \Delta E_{(0)} + \int_{0}^{T} \Delta C_V \, dT, \tag{14}$$

$$\Delta H_{(T)} = \Delta H_{(0)} + \int_{0}^{T} \Delta C_P \, dT, \tag{15}$$

where $\Delta E_{(0)}$ and $\Delta H_{(0)}$ are the values of $(E_B - E_A)$ and $(H_B - H_A)$

---

† See note † on p. 48.
‡ Eastman and McGavock, *J. Amer. Chem. Soc.*, 1937, **59**, 145.

at absolute zero. (This does not imply that the change could be carried out at absolute zero; we are merely taking the difference between E or H for products and reactants, each at absolute zero.) It is these quantities $\Delta E_{(0)}$ and $\Delta H_{(0)}$ that should, strictly speaking, be used in calculations of bond energies, in discussions of potential energy diagrams, and in calculations of equilibrium constants with the aid of statistical mechanics. As an example, for the reaction

$$\text{C (graphite)} + \tfrac{1}{2}O_2 \text{ (gas)} = \text{CO (gas)},$$

the value of ΔH at $298 \cdot 15°$ K from calorimetric data is $-26{,}407$ cal/mole. To obtain the value of ΔH at $0°$ K we must subtract $\Delta(H_{(298)} - H_{(0)})$, obtained by the use of equation 6. For CO, the value of $H_{(298)} - H_{(0)}$ is $2{,}070 \cdot 9$ cal/mole at $298 \cdot 15°$ K; for oxygen the value for half a mole is $1{,}035 \cdot 2$ cal/mole and for carbon the value for one gramme-atom is $251 \cdot 4$ cal/mole. Thus

$$\Delta(H_{(298)} - H_{(0)}) = 783 \cdot 3 \text{ cal/mole},$$

and the value of ΔH at $0°$ K is

$$\Delta H_{(0)} = -26{,}407 - 783 = -27{,}190 \text{ cal/mole.†}$$

The difference between ΔH and $\Delta H_{(0)}$ is thus significant in accurate work. In many applications, however, it is enough to know ΔH to the nearest kilocalorie, and the difference may then be negligible.

Determination of heat capacities, and computation of $(E - E_{(0)})$ *and* $(H - H_{(0)})$ *for closed systems.* Much experimental work has been done on the determination of heat capacities, partly because they are continually needed in thermochemical calculations such as the above, and partly because they may be compared with the predictions of molecular theories.‡

The *calorimetric* methods for the determination of heat capacities generally depend on measuring the temperature rise of a

† This calculation applies strictly when the gases are at 1 atm pressure and when correction has been made for deviation from perfect-gas behaviour. Cf. section 3.12, p. 72.

‡ For a general review of experimental methods, see Sturtevant in *Physical Methods of Organic Chemistry*, ed. Weissberger (1949), vol. i, chap. 14; Partington, *Treatise on Physical Chemistry* (Longmans, 1949), vol. i, pp. 792 seq.

known mass of material when a known amount of electrical energy is supplied to it. For solids, a cylinder of the substance may be wound with a resistance wire which is used both as a heater and as a resistance thermometer; the experiment is then conducted at atmospheric pressure and gives C_P. A condensible gas such as carbon dioxide may be distilled into a metal calorimeter wound in the same way. A heavy copper block provides an environment of constant temperature; or the principle of adiabatic calorimetry may be used. This method, due originally to Nernst, has been used to measure heat capacities down to low temperatures, with an uncertainty of the order of ± 0.2 per cent. (fig. 6 a).† C_V for gases may be similarly measured, with the gas enclosed in a thin-walled steel cylinder; that of hydrogen was measured in this way.‡ C_P may then be found from a determination of the ratio C_P/C_V by one of the methods discussed later (section 3.52), some of which can be used at low temperatures; or C_P and C_V can both be found by combining the value of C_P/C_V with that of $C_P - C_V$ (cf. section 4.52), as has also been done for hydrogen at low temperatures.§ At ordinary temperatures, the capacity of the gas is not large compared with that of the container, and it is usually preferable to determine C_P. This is commonly done by a streaming method; gas is passed at a constant known rate over an electrically heated wire from which it receives in unit time a known amount of energy, and the initial and final temperatures of the gas stream are determined by platinum resistance thermometers (fig. 6 b).‖ The same method may be applied to vapours near the boiling-point (fig. 6 c).†† A correction may be made for heat-losses by varying the rate and plotting the apparent value of C_P against the reciprocal of the rate; extrapolation then gives the value at infinite rate, corresponding to conditions of zero heat-loss.

The heat capacities of gases at constant volume can also be

† Giauque and Egan, *J. Chem. Phys.*, 1937, **5**, 45; Giauque and Meads, *J. Amer. Chem. Soc.*, 1941, **63**, 1897.

‡ Eucken, *Ber. dtsch. phys. Ges.*, 1916, **18**, 4.

§ Cornish and Eastman, *J. Amer. Chem. Soc.*, 1928, **50**, 627.

‖ Scheel and Heuse, *Ann. Phys. Lpz.* (4), 1912, **37**, 79.

†† Pitzer, *J. Amer. Chem. Soc.*, 1941, **63**, 2413.

obtained by the combination of spectroscopy and statistical mechanics based on the quantum theory (cf. section 3.11, p. 68).† The results have been so successful wherever they

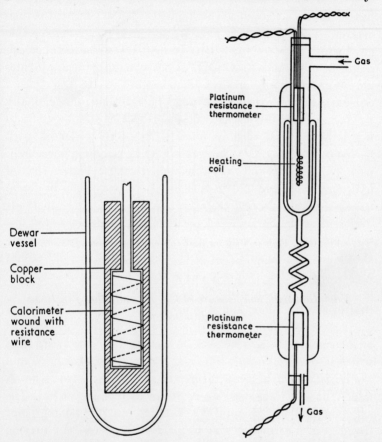

FIG. 6 (a). Apparatus for measuring heat capacities of solids at low temperatures (Giauque and Egan; diagrammatic).

FIG. 6 (b). Flow method for heat capacities of gases (Scheel and Heuse; diagrammatic).

have been tested that they are regarded as giving values generally more accurate than the calorimetric values for simple molecules.

† Cf., for example, Rushbrooke, *Introduction to Statistical Mechanics*, chap. 6; Taylor and Glasstone, *Treatise on Physical Chemistry* (van Nostrand, 1942), vol. i, pp. 559 seq.

A typical set of calorimetric results on the heat capacity of a solid from near absolute zero to room temperature is given in Table 5, which summarizes the results of Giauque and

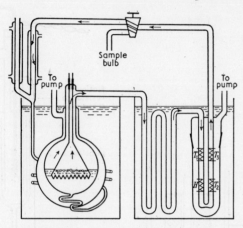

FIG. 6 (c). Flow method for heat capacities of vapours (Pitzer).

TABLE 5

Variation with temperature of C_P, H, and other functions for aluminium

T °K	C_P cal mole^{-1}	C_V cal mole^{-1}	$\dfrac{C_V}{C_V \text{ (Debye)}}$	$\dfrac{H_{(T)}-H_{(0)}}{T}$ cal mole^{-1} deg.$^{-1}$	$S^0_{(T)}-S^0_{(0)}$ cal mole^{-1} deg.$^{-1}$	$\dfrac{-(G^0_{(T)}-H^0_{(0)})}{T}$ cal. mole^{-1} deg.$^{-1}$
15	0·022	0·022	0·827	0·005	0·007	0·002
50	0·913	0·912	1·033	0·236	0·313	0·077
100	3·116	3·084	1·000	1·147	1·650	0·503
150	4·427	4·361	1·001	2·044	3·189	1·145
200	5·138	5·039	1·015	2·740	4·572	1·832
250	5·557	5·383	1·017	3·267	5·769	2·502
298·1	5·817	5·592	1·020	3·668	6·769	3·101
300	5·826	5·599	1·021	3·672	6·806	3·134

Meads† on the heat capacity of aluminium at constant pressure. The first column gives the temperature, the second the observed value of C_P, and the fifth gives the value of $(H_{(T)}-H_{(0)})$, expressed as $(H_{(T)}-H_{(0)})/T$, derived from the plot of C_P against

† See note † on p. 60.

T (p. 55). The third column of the table gives C_V, derived from C_P by a method described later (section 4.52), and in the fourth column this experimental value is compared with that calculated on Debye's theory of solids. The sixth and seventh columns give values for the standard entropy and free energy; these quantities will be considered later.

2.73. *Partial derivatives with respect to V and P*

The most interesting of these are $(\partial E/\partial V)_{T,n_i}$ and $(\partial E/\partial P)_{T,n_i}$, which measure the variation of E with V or P for a closed system, at constant temperature. These quantities are related to one another by the compressibility $(\partial V/\partial P)_T/V$, since $(\partial E/\partial P)_T = (\partial E/\partial V)_T(\partial V/\partial P)_T$. They are important because they depend upon intermolecular forces; $(\partial E/\partial V)_T$ represents the change in E due solely to changes in intermolecular distances. If there were no intermolecular attractions and repulsions, E would be independent of volume and pressure and would depend only on the temperature, as in the simple kinetic theory of gases. Consequently $(\partial E/\partial V)_T$ is of interest for gases. Another field in which $(\partial E/\partial V)_T$ is of interest is the theory of liquids and of regular solutions (section 11.2); here it is known as the 'internal pressure'.†

The corresponding changes in H can be found from the changes in E as follows. Since

$$H \equiv E + PV, \qquad dH = dE + P\,dV + V\,dP,$$

and so

$$\left(\frac{\partial H}{\partial V}\right)_T = \left(\frac{\partial E}{\partial V}\right)_T + \left(\frac{\partial (PV)}{\partial V}\right)_T = \left(\frac{\partial E}{\partial V}\right)_T + P + V\left(\frac{\partial P}{\partial V}\right)_T.$$

From $(\partial H/\partial V)_T$, $(\partial H/\partial P)_T$ can be found by multiplying by $(\partial V/\partial P)_T$. Thus the variation of H with P and V is fixed by the relation between E and V, together with the compressibility relation between P and V, at constant temperature.

† Hildebrand and Scott, *Solubility of Non-electrolytes* (Reinhold, 1950).

III

APPLICATION OF THE FIRST LAW TO GASES

WHETHER we approach them experimentally or theoretically, the simplest of the thermodynamic properties of gases that depend on the First Law fall into two classes. The first class comprises the heat capacities of gases, representing the variation of E and H with temperature. The second class comprises equations of state and quantities such as $(\partial E/\partial V)_T$. Thermodynamically, we cannot deduce properties in one of these classes from those in the other class; for instance, we cannot deduce C_P for a given gas from its equation of state. Statistical interpretations show why this is so: heat capacities depend (at low pressures) on the mean translational, rotational, and vibrational energy of isolated molecules, while equations of state and related quantities are affected by molecular interactions.

In this chapter we begin with heat capacities at low pressures (section 3.1), and then turn to equations of state and other properties of the second class (sections 3.2, 3.3, 3.4). Finally (section 3.5) we consider some phenomena that depend on properties of both classes; the treatment will serve as an introduction to the discussion of the Second Law in the next chapter. We shall return in section 5.1, armed with the Second Law, to reconsider some of the relations of sections 3.2, 3.3, and 3.4.

3.1. The internal energy and heat content of a gas, as a function of temperature

In an earlier section (2.72, p. 53) we obtained some general relations between heat capacities and the thermodynamic functions E and H, which are based on the First Law. We now apply these to gases.

3.11. *Heat capacities of gases*

The heat capacities of gases have been measured† over considerable ranges of temperature and pressure, and found to vary with both. At pressures above one atmosphere the variation with pressure is appreciable, especially with gases near their boiling-points, as the data on carbon dioxide show (fig. 7).

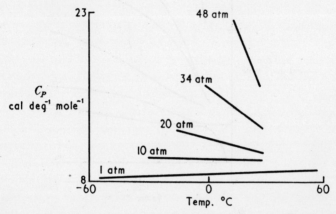

FIG. 7. Variation of C_P with temperature and pressure, for carbon dioxide.

At low enough pressures, however, it is found for all gases that C_P and C_V become practically independent of pressure. The pressure-range in which this occurs depends on the gas; for carbon dioxide it is below 1 atm, while for helium C_P is constant within 0·1 per cent. from 1 to 40 atm at ordinary temperatures.‡ It is also found that if we express C_P and C_V in calories per degree per mole§ of gas, then $(C_P - C_V)$ is always positive and equal to about 2 calories per degree.

The temperature-dependence of C_P and C_V at low pressures is more complex and is found to depend on the molecular structure of the gas. Some values of C_P and C_V are given in Table 6

† For methods of measurement cf. section 2.72, p. 59, and section 3.52, p. 110.

‡ This variation is measured indirectly; cf., for example, Keesom, *Helium* (Elsevier, 1942), p. 86.

§ A mole of gas here means a mass in grammes equal to the sum of the atomic weights in the accepted formula of the gas. We shall later (section 3.33, p. 92) give a thermodynamic definition.

and plotted in fig. 8.† Some values of C_P/C_V extrapolated to zero pressure, at ordinary temperature, are given in Table 7 (the method of determination is described in section 3.52).

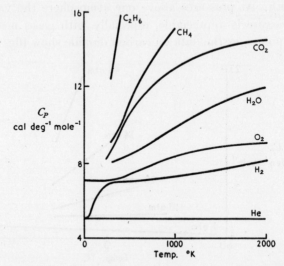

FIG. 8. Heat capacity C_P for various gases at low pressure, plotted against temperature.

Values of C_P/C_V and of $(C_P - C_V)$ over a range of temperatures are given in Table 8.‡ The data may be summarized as follows:

(i) *Monatomic gases* (helium, argon, neon, and most metal vapours) have C_V and C_P nearly constant over a wide temperature-range from $20°$ K to $2,000°$ K; C_V is near to 3 cal deg^{-1} mole^{-1} and C_P is near to 5 cal deg^{-1} mole^{-1}, so that the ratio C_P/C_V is constant and near to 1·67.

(ii) *The 'permanent' diatomic gases* (H_2, D_2, O_2, N_2, NO, CO) have C_V and C_P nearly constant at ordinary temperatures, at which C_V and C_P are approximately 5 and 7 cal deg^{-1} mole^{-1} respectively, so that C_P/C_V is nearly 1·40. As the temperature

† These values are calculated by the statistical-spectroscopic method (see below, pp. 68–70) and refer to undissociated molecules. They are taken from *Selected Values of Chemical Thermodynamic Properties*, series iii, ed. Rossini *et al.* (U.S. National Bureau of Standards). Temperatures are given in degrees absolute (°K), which will be explained in section 4.43 (p. 139).

‡ Data from *International Critical Tables* (McGraw-Hill, 1926).

TABLE 6

C_P for various gases at low pressures (perfect-gas conditions)
in calories per degree per mole

	Temperature, °K					
Gas	200	300	500	1,000	1,500	2,000
He	4·99	4·99	4·99	4·99	4·99	4·99
H_2	6·56	6·89	6·99	7·22	7·71	8·18
N_2	6·96	6·96	7·07	7·82	8·33	8·60
O_2	6·96	7·02	7·43	8·34	8·74	9·03
Cl_2	..	8·12	8·62	8·96	9·08	..
Br_2	..	8·60	8·86	9·01	9·08	..
I_2	..	8·82	8·95	9·06	9·13	..
H_2O	..	8·03	8·42	9·86	11·26	12·01
CO_2	..	8·89	10·66	13·00	13·99	14·5
CH_4	..	8·55	11·13	17·21	20·71	..
C_2H_6	..	12·65	18·66	29·33	34·90	..
C_6H_6	..	19·65	32·80	50·16	57·67	..

TABLE 7

C_P/C_V for various gases at about 25° C,
(a) at 1 atm pressure, (b) extrapolated to zero pressure

	C_P/C_V	
Gas	$P = 1$ atm	$P = 0$
He	1·666$_7$	1·666$_9$
A	1·670$_2$	1·666$_7$
H_2	1·404$_7$	1·404$_5$
N_2	1·402$_8$	1·400$_6$
CO_2	1·300$_0$	1·294$_8$
SO_2	1·283$_7$	1·264$_2$
N_2O	1·284$_7$	1·278$_3$

rises, C_V increases; C_P also increases, (C_P-C_V) remaining constant, so that C_P/C_V decreases. As the temperature falls below 0° C, there is little change in C_P and C_V for most gases until very low temperatures are reached, thus for oxygen C_P is measured as 6·98 cal deg.⁻¹ mole⁻¹ at 293° K and 6·90 at 92° K. For hydrogen, however, C_P and C_V begin to decrease at once; when 50° K is reached, C_P has fallen to 5 and C_V to

TABLE 8

Experimental values at 1 atm pressure of (C_P/C_V) and of $(C_P - C_V)$ in calories per mole per dyne

Gas	Temp. °C	$\dfrac{C_P}{C_V}$	$C_P - C_V$
He	-269	1.66_9	..
	-183	1.66_3	1.99
	23	1.667	..
H_2	-238	1.67	..
	-173	1.58	1.99
	15	1.40	1.99
O_2, N_2	0	1.402	1.99_8
	100	1.399	1.99_1
	600	1.383	1.98_8
	$1,000$	1.365	1.98_7
	$1,400$	1.342	1.98_7
	$2,000$	1.303	1.98_7
CO_2	0	1.310	2.055
	100	1.281	2.014
	600	1.217	1.989
	$1,000$	1.195	1.988
	$1,400$	1.184	1.987
	$2,000$	1.171	1.987

3 cal deg.$^{-1}$ mole^{-1} (fig. 8), so that C_P/C_V is about 1.67 as for monatomic gases.

(iii) *Polyatomic gases and some diatomic gases* such as CO_2, NH_3, CH_4, Cl_2, Br_2, show variations of C_P, C_V, and C_P/C_V with temperature which are different for each gas, and complex. The heat capacities increase with the complexity of the molecule (cf. Table 6 and fig. 8).

These results are in excellent agreement with the predictions of statistical mechanics using the following assumptions. (i) A gas at low pressure can be treated as an assembly of independent non-localized molecules. (ii) The energy of a molecule is made up of kinetic energy of translation of the molecules as a whole together with energy associated with the rotations and vibrations of the molecule, and (at higher temperatures) with electronic transitions. (iii) These energy terms can have only certain discrete values. The energy-levels for rotational and vibrational motion and for electronic transitions are revealed by analysis of band spectra.[†] Those for translation are only inferred from the wave-theory of matter; they are closer together the larger the mass of the particle (i.e. the larger the molecular weight of the gas) and the larger the volume.[‡] They are so close together that the translational energy may generally be treated as if it were continuous. The energy of an assembly of molecules—say one mole of gas, containing $N^0 = 6 \cdot 02 \times 10^{23}$ molecules—is the sum of the energies of the individual molecules, provided that the molecular interactions are negligible, i.e. at low pressures. To find an average value for this energy we need to know the fraction of the total number of molecules in each of the energy states. This we assume to be given by the Boltzmann distribution law, according to which the fraction of molecules in the state of energy ϵ_i is (omitting weight factors) equal to $e^{-\epsilon_i/kT} / \sum e^{-\epsilon_i/kT}$, where k is a universal constant.[§] The energy contributed by the molecules in this state is equal to this fraction, multiplied by the total number of molecules, multiplied by the energy of the state (ϵ_i). For one mole the product is thus

$$N^0 \epsilon_i \, e^{-\epsilon_i/kT} / \sum e^{-\epsilon_i/kT}.$$

The total energy of one mole of gas, relative to that at the absolute zero of temperature, is the sum of such terms contributed by all the energy levels, so that

$$E - E_{(0)} = N^0 \sum \epsilon_i \, e^{-\epsilon_i/kT} / \sum e^{-\epsilon_i/kT}.$$

The quantity $\sum e^{-\epsilon_i/kT}$, which is characteristic of the gas at a given temperature, is called the *partition function*. Writing this

† See, for example, Bowen, *Chemical Aspects of Light* (Oxford, 2nd edn. 1946), or Herzberg, *Molecular Spectra and Molecular Structure: Diatomic Molecules* (Prentice Hall, 2nd edn. 1952), for charts of energy-levels for various diatomic molecules.

‡ For a particle of mass m in a box of sides a, b, and c, the energy-levels are given by $\epsilon = (h^2/8m)(n_x^2/a^2 + n_y^2/b^2 + n_z^2/c^2)$, where h is Planck's constant and n_x, n_y, n_z are integers. This gives the partition function for translation alone as $V(2\pi mkT/h^2)^{\frac{3}{2}}$, where V is the volume.

§ Cf., for example, Rushbrooke, *Introduction to Statistical Mechanics* (Oxford, 1949); Ubbelohde, *Modern Thermodynamics* (Oxford, 2nd edn. 1952); Guggenheim, *Boltzmann's Distribution Law* (North Holland Publishing Co., 1955).

as f, it is a matter of algebra to show that for n moles

$$E-E_{(0)} = nRT^2(\partial \ln f/\partial T)_V, \qquad (1)$$

where $R = kN^0$ and is identical with the gas constant discussed later (section 3.33). Thus if we know the energy-levels for the gas, from its spectrum, we can find the internal energy of the gas, at pressures low enough for molecular interactions to be negligible. For accurate results, laborious summations are needed; but approximate values that suffice for many purposes can be found from values of the moments of inertia and force-constants, derived from analysis of the spectra.† From the energy-function E we can determine C_V at low pressure (by differentiation with respect to temperature), and hence C_P, since $C_P-C_V = $ constant.

From such an investigation it emerges that, on these quantum theory assumptions, the contributions of translation, rotation, vibration, and electronic transitions should lead to an equation for C_P of the form $C_P = $ constant$+f(T)$. Here the constant term results from translation and rotation, and is $\frac{5}{2}R$ or about 5 cal deg^{-1} mole^{-1} for all monatomic gases, and $\frac{7}{2}R$ or about 7 cal deg^{-1} mole^{-1} for all diatomic gases (except hydrogen). The term $f(T)$ is a complex function depending on the vibrations of the parts of the molecule; it decreases with temperature and tends to zero at the absolute zero. Because it depends only on these internal motions, it is often written C_i. Thus $C_P = C_i+\frac{5}{2}R$ for monatomic gases, and $C_P = C_i+\frac{7}{2}R$ for diatomic gases.

The experimental findings, then, can be fully interpreted in molecular terms. This interpretation is in fact so firmly established that the values of C_P calculated from spectra are often more reliable than the calorimetric values; they have been used in Table 6, for example. (It should, however, be remembered that the calculated values take no account of molecular dissociation, and must be corrected if this is appreciable.) Again, the ortho- and para-forms of hydrogen were discovered because of

† Cf., for example, Rushbrooke, *Introduction to Statistical Mechanics* (1949); Taylor and Glasstone, *Treatise on Physical Chemistry* (van Nostrand, 1942), vol. i, chap. 4.

a discrepancy between the observed and calculated heat capacities at low temperatures,[†] which was removed when the calculation was amended to take account of the two forms.

Empirical equations for the variation of the heat capacities of gases with temperature. For many purposes the exact equations are unnecessarily complex, and rough empirical equations suffice to describe the variation of heat capacities with temperature. The simplest of these empirical equations are those given by Lewis and Randall,[‡] which are of the form

$$C_P = a + bT + cT^2. \tag{2}$$

For hydrogen, for example, $C_P = 6 \cdot 50 + 0 \cdot 0009T$; for ammonia, $C_P = 8 \cdot 04 + 0 \cdot 0007T + 0 \cdot 0^551T^2$. These equations are accurate to 1 or 2 per cent. in the temperature range 300–1,500° K, at ordinary pressures.

Such equations are useful in computing the heat change in a reaction at a given temperature from an observed value at a different temperature. We know from Kirchhoff's equations (section 2.72, p. 57) that $d(\Delta H)/dT = \Delta C_P$, where ΔC_P is the difference of the heat capacities of the products and reactants. Using equations for C_P such as 2 above, and subtracting, we obtain equations of the form

$$d(\Delta H)/dT = \Delta C_P = a' + b'T + c'T^2. \tag{3}$$

Integrating, the value of ΔH at temperature T is given by

$$\Delta H = \Delta H' + \alpha T + \beta T^2 + \gamma T^3, \tag{4}$$

where $\Delta H'$ is an integration constant having the dimensions of H, and α, β, γ are constants known in terms of the constants of the heat capacity equations. Thus if ΔH is known at one temperature within the range covered by the empirical equations for C_P, the integration constant $\Delta H'$ can be determined

---

[†] Cf., for example, Rushbrooke, *Introduction to Statistical Mechanics* (1949), chap. 7; Fowler and Guggenheim, *Statistical Thermodynamics* (Cambridge, 1939), p. 91.

[‡] Lewis and Randall, *Thermodynamics* (McGraw-Hill, 1923), p. 80. More accurate empirical equations have since been proposed; thus the specific heats of H_2, CO, and CO_2 are represented within $0 \cdot 1$ per cent. in the range 400–2,000° K by the equations of the form $Cp = a + bT + cT^{-\frac{1}{2}}$ (Chipman and Fontana, *J. Amer. Chem. Soc.*, 1935, **57**, 48).

once and for all, and the value of ΔH at other temperatures can be calculated.

The equation just derived for ΔH may be compared with the general equation 15 of section 2.72 (p. 58) obtained from Kirchhoff's equations in terms of $\Delta H_{(0)}$:

$$\Delta H = \Delta H_{(0)} + \int_0^T \Delta C_P \, dT.$$

The empirical integration constant $\Delta H'$ in equation 4 is *not* equal to $\Delta H_{(0)}$, the value of ΔH at absolute zero, because the empirical equations for C_P do not hold at low temperatures, so that $\int_0^T \Delta C_P \, dT$ is not equal to $(\alpha T + \beta T^2 + \gamma T^3 ...)$. It is important, when using these equations for C_P, to remember their limitations as regards both accuracy and range of temperature.

3.12. *E and H for gases*

If a gas is cooled at moderate pressures, say one atmosphere, it will of course condense to a liquid and at a lower temperature this will solidify. Both liquid and solid have, however, a certain vapour pressure, so that at a low enough pressure we could always investigate the gaseous form. There are two alternative ways of expressing E and H for gases as functions of temperature, according as we suppose the pressure to be kept very low or to be kept at one atmosphere.

If the pressure is kept always below the vapour-pressure of the condensed phase at the lowest temperature investigated, the system will be gaseous over the whole temperature range. E and H in general vary somewhat with pressure, but at low enough pressures, when the gas behaves as a 'perfect gas', they are both independent of pressure (section 5.11), and for gases at $25°$ C and one atmosphere the corrections are small, a few calories per mole. Values at the standard pressure of one atmosphere can therefore be obtained, even though the gas does not exist at this pressure at any temperature below its boiling-point. These values are commonly written E^0 and H^0. E^0 and H^0 will be given, relative to the values for the gases at absolute zero, by equations 3 and 5 of section 2.72 (p. 54). If we represent the values for one mole of gas at $T°$ by $E_{G(T)}$ and $H_{G(T)}$, and at $0°$ K by $E_{G(0)}$ and $H_{G(0)}$, we find

$$E^0_{G(T)} - E^0_{G(0)} = \int_0^T (C_V)_G \, dT, \tag{1}$$

$$H^0_{G(T)} - H^0_{G(0)} = \int_0^T (C_P)_G \, dT. \tag{2}$$

Heat capacities at very low pressures are not conveniently determined by calorimetry, but the statistical-spectroscopic values refer to just these conditions, since they depend on the energy-levels of isolated molecules, and can be computed for low temperatures just as well as for high ones. From these values we can find the internal energy function and the heat content of the gas down to the lowest temperatures. We have seen (p. 70) that C_P can be divided into (a) a temperature-variable term C_i, which depends on the gas but always tends to zero as the temperature approaches $0°$ K, and (b) a term independent of temperature, which may be written $(C_P - C_i)$, and takes the value $\frac{5}{2}R$, $\frac{7}{2}R$, etc., according to the complexity of the gas molecule. It is therefore convenient to rewrite equations 1 and 2 as

$$E^0_{G(T)} - E^0_{G(0)} = \int_0^T C_i \, dT + T(C_V - C_i), \tag{3}$$

$$H^0_{G(T)} - H^0_{G(0)} = \int_0^T C_i \, dT + T(C_P - C_i). \tag{4}$$

The integral can be determined graphically, as the area under a plot of C_i against T.

Some values for $H^0_{G(T)} - H^0_{G(0)}$ for common gases at various temperatures are given in Table 9† and plotted in fig. 9. It is evident that the more complex molecules have the larger values, corresponding to their larger heat capacities throughout the temperature range.

† By permission from chapter 5 by L. Brewer in *Chemistry and Metallurgy of Miscellaneous Substances; Thermodynamics*, ed. Quill. Copyright, 1950, McGraw-Hill Book Company, Inc.

TABLE 9

*The heat content for various gases, relative to that of the gas at 0° K,
and corrected for deviations from the perfect-gas laws*

Gas	$H^0_{G(T)} - H^0_{G(0)}$, kcal/mole				
	298° K	500° K	1,000° K	1,500° K	2,000° K
H_2	2·02	3·43	6·97	10·69	14·68
N_2	2·08	3·48	7·20	11·25	15·52
O_2	2·07	3·52	7·50	11·78	16·22
F_2	2·11	3·70	7·98	12·36	16·79
Cl_2	2·19	3·89	8·39	12·75	17·34
Br_2	2·32	4·09	8·57	13·10	17·68
I_2	2·42	4·22	8·68	13·22	17·97
HF	2·06	3·46	6·97	10·72	14·69
HCl	2·07	3·47	7·06	10·98	15·16
HBr	2·07	3·48	7·16	11·08	15·40
HI	2·07	3·52	7·28	11·40	15·54
CO	2·07	3·49	7·26	11·36	15·64
CO_2	2·24	4·22	10·22	17·00	24·16
SO_2	2·52	4·61	10·69	17·28	24·05
NH_3	2·40	4·27	10·13	17·47	25·74
H_2O	2·37	4·02	8·58	13·88	19·78

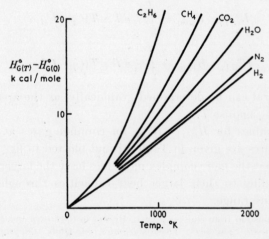

FIG. 9. Heat content of various gases, plotted against temperature.

If, alternatively, the pressure of the gas is kept at (say) one atmosphere, so that the gas condenses on cooling, the changes in E and H on raising the temperature from $0°$ K will have to include the heats of fusion and evaporation under one atmosphere pressure. The value at $0°$ K will refer to the solid and

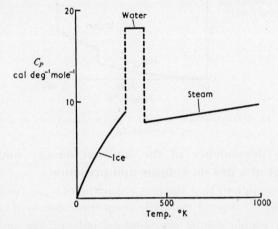

FIG. 10. Heat capacities of ice, water, and steam, plotted against temperature.

may be written $H_{S(0)}$. The heat content will be relative to $H_{S(0)}$ and will be given by

$$H^0_{G(T)} - H_{S(0)} = \int_0^{T_f} C_S \, dT + L_f + \int_{T_f}^{T_e} C_L \, dT + L_e + \int_{T_e}^{T_f} C_G \, dT \quad (5)$$

and there will be a similar equation for $E^0_{G(T)}$. Here C_S, C_L, and C_G are respectively the heat capacities at constant pressure of the solid, liquid, and gas; L_f is the latent heat of fusion at temperature T_f; and L_e is the latent heat of evaporation at the boiling-point T_e (at 1 atm). Some substances, such as nitrogen, undergo transitions in the solid state, with a heat of transition and a change of heat capacity; extra terms must then be added. The plots of C_P and of H^0 against T will have a form such as that shown in figs. 10 and 11, which represent calorimetric results for water at 1 atmosphere.†

† Giauque and Stout, *J. Amer. Chem. Soc.*, 1936, **58**, 1154.

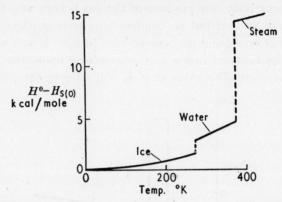

Fig. 11. Heat content of ice, water, and steam, plotted against temperature.

3.2. The dependence of the internal energy and heat content of a gas on volume and pressure

We have noticed that the heat capacities of a gas (and therefore E and H) depend markedly upon the pressure of the gas, and that simple results are obtained only at low pressures. The variation with pressure and volume of the internal energy and heat content must depend upon the intermolecular forces. If we increase the volume of a gas, we increase the average distance between the molecules and reduce the frequency of collision, so that the effects of intermolecular forces will be less marked. If the effects of intermolecular forces could be reduced to zero, the internal energy E would become independent of the volume. In real gases, E is not independent of V; the magnitude of $(\partial E/\partial V)_T$ is a measure of the effects of intermolecular forces.

Before we discuss methods of measuring $(\partial E/\partial V)_T$, we must mention that it is an experimental fact that the pressure, volume, and temperature of a fixed mass of gas cannot all be varied independently. If two of these three variables are fixed by the experimental apparatus, the third takes up a value which (other factors remaining constant) is reproducible and which it maintains indefinitely. If, for instance, some gas is enclosed in a vessel of fixed volume immersed in a thermostat, the pressure will assume an equilibrium value and remain steady, and this pressure is reproducible. Since any two of the three variables P, V, and T determine the third, there is some equation relating P, V, and T; this is called the *equation of state* of the gas. Various equations of state are considered later in this chapter.

3.21. *Joule effect: adiabatic expansion of gas without performance of work*

Suppose that some gas is contained in a vessel A and is allowed to expand into another vessel B containing the same gas at a pressure below that in A. We suppose that the heat

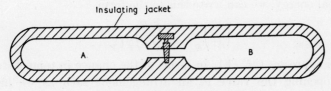

Fig. 12. Joule effect (schematic).

capacity of the vessel can be made negligible in comparison with that of the gas, and that the whole arrangement is enclosed in an insulating jacket. The thermodynamic system that we consider is the whole mass of gas present in A and B. This is a closed system, and since the total volume is fixed it has performed no work on its surroundings. (If we take the gas initially in A alone as the system to be considered, and the gas in B as the surroundings, then the system does do work on its surroundings; we are interested, however, in the heat and work exchanges between the gas and the world outside, and therefore take the whole mass of gas as our system.) In general the temperature will change, as well as the volume, so we must consider the variation of E with V and T together. (There is no need to consider P as well, since it is fixed by V and T and the equation of state.) E is characteristic of the state of the system, and therefore in this case it is a single-valued function of V and T. We can therefore write (as in section 2.4, p. 33) for the variation of E with both V and T together:

$$dE = \left(\frac{\partial E}{\partial T}\right)_V dT + \left(\frac{\partial E}{\partial V}\right)_T dV$$

$$= C_V \, dT + (\partial E/\partial V)_T \, dV. \tag{1}$$

For a system undergoing an adiabatic change in which no work is done on the surroundings, the First Law gives us (p. 40):

$$dE = dq - dw = 0.$$

Hence we obtain, on rearranging equation 1,

$$\frac{dT}{dV} = -\left(\frac{\partial E}{\partial V}\right)_T \frac{1}{C_V}. \tag{2}$$

If we wish to emphasize that the change occurs at constant internal energy, we can write this in the form

$$\left(\frac{dT}{dV}\right)_E = -\left(\frac{\partial E}{\partial V}\right)_T \frac{1}{C_V}.$$

This expresses $(\partial E/\partial V)_T$ in terms of the change in temperature on opening the valve in an arrangement such as we have imagined, and so relates $(\partial E/\partial V)_T$ to a quantity that is in principle measurable. Attempts were made by Joule to realize experimentally the conditions required, but in practice the heat capacity of a vessel cannot be made small enough compared with that of the gas it contains, and although temperature changes were observed they were too small to be measured with any accuracy.

3.22. *Joule–Kelvin effect: adiabatic expansion of gas with performance of work*

A better experimental arrangement is one which uses a stream of gas, rather than a fixed amount, so that a steady state is set up. In the experiment first performed by Thomson (later Lord Kelvin) and Joule,† a stream of gas passes adiabatically from high pressure to low, and the change of temperature is observed. Adiabatic expansion occurs in turbines and jet engines (section 3.53); but under such conditions of free expansion the

† Joule and Thomson, *Phil. Trans. Roy. Soc.*, 1853, **143**, 357; 1854, **144**, 321.

stream of gas accelerates, whereas for the present purpose we need a small rate of flow and negligible change of kinetic energy of the gas. This is achieved by means of a porous plug, or a throttle-valve. A considerable excess pressure can then be maintained on one side of the plug with a reasonable rate of flow; a steady temperature-difference results, and can easily be

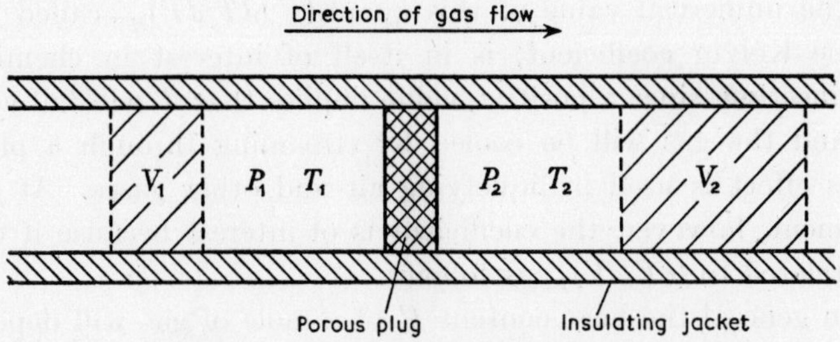

Direction of gas flow

FIG. 13. Joule–Kelvin effect (schematic).

measured. The essential parts of the apparatus can be thermally insulated with relative ease.

Under these conditions the work performed is not zero. Suppose one mole of gas passes from the high-pressure side of the plug, where the temperature is T_1, the pressure P_1, and the molar volume of the gas V_1, to the low-pressure side, where the pressure has dropped to P_2 and the temperature to T_2 while the molar volume has increased to V_2. The 'surroundings' of the chosen portion of the gas are the elements of the gas stream adjacent to it. When it is expelled from the high-pressure side, work $P_1 V_1$ is done *on* it; when it enters the low-pressure side, work $P_2 V_2$ is done *by* it. Thus the net work performed by this element of gas on its surroundings is

$$w = P_2 V_2 - P_1 V_1.$$

This would be zero if Boyle's law were exactly obeyed, which is not the case with real gases at ordinary pressures (section 3.4).

We can apply the First Law as follows. For an adiabatic change such as this, where the heat change q is zero,

$$\Delta E = E_2 - E_1 = q - w = -w = P_1 V_1 - P_2 V_2$$

so that
$$E_2 + P_2 V_2 = E_1 + P_1 V_1,$$

or $$H_2 = H_1,$$

where E_1 and H_1 refer to the initial state and E_2 and H_2 to the final state. Thus the adiabatic expansion of a gas stream in the steady state occurs at constant H, not at constant E as in the Joule experiment. The dependence of the temperature on the pressure-drop may thus be written as $(dT/dP)_H$.

The numerical value of this quantity $(dT/dP)_H$, called the Joule–Kelvin coefficient, is in itself of interest in chemical engineering, since a positive value implies that T will fall with P and the gas will be cooled by streaming through a plug. This effect is used in liquefying air and other gases. At the moment, however, the coefficient is of interest because it can be related to $(\partial E/\partial V)_T$, as follows.

In general the heat content H of a mole of gas will depend upon both temperature and pressure, and since H is a single-valued function of T and P, we may express its variation with T and P generally by the equation

$$dH = \left(\frac{\partial H}{\partial T}\right)_P dT + \left(\frac{\partial H}{\partial P}\right)_T dP.$$

In the Joule–Kelvin experiment, as we have just shown, H is constant and so $dH = 0$. Substituting this, and also writing C_P for $(\partial H/\partial T)_P$, we obtain

$$0 = (\partial H/\partial T)_P dT + C_P dP.$$

Rearranging, and noting that (dT/dP) refers to constant H, we obtain

$$\left(\frac{dT}{dP}\right)_H = -\frac{1}{C_P}\left(\frac{\partial H}{\partial P}\right)_T. \tag{1}$$

This expresses the dependence of H on P in terms of the measurable quantity $(dT/dP)_H$. We can also derive from it an expression for $(\partial E/\partial V)_T$, as follows.

Since $H = E + PV$, $dH = dE + d(PV)$. Dividing through by dP, and restricting ourselves to changes at constant temperature,

$$\left(\frac{\partial H}{\partial P}\right)_T = \left(\frac{\partial E}{\partial P}\right)_T + \left(\frac{\partial(PV)}{\partial P}\right)_T = \left(\frac{\partial E}{\partial V}\right)_T\left(\frac{\partial V}{\partial P}\right)_T + \left(\frac{\partial(PV)}{\partial P}\right)_T. \tag{2}$$

Substituting this value of $(\partial H/\partial P)_T$ in equation 1, we obtain

$$\left(\frac{dT}{dP}\right)_H = -\frac{1}{C_P}\left\{\left(\frac{\partial E}{\partial V}\right)_T\left(\frac{\partial V}{\partial P}\right)_T + \left(\frac{\partial(PV)}{\partial P}\right)_T\right\}. \qquad (3)$$

Of the quantities in this equation, the left-hand side is experimentally determined by the Joule–Kelvin experiment; C_P may be obtained calorimetrically or spectroscopically (p. 59); while $(\partial V/\partial P)_T$ and $(\partial(PV)/\partial P)_T$ can be obtained from data on the compressibility of the gas at constant temperature (or from the equation of state; cf. section 3.4). Hence we can determine $(\partial E/\partial V)_T$ for any gas.

Before we discuss the values obtained, the experimental arrangement for measuring the Joule–Kelvin effect may be briefly described.†

The central part of Roebuck's apparatus is shown in fig. 14. Gas from a storage vessel is led at a constant pressure through a coil immersed in a thermostat to bring it to a known temperature, then into a vessel in the same thermostat where it passes over a platinum resistance thermometer, through a porous plug, and over another platinum resistance thermometer. The gas escapes through a valve which controls the final pressure. The initial pressure must be controlled within fine limits, since a change would lead to adiabatic expansion or compression and so to a change of temperature. The temperature-difference on the two sides of the plug (which may be as much as 25° C) is read to about 0·001° C. A needle-valve may be used instead of a porous plug; to keep down thermal losses, it must be made of non-conducting materials. Care must be taken that the gas does not gain appreciable kinetic energy during the expansion; this may be checked by varying the rate of flow, which should make no difference to the results. Keeping initial temperature and pressure constant, the final pressure is varied and the temperature-difference observed; from the

† Descriptions of apparatus for measuring the Joule–Kelvin effect are given by (a) Hoxton, *Phys. Rev.*, 1919, **13**, 438; (b) Roebuck, *Proc. Amer. Acad. Arts Sci.*, 1925, **60**, 537; (c) Sage and Lacy, *Industr. Engng. Chem.*, 1939, **32**, 369; (d) Johnston *et al.*, *J. Amer. Chem. Soc.*, 1946, **68**, 2362, 2367, 2373; (e) Roebuck, *J. Amer. Chem. Soc.*, 1942, **64**, 400.

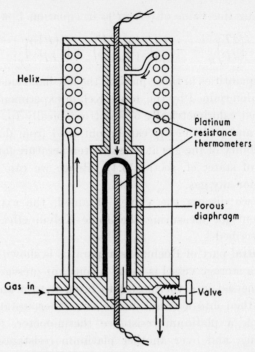

Helix

Platinum resistance thermometers

Porous diaphragm

Gas in

Valve

FIG. 14. Apparatus for measuring the Joule–Kelvin effect.

results, $(\partial T / \partial P)_H$ is obtained for a series of pressures and temperatures. Some results for gases at 1 atmosphere are given in Table 10.†

TABLE 10

Joule–Kelvin coefficients for gases at 1 atm

Temp., °C	$(\partial T / \partial P)_H$ degree/atm	
	Helium	*Nitrogen*
300	−0·0597	+0·0139
200	−0·0641	+0·0558
100	−0·0638	+0·1291
0	−0·0616	+0·2655
−100	−0·0584	+0·6487
−180	−0·0412	+2·391

† Roebuck and Osterberg, *Phys. Rev.*, 1934, **45**, 335.

Some values of $(\partial E/\partial V)_T$ for helium, derived from such results, are given in Table 11.† The accuracy of these figures is not high—the uncertainty is of the order of ± 10 per cent.—since they are found as the difference of two large quantities (cf. equation 3). It will be noted that the numerical value of $(\partial E/\partial V)_T$ decreases rapidly with decrease of pressure.

TABLE 11

Values of $-(\partial E/\partial V)_T$ *(in atm) for helium gas*

Pressure atm	Temperature, °C				
	−50	0	50	100	200
1	0·002	0·004	0·006	0·008	0·008
5	0·05	0·09	0·09	0·19	0·19
10	0·21	0·37	0·49	0·79	0·79
20	0·83	1·51	2·34	3·13	3·15
30	1·85	3·36	5·28	7·07	7·08

The expansion of a gas against the atmosphere can also be carried out *isothermally*, by adding heat to counteract the drop in temperature. A stream of gas may be used, as in the Joule–Kelvin experiment, and an electrical heating element placed next to the porous plug or expansion valve.‡ Application of the First Law shows that the heat supplied is equal to ΔH; hence one can plot ΔH against ΔP and so determine $(\partial H/\partial P)_T$. Another isothermal method is to allow compressed gas to escape from a steel vessel to the atmosphere through a coil of tubing, the apparatus being immersed in water whose temperature is kept constant by electrical heating;§ this gives $(\partial E/\partial P)_T$. From such measurements $(\partial E/\partial V)_T$ can be obtained, and compared with the results of Joule–Kelvin experiments. The results of the three methods agree satisfactorily where they can be compared; they also agree with results derived from the deviations of gases from the perfect-gas equation of state (p. 181). Such results provide important data on molecular interactions (section 3.43).

† See note † on p. 82.
‡ Charnley, Isles, and Townley, *Proc. Roy. Soc.* A, 1953, **218**, 133.
§ Rossini and Frandsen, *Bur. Stand. J. Res.*, 1932, **9**, 733; cf. Zemansky, *Heat and Thermodynamics* (McGraw-Hill, 1943), chap. 6.

For our purposes in the next section, the most important thing revealed by the experimental results is that $(\partial E/\partial V)_T$ decreases rapidly with decrease of pressure and *tends to zero as the pressure tends to zero*. In other words, the lower the pressure, the less does the internal energy of a gas depend on the volume, and the more closely does it become a function of temperature alone. We shall later find that the same is true of the heat content (p. 93). These results, moreover, appear to be true for all gases.

3.3. The pressure-volume relations of gases at low pressures; perfect-gas behaviour and scales of temperature

3.31. *Pressure-volume relations at low pressures*

The relations between pressure and volume for gases, like the relations between internal energy and volume (section 3.2), become simple for low pressures, provided that the gases are not too close to their critical temperatures. (At higher pressures and lower temperatures the relations are much more complex; they are treated in section 3.4.) At constant temperature, the product PV is nearly constant, varying slightly with P according to the linear relation

$$PV = (PV)^0(1-AP), \qquad (1)$$

where A is a constant depending on the temperature, and $(PV)^0$ is the value of PV in the limit as the pressure tends to zero. Linear plots of PV against P are found for many gases at pressures below one atmosphere. Fig. 15† shows the plots for hydrogen, oxygen, carbon dioxide, nitrous oxide, silicon tetrafluoride, ammonia, sulphur dioxide, and dimethyl ether, at 25° C.

The general conclusion may be drawn that as the pressure is reduced, at constant temperature, the P–V relations tend more and more closely to

$$(PV)_T = \text{constant} \qquad (2)$$

as the limiting form of relation.

† From Whytlaw-Gray, *Quart. Rev. Chem. Soc.*, 1950, **4**, 153.

We shall show later (section 5.1) that this limiting law may be thermodynamically related to the other limiting law for low pressures that we have already found (p. 84), namely $(\partial E/\partial V)_T = 0$. We can, however, easily see a connexion in terms of a molecular interpretation. Simple kinetic theory gives

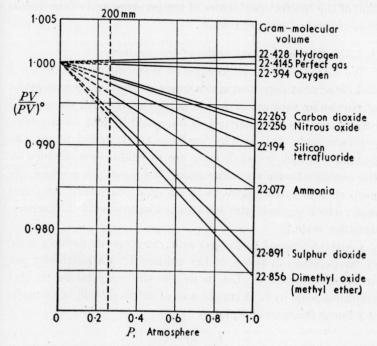

FIG. 15. $PV/(PV)^0$ for various gases below 1 atm at 25°C plotted against pressure.

for an assembly of monatomic gas molecules which are of negligible size and exert no intermolecular forces,

$$PV = \tfrac{2}{3} \text{ (kinetic energy of gas).}$$

The internal energy of a monatomic gas may be identified with the sum of the kinetic energies of its molecules. Thus PV is proportional to E. Hence, if E is independent of volume at low pressures, provided the temperature is constant, so is PV. From the alternative point of view of quantum statistics, the constancy of PV for such an assembly results from the fact that the partition-function for translation alone is proportional to the first power of the volume.[†]

We have as yet said nothing about the value of the constant in equation 2, nor about the way it depends on the temperature and mass of the gas. These matters will lead us to the formulation of the 'perfect-gas' scales of temperature and of the definition of 'perfect-gas behaviour'.

3.32. *The 'perfect-gas' scales of temperature*

We introduced the conception of temperature in Chapter I and noted that empirical scales which depend on the properties of particular substances do not agree exactly. All the general results that we have derived so far would be true on any temperature scale; this is why we have not scrupled to use the symbol T which we shall later use to denote temperature on the absolute thermodynamic scale. We must now see how the properties of gases enable us to set up a convenient empirical scale, which we shall later show to be identical with the thermodynamic scale.[‡]

Constant-pressure perfect-gas scale. Suppose we define a scale of temperature in terms of the volume V of a particular gas at constant pressure. Let us denote the temperature on this empirical scale by t. A simple way of defining t will be to make it a linear function of V, i.e.

$$t = \alpha V + \beta, \tag{3}$$

where α and β are constants. To fix these constants we need two independent equations involving them. We therefore define the value of t at two reproducible temperatures: we call '$0°$' the temperature at which ice is in equilibrium with water, saturated with air at one atmosphere pressure, and '$100°$' the temperature at which steam is in equilibrium with water at one atmosphere pressure. These fixed points, $0°$ and $100°$, fix a 'Celsius' scale; the unit of temperature is a 'centigrade degree'.

[†] Cf. note [‡], p. 69, and, for example, Rushbrooke, *Introduction to Statistical Mechanics* (1949), chap. 3.

[‡] An excellent account of temperature scales is given by Zemansky, *Heat and Thermodynamics* (1943), chap. 1.

If V_i is the volume corresponding to the ice-point (t_i), and V_s the volume corresponding to the steam-point (t_s), this gives us

$$0 = t_i = \alpha V_i + \beta \quad \text{and} \quad 100 = t_s = \alpha V_s + \beta.$$

Subtraction gives us $100 = \alpha(V_s - V_i)$, whence

$$\beta = -\alpha V_i = -100 V_i/(V_s - V_i).$$

Substituting these values for α and β in equation 3 which defines t, we obtain a definition of t in terms of the observable quantities V, V_s, and V_i:

$$\frac{t}{100} = \frac{(V - V_i)}{(V_s - V_i)}. \tag{4}$$

This expresses a simple proportionality between the temperature-intervals, $0°$ to $t°$ C and $0°$ to $100°$ C, and the corresponding volume increments. The temperature of any system can now be measured on this scale by means of a constant-pressure gas thermometer containing the particular gas chosen.

If we always use the same gas in the constant-pressure thermometer, under the same conditions, we have a self-consistent temperature scale. This scale, like all empirical scales, depends on the properties of the particular gas. When we use different gases, however, we find that the temperature-scales differ among themselves much less than do other empirical temperature scales (p. 9). Thus the temperature which would be indicated as $50°$ C by the constant-pressure helium thermometer, when working at a pressure of 1,000 mm Hg, would be given as follows if different gases were used in the gas-thermometer under the same conditions:

Gas:	Helium	Hydrogen	Neon	Nitrogen	Argon	Oxygen
$t = \dfrac{100(V - V_i)}{(V_s - V_i)}$	50·000	50·004	50·002	50·032	50·034	50·035

Moreover, the differences diminish as the pressure at which the thermometer works is reduced. In the limit at zero pressure, the temperatures indicated by the several gases (determined by extrapolation) are found to coincide. This result is extremely important both for our knowledge of gases (section 3.33), and for the temperature scales which are our present concern. It allows us to take a step towards emancipating our temperature-scale from the properties of a particular substance. The common limiting values on the several gas-scales, as the pressure tends to zero, define the *'perfect-gas' constant-pressure scale of temperature*. In mathematical terms,

$$t = \lim_{P \to 0}\left[\frac{100(V-V_i)}{(V_s-V_i)} \right]. \tag{5}$$

Constant-volume perfect-gas scale. Instead of defining temperature as varying linearly with the volume of a gas at constant pressure, we can define another scale on which it varies linearly with the pressure of the gas at constant volume. With the same fixed points, a Celsius scale is then defined by an equation analogous to equation 4:

$$\frac{t}{100} = \frac{(P-P_i)}{(P_s-P_i)}, \tag{6}$$

where P is the pressure of the gas at temperature t, P_i at the ice-point, and P_s at the steam-point, the volume being constant throughout. Temperature on this scale can be measured on a constant-volume gas thermometer. Experiments with various gases show that the temperature indicated by the different gases are nearly equal among themselves and nearly equal to that indicated by constant-pressure thermometers. The following results are obtained when the pressure of the gas at the ice-point is 1,000 mm, for the temperature given as 50° C by the constant-pressure helium thermometer working at 1,000 mm.

Gas:	Helium	Hydrogen	Neon	Nitrogen	Argon	Oxygen
$t = \dfrac{100(P-P_i)}{P_s-P_i}$	50·001	50·003	50·001	50·010	50·014	50·016

Moreover, as the pressure-range at which the thermometer works is reduced, the extremely important result is obtained that the temperatures on these several scales approach not only one another but also the temperature on the constant-pressure scale. The common limiting values define the 'perfect-gas' constant-volume scale of temperature, which coincides with the perfect-gas constant-pressure scale:

$$t = \lim_{P \to 0}\left[\frac{100(P-P_i)}{(P_s-P_i)}\right] = \lim_{P \to 0}\left[\frac{100(V-V_i)}{(V_s-V_i)}\right]. \qquad (7)$$

The absolute perfect-gas scale. There is one more very important property of gases which is revealed by gas thermo-

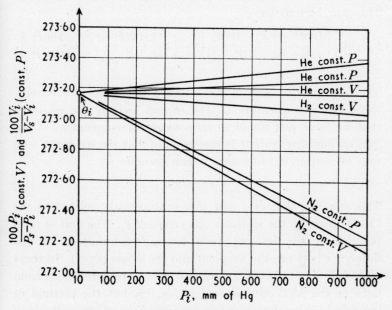

FIG. 16. $100V_i/(V_s-V_i)$ and $100P_i/(P_s-P_i)$ for various gases plotted against pressure.

metry. If, using the experimental data at the ice-point and at the steam-point, we compute values of $V_i/(V_s-V_i)$, or of $P_i/(P_s-P_i)$, for various gases, we find that these quantities depend slightly on the pressure, but that when extrapolated to zero pressure the values coincide and are *equal for all gases* within experimental error. This is illustrated in fig. 16.†

This experimental fact allows us to define a new temperature-scale, in which temperature is *directly proportional* to the volume

† By permission from *Heat and Thermodynamics* by Zemansky. Copyright, 1943, McGraw-Hill Book Company, Inc.

of any gas at constant pressure, or to the pressure at constant volume, in the limit at low pressures. (This corresponds to $\beta = 0$ in equation 3 above.) If we use θ to denote the temperature on this new scale, our definition of θ is

$$\theta = \lim_{P \to 0}\left[\frac{100V}{(V_s - V_i)}\right] = \lim_{P \to 0}\left[\frac{100P}{(P_s - P_i)}\right]. \tag{8}$$

This may be rewritten:

$$\theta = \lim_{P \to 0}\left[\frac{100(V - V_i)}{(V_s - V_i)} + \frac{100V_i}{(V_s - V_i)}\right] = \lim_{P \to 0}\left[\frac{100(P - P_i)}{(P_s - P_i)} + \frac{100P_i}{(P_s - P_i)}\right]. \tag{9}$$

The first term in each of the square brackets is, in the limit, the Celsius temperature t. The second term is the quantity that we have just found to be a constant independent of the gas; on our new scale it is the value of θ at the ice-point, and may be written θ_i. Equation 9 then becomes

$$\theta = t + \theta_i. \tag{10}$$

This equation defines a new temperature-scale, related to the Celsius scale by the addition of a constant θ_i. The unit of temperature is still the centigrade degree (one-hundredth of the difference between the ice-point and the steam-point). In these units θ_i is about $273 \cdot 2°$. In principle it may be determined from data of the kind summarized in fig. 16, but the method of graphical extrapolation is less accurate than other methods of correction (section 5.13), which give $\theta_i = 273 \cdot 16 \pm 0 \cdot 01$ centigrade degrees. Thus a temperature on the absolute gas scale is given by

θ (absolute perfect-gas scale temp.)

$$= t \text{ (Celsius gas scale temp.)} + 273 \cdot 16. \tag{11}$$

The absolute perfect-gas scale, though independent of the particular gas used, is yet an empirical scale in the sense that it depends on the properties of a particular group of substances and is not defined in terms of mechanical quantities alone. We shall later show, however, that it is *identical with the absolute thermodynamic scale*. It provides an important means of setting up that scale experimentally. In the rest of the present chapter, we shall continue to write θ instead of T, but in all the relations that we derive T can be substituted directly for θ.

3.33. *Pressure-volume-temperature relations at low pressures*

The experimental data, as we have just seen, allow the deduction that, as the mathematical limit at low pressures, the absolute temperature θ of a mass of gas is proportional to the pressure P at constant volume and to the volume at constant pressure. Consequently, when both P and V vary,

$$\theta \propto PV, \quad \text{or} \quad PV = \theta \times \text{constant}.$$

The constant in the equation is independent of P, V, and θ, and for a given gas it depends only on the mass of the sample, to which it is evidently proportional, since V is an extensive variable while P and θ are intensive. For one-gramme samples of different gases, the constant is found to have different values. It is therefore convenient to measure the masses of different gases in *different units*, chosen so that we can adopt one single value for the constant. The units adopted are called *moles*—the mole having a different value in grammes for each gas—and the constant is then a universal constant for all gases. It is called the *gas constant*, and is commonly written R. The pressure-volume-temperature relation for n moles of any gas, in the limit at low pressure, is thus

$$PV = nR\theta. \tag{12}$$

We shall find that the gas constant R occurs in many thermodynamic relations, and it is important to have an accurate value for it. For oxygen, the mole is defined as 32 grammes exactly. From this we can calculate R from the experimental data.† The limiting value of PV at low pressure for 32 grammes of oxygen at the ice-point is found experimentally to be $2271 \cdot 16 +$ $0 \cdot 04$ joules per mole. (It will be remembered that quantities

† The numerical data are given by Rossini *et al.*, *J. Amer. Chem. Soc.*, 1952, **74**, 2699.

with the dimensions of energy are best expressed in joules in the most accurate work.) Hence

$$R = (2271 \cdot 16 \pm 0 \cdot 04)/(273 \cdot 16 \pm 0 \cdot 01)$$

$$= 8 \cdot 3143_9 \pm 0 \cdot 00044 \text{ joule deg}^{-1} \text{ mole}^{-1}.$$

Changing the unit of energy to litre-atmospheres (1 atmosphere by definition = 1,013,250 dyne cm^{-2}; 1 litre = volume of 1,000 gm of water = $1000 \cdot 028 \pm 0 \cdot 004$ cm^3), we find

$$R = 0 \cdot 08205 \pm 0 \cdot 0^5 44 \text{ litre-atm deg}^{-1} \text{ mole}^{-1}.$$

In thermal units (1 calorie = $4 \cdot 1840$ joules by definition, p. 15)

$$R = 1 \cdot 9871_9 \pm 0 \cdot 0001 \text{ cal deg}^{-1} \text{ mole}^{-1}.$$

For any gas other than oxygen, the mole is defined thermo-dynamically as that mass of gas for which the limiting value at low pressures of PV/θ equals R as determined above. This is a purely *thermodynamic definition of the mole*, without any appeal to atomic theory or to atomic weights. Molecular con-cepts are not necessary to thermodynamics, though they are used to interpret its conclusions. There is, as a matter of fact, nearly always excellent agreement between the value in grammes of the mole of gas as determined on this thermodynamic defini-tion (by the limiting-density method†, for instance) and the sum of the atomic weights in grammes measured by chemical or mass-spectograph methods; this is strong evidence in favour of the atomic theory.

Kinetic theory or statistical mechanics based on the assump-tion that a gas consists of independent non-localized molecules leads to the conclusion that the number of molecules in a mole is the same for every gas. This number is called Avogadro's number, N^0. It may be determined experimentally in various ways—for instance, by finding the ratio of the Faraday to the electronic charge, or most accurately by measuring the spacings of atoms in crystals using X-rays of known wavelength—and is found to be $6 \cdot 023 \times 10^{23}$.

† Whytlaw-Gray, *Quart. Rev. Chem. Soc.*, 1950, **4**, 153.

3.34. *Thermodynamic properties of gases at low pressures. Perfect-gas behaviour*

For many practical purposes, the behaviour of a gas not too close to its critical temperature can be described accurately enough by equation 12. In accurate work, deviations from this equation become important. However, equation 12 is the mathematical limit at low pressures of equations describing the actual behaviour of gases (section 3.4).

We have thus found from independent experimental data† two tendencies in the behaviour of gases at low pressures which in the limit may be expressed by the equations

$$(\partial E/\partial V)_T \to 0 \quad \text{and} \quad PV \to nR\theta.$$

Later on, we shall be able to show by the aid of the Second Law that these two equations are related (section 5.1). This is not surprising, since both can be interpreted in terms of a picture of a perfect gas as an assembly of independent molecules. Either equation defines *perfect-gas behaviour*.

In the limit at low pressures when these equations become true, the thermodynamic properties of gases are much simplified. The relations of sections 2.72 (p. 53) and 2.73 (p. 63) give us, for perfect-gas behaviour:

(i) $(\partial E/\partial V)_\theta = (\partial E/\partial P)_\theta = 0$; that is, E is independent of volume or pressure and depends only on temperature.

(ii) Hence $C_V = (\partial E/\partial \theta)_V$ depends only on temperature (cf. p. 65).

(iii) $C_P - C_V = R$, by equation 9 of section 2.72 (p. 56), since

$$(\partial E/\partial V)_T = 0 \quad \text{and} \quad (\partial V/\partial P)_T = R/P.$$

(iv) Hence C_P depends only on temperature (cf. p. 65).

(v) By equation 2 of section 3.22 (p. 80), $(\partial H/\partial P)_\theta = 0$; that is, H is independent of pressure and depends only on the temperature.

Although no gas behaves exactly according to these equations at finite pressures, it is often convenient, as a theoretical device or as a first approximation, to work out the behaviour in given

† Cf. section 3.22, p. 84.

circumstances of a hypothetical 'perfect gas' for which the equation is true at ordinary pressures (as, for instance, in section 3.5 below). It is also convenient sometimes to take such an imaginary gas as a standard, and apply corrections to observed quantities—such as the entropy of a gas—for the deviations of the gas from perfect-gas behaviour. These theoretical devices must not be taken to imply that any real gas ever follows exactly the above relations.

3.4. Equations of state of gases

3.41. *P–V–T relations of gases over a wider range of pressure and temperature*

The behaviour of any actual gas is represented only as a first approximation by the equation

$$PV = nR\theta \tag{1}$$

which we have just been discussing. At constant temperature, PV is not independent of P, so that the plot of PV against P is not a perfectly horizontal line. The deviations depend on the gas, and are greater the lower the temperature. We have seen (p. 84) that below one atmosphere the plots of PV against P are linear, if the temperature is not too low; thus for this range we have accurate equations of the type

$$PV = (PV)^0(1-AP) = R\theta(1-AP). \tag{2}$$

But at higher pressures and lower temperatures, accurate measurements reveal more complex phenomena. Some examples are represented in figs. 17 a and 17 b,† which show isothermal plots of PV against P for hydrogen and carbon dioxide respectively, at various temperatures. Similar plots for various gases at $0°$ C are shown in fig. 18.

It is evident that the deviations from perfect-gas behaviour at a given temperature are larger for carbon dioxide than for hydrogen, and are greater the lower the temperature. At a low enough temperature it is possible to liquefy the gas by increasing the pressure. This is shown in fig. 19, which represents

† From *Handbuch der Experimentalphysik* (Akademische Verlagsgesellschaft, 1929), vol. viii (2).

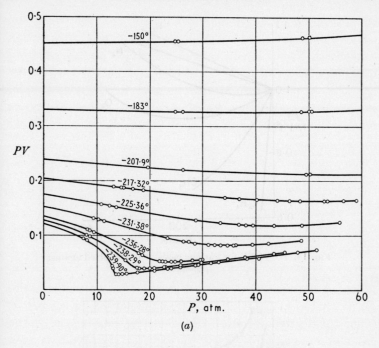

(a)

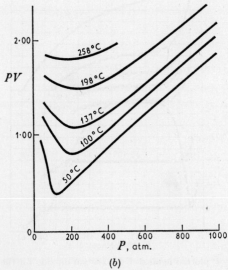

(b)

Fig. 17. PV plotted against P at various temperatures for (a) hydrogen, (b) carbon dioxide. (P in atm.; $V = 1$ at $0°$ C and 1 atm.)

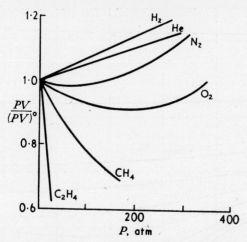

FIG. 18. $PV/(PV)^0$ for various gases at 0° C plotted against pressure.

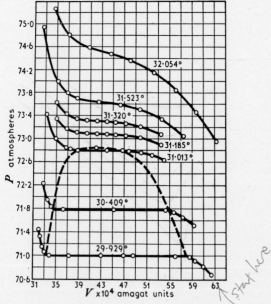

FIG. 19. P plotted against V for carbon dioxide for the range 29° to 32° C.†

† From Michels, Blaisse, and Michels, *Proc. Roy. Soc.* A, 1937, **160**, 367.

isothermal $P–V$ plots for carbon dioxide, including measurements at lower temperatures than those of fig. 17 b.

Suppose, for example, that carbon dioxide is kept at $29\cdot9°$ C and subjected to increasing pressure. From fig. 19 we see that if we continue to compress the gas after the pressure has reached about 71 atmospheres, we simply cause the gas to liquefy at constant pressure (the vapour pressure of the liquid at this temperature being about 71 atm). The curve therefore becomes a horizontal line. When the gas is completely liquefied, the pressure can be increased. This makes little difference to the volume, since the compressibility of the liquid is relatively small; the curve accordingly rises sharply. The length of the horizontal part evidently depends on the difference of density between gas and liquid. From the plots it is seen that this difference is greater the lower the temperature. As the temperature is increased, the two densities approach each other, the horizontal part becoming shorter, and they become equal at the temperature (about $31°$ C) corresponding to the peak of the dashed line. This is called the critical temperature and the pressure here is called the critical pressure; the $P–V$ curve passing through this critical point is called the critical isotherm. Inside the area bounded by the dashed line in fig. 19, liquid and gas can coexist, as two phases in equilibrium at the vapour pressure of the liquid; outside, liquid cannot exist in equilibrium with the gas (though it may in a metastable superheated condition). The critical point is a characteristic property of a gas; it may be accurately determined by various methods, for instance by measuring the liquid and vapour densities and finding graphically the point at which they are equal.[†] We deal later (Chapter VII) with two-phase systems and vapour pressures; we mention the condensation of a gas at this point because, like the deviations from perfect-gas behaviour, it must depend on molecular interactions, and to predict the critical point is a rather severe test of any theory of intermolecular forces.

The relations between pressure, volume, and temperature for a pure substance may be represented compendiously on a three-

[†] For a review see Kobe and Lynn, *Chem. Rev.*, 1953, **52**, 117.

dimensional diagram. Those for water are shown in fig. 20.†
P–V curves such as those shown in fig. 19 may be regarded
as projections of the P–V–T surface on the vertical plane
representing a particular temperature.

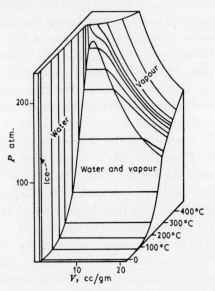

FIG. 20. Pressure-volume-temperature relations for water.

3.42. *Empirical equations of state*

Our present problem is to represent mathematically the relations of pressure, volume, and temperature for gases; some of
these have been represented graphically in the figures above.
Several hundred equations have been proposed. They become
more accurate as the number of adjustable constants is increased. We begin with a two-constant equation, the *van der
Waals equation*. Expressed for one mole of gas this is

$$\left(P + \frac{a}{V^2}\right)(V - b) = R\theta, \tag{3}$$

where a and b are two constants, assumed to be independent

† By permission from *Introduction to Chemical Physics*, by Slater. Copyright, 1937, McGraw-Hill Book Company, Inc.

of P, V, and temperature. Compared with the perfect-gas law, this gives a much improved account of the behaviour of real gases at relatively high pressures and low temperatures. It reproduces the forms of the isothermals above the critical point (fig. 19) and predicts quantitatively the position of the critical point, below which the equation has three roots instead of one. At the critical point, there is a point of inflection in the isotherm, so that $(\partial P/\partial V)_{\theta=\theta_c} = (\partial^2 P/\partial V^2)_{\theta=\theta_c} = 0$. Writing the van der Waals equation as

$$P = [R\theta/(V-b)] - (a/V^2), \qquad (4)$$

these conditions give the following expressions for the critical volume, temperature, and pressure: $V_c = 3b$, $\theta_c = 8a/27bR$, $P_c = a/27b^2$. Combining these gives $R\theta_c/P_cV_c = 8/3 = 2\cdot 67$ (instead of 1 for perfect-gas behaviour). We can thus test the van der Waals equation by calculating a and b from the critical constants and comparing the values with those derived from the isothermals. The comparison is shown in Table 12, and it is seen that the agreement is moderately good for the 'permanent' gases. Another test is to calculate $R\theta_c/P_cV_c$ from the critical constants and compare with the van der Waals value $2\cdot 67$. This is a severe test and the agreement is only fair. For instance, $R\theta_c/P_cV_c$ has the value 3 to $3\cdot 5$ for the simpler gases (Table 12).

The van der Waals equation can be used to interpret the curves of PV or of $(PV)/(PV)^0$ against P at various temperatures, of which we have shown examples in figs. 17 and 18, to summarize the deviations of gases from perfect-gas behaviour. For a given gas, the initial slope of the plot decreases with temperature; in some cases, it changes sign. Generally the plot is concave upwards. This behaviour can be reproduced by the van der Waals equation; indeed this is one great advantage of two-constant equations such as 3 over the one-constant equations such as 2. We write the equation in the form

$$PV = bP - \frac{a}{V} + \frac{ab}{V^2} + R\theta. \qquad (5)$$

At constant temperature the slope of a plot of PV against P is given, by differentiating this equation, as

$$\frac{d(PV)}{dP} = b - a\,\frac{d(1/V)}{dP} + ab\,\frac{d(1/V^2)}{dP}.$$

The last two terms are small, and are given accurately enough by differentiating the equation $PV = R\theta$, which gives

$$\frac{d(1/V)}{dP} = \frac{1}{R\theta} \quad \text{and} \quad \frac{d(1/V^2)}{dP} = \frac{2P}{R^2\theta^2}.$$

Substituting these values,

$$\frac{d(PV)}{dP} = b - \frac{a}{R\theta} + \frac{2abP}{R^2\theta^2}. \tag{6}$$

TABLE 12

Van der Waals constants a and b, and critical constants, for various gases

To obtain values independent of the units of pressure and volume, the van der Waals constants are expressed as the dimensionless quantities $a/P_0 V_0^2$ and b/V_0, where P_0 and V_0 are the pressure and volume under standard conditions ($0°$ C and 1 atm). The 'observed' values are those that fit the P–V curves at $0°$ C; the 'calculated' values are those derived from the critical constants (see text). 'Observed' values are from Kennard, *Kinetic Theory of Gases* (McGraw-Hill, 1938), p. 224; critical constants are from the tables of Kobe and Lynn.†

Gas	$10^3 a/P_0 V_0^2$		$10^3 b/V_0$		T_c K	P_c atm	V_c c.c. per mole	$\dfrac{RT_c}{P_c V_c}$
	obs.	calc.	obs.	calc.				
He	−0·04	0·06	0·46	0·86	5·3	2·26	57·8	3·4
Ne	0·30	0·34	0·77	0·62	44·5	26·9	41·7	3·3
A	3·04	2·1	2·06	1·12	151	48·0	75·2	3·4
H_2	0·34	0·40	0·95	0·97	33·3	12·8	65·0	3·3
N_2	3·07	2·1	2·55	1·34	126·2	33·5	90·1	3·4
O_2	3·60	2·2	2·60	1·16	154·8	50·1	78	3·1
CO_2	(17·5)	5·2	(9·9)	1·40	304·2	72·9	94·0	3·6
CH_4	..	..	..	..	191·1	45·8	99·0	3·4
C_2H_6	..	..	..	..	305·5	48·2	148	3·4
C_6H_6	..	..	..	..	562	48·6	260	3·3
$(C_2H_5)_2O$	..	..	..	..	467	35·6	281	3·8

† See note on p. 97.

The predictions of this equation agree qualitatively with the observed facts about the PV–P plots:

(i) At low pressures, and constant temperature, the slope of the plot $d(PV)/dP$ will become $(b-a/R\theta)$ and so will be independent of pressure; this agrees with the linear low-pressure plots in fig. 15 (p. 85) and the tendency of the plots in fig. 18 (p. 96) at the lower pressures.

(ii) At higher pressures the slope will increase, so that the curve of PV against P will be concave upwards, as in figs. 17 and 18.

(iii) For a given gas, the initial slope at $P = 0$ will depend on the temperature. It will be positive, as with hydrogen at $0°$ C, if $b > a/R\theta$; negative, as with hydrogen at $-200°$ C and most gases at ordinary temperatures, if $b < a/R\theta$. At the temperature when these quantities are equal ($\theta = a/Rb$), the initial slope becomes zero, as for perfect-gas behaviour. This temperature is called the 'Boyle temperature'.

(iv) Comparing different gases, this Boyle temperature will be lower, the smaller the constant a.

The flexibility of a two-constant equation in representing the observed facts is thus considerable, though quantitatively the fit is imperfect (see also p. 181). The agreement is somewhat improved by using another two-constant equation, the *Berthelot equation*, which for one mole of gas is

$$\left(P+\frac{a}{\theta V^2}\right)(V-b) = R\theta. \tag{7}$$

Since this equation gives better values of $R\theta_c/P_c V_c$ from its values for the critical constants,

$$P_c^2 = aR/216b^3, \quad V_c = 3b, \quad \theta_c^2 = 8a/27Rb,$$

it may be used in a form in which the critical constants appear in place of a and b:

$$PV = R\theta + P\left[\frac{V_c}{3} - \frac{27V_c\,\theta_c^2}{24\theta^2}\right]. \tag{8}$$

For accurate representation of the data, especially at high pressures, more adjustable constants are needed. A five-constant equation for which the constants have been determined for many gases is the *Beattie–Bridgman equation*, which for one mole of gas is

$$P = \frac{RT(1-\epsilon)(V+B)}{V^2} - \frac{A}{V^2}, \qquad (9)$$

where

$$A = A^0\left(1 - \frac{a}{V}\right), \qquad B = B^0\left(1 - \frac{b}{V}\right), \qquad \epsilon = C/VT^3,$$

the five adjustable constants being a, b, c, A^0, B^0. This equation is fairly satisfactory from high pressures down to the critical pressure, for temperatures above the critical.†

The behaviour of gases may be expressed, to whatever accuracy the experimental data present, by equations of the type used by the Berlin school of Holborn and Otto:

$$PV = R\theta + BP + CP^2 + DP^3 + \dots. \qquad (10)$$

For a fixed mass of gas, B, C, etc., depend only on the temperature; they are called the *second virial coefficient*, third virial coefficient, and so on. Another equation has been used by the Leiden school following Kammerlingh Onnes:

$$PV = R\theta(1 + B'/V + C'/V^2 + \dots), \qquad (11)$$

where the virial coefficients B', C', etc., again depend only on the temperature. When the highest accuracy is not necessary, the *second virial coefficient* B provides a useful second approximation to the behaviour of gases.‡ It may be related to the van der Waals 'constants' a and b by comparing equations 5 and 10; neglecting second-order terms, we find $B = b - a/R\theta$, an equation which represents the temperature-dependence of B with fair accuracy above the Boyle temperature.

---

† For data see Beattie and Stockmayer, in Taylor and Glasstone's *Treatise on Physical Chemistry* (1951), vol. ii, p. 206.

‡ An equation including the second virial coefficient is used systematically in Guggenheim, *Thermodynamics* (North Holland Publishing Co., 1957). Plots of B against T for various gases are given by Kennard, *Kinetic Theory of Gases* (McGraw-Hill, 1938), p. 222.

All these equations give at low pressures and constant temperature an equation of the form $PV = $ constant, and as the next approximation $PV = (PV)^0(1-AP)$, in agreement with experiment (equations 1 and 2, p. 84).

TABLE 13

Virial coefficients for helium†

Unit of pressure: metres of mercury.
Unit of volume: that of 1 mole at 0° C and 1 m mercury.

Temp., °C	$R\theta$	10^3B	10^6C	10^6D	10^9E
400	2·46244	0·59451	..	..	..
300	2·09665	0·61600	..	..	..
200	1·73091	0·64933	..	..	..
100	1·36518	0·6680	..	..	..
50	1·18223	0·68887	..	..	..
0	0·99931	0·6900	..	..	..
−50	0·81642	0·70000	0·163	..	..
−100	0·66352	0·69900	0·285	..	..
−150	0·45062	0·67000	0·449	..	..
−183·0	0·32992	0·62286	0·735	..	..
−208·0	0·23847	0·55080	2·384	−0·0141	..
−252·8	0·07460	−0·16424	18·529	−0·1105	..
−258·0	0·05558	−0·79740	54·370	−0·7513	+3·796

We shall later mention another general way of expressing the behaviour of gases, in terms of a function called the fugacity (section 5.15).

3.43. *Molecular interpretations of equations of state*

We have mentioned that the perfect-gas equation of state, $PV = R\theta$, agrees with that predicted for an assembly of non-interacting point molecules (p. 85). To account for the deviations from this equation, an investigation of intermolecular forces is the obvious line of attack.

The 'constants' of the van der Waals equation have a simple molecular interpretation. The term b is a correction to V arising from the finite size of the molecules, which reduces the free space. The term a/V^2 is a correction to the pressure to take account of intermolecular attractions, which will reduce the

† From Keesom, *Helium* (1942), p. 41. This book describes experimental methods, results, and theoretical interpretations.

average kinetic energy with which molecules strike the walls of the vessel. Rigorous examination shows, however, that the van der Waals equation can only be derived from theory under rather restricted conditions, and even then will give only a first-

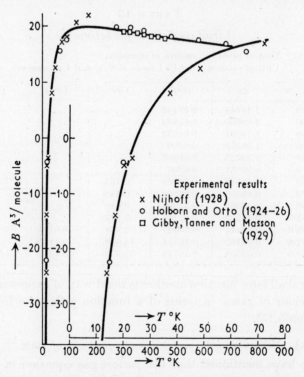

Fig. 21. Comparison of observed and calculated values of the second virial coefficient B for helium at various temperatures. The curves represent the calculated values.

order correction to the perfect-gas law; beyond this it is purely empirical.

More exact treatments of intermolecular forces such as that of Lennard-Jones have considered the repulsion forces that must operate at short distances, as well as the attractive forces, and have taken into account collisions between more than two molecules at a time. The energy of interaction of helium mole-cules, for instance, is expressed as the difference between a repulsion energy which falls off with r^{-12} (where r is the distance between molecular centres), and an energy due to attractive van der Waals forces which falls off with r^{-6}. The theory has been tested by calculating the second virial coefficient B at various temperatures and comparing with the experimental values. The agreement is good, as fig. 21 shows.[†] For fuller treatment of these theoretical calculations the reader is referred to works on statistical mechanics.[‡]

3.5. Work and heat changes for gases showing perfect-gas behaviour

Partly for their own interest, and partly because they serve as a bridge to a discussion of the Second Law, we now turn to the work and heat changes associated with processes of certain simple types in gases. These we can calculate with the aid of (i) the First Law and (ii) an equation of state. We shall throughout suppose the gas to exhibit *perfect-gas behaviour*, so that its equation of state is $PV = R\theta$; our conclusions will therefore be a first approximation to the behaviour of real gases. These conclusions will, however, be enough for our purposes, which are mainly concerned with principles rather than specific instances. We shall frequently have to idealize the processes in another way also, namely by assuming that the pressure of the gas while it expands or contracts is opposed by a pressure only infinitesimally different, and that heat exchanges occur because of a temperature-difference that is only infinitesimal. Such changes are called *reversible* or *quasi-static*, while ordinary changes with a finite pressure or temperature-difference are called *irreversible*. These types of change will be fully discussed in the next chapter (section 4.2) since they turn out to be important in connexion with the direction taken by a physical or

---

[†] From Fowler and Guggenheim, *Statistical Mechanics* (Cambridge, 1939).

[‡] Rushbrooke, *Introduction to Statistical Mechanics* (1949), chap. 16; Guggenheim, *Mixtures* (Oxford, 1952), chap. 8; Fowler and Guggenheim, *Statistical Thermodynamics* (1939), chap. 7; Mayer and Mayer, *Statistical Mechanics* (Wiley, 1940), chaps. 12 and 13. Cf. also Taylor and Glasstone, *Treatise on Physical Chemistry* (1951), vol. ii, chap. 2; Keesom, *Helium* (1942), chap. 2; Hirschfelder, Curtiss, and Bird, *Molecular Theory of Gases and Liquids* (Chapman & Hall, 1954); Rowlinson, *Ann. Rep. Chem. Soc.*, 1955, pp. 57 seq.

chemical change. At present we shall consider a few examples, from the point of view of the work and heat changes.

3.51. *Work and heat of reversible isothermal expansion of a fixed quantity of a perfect gas*

We consider a fixed mass of gas, say one mole for convenience. Heat is supplied to the gas while it expands, in such a way that its temperature remains constant. The expansion occurs against

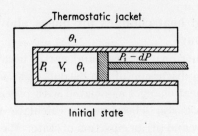

Initial state

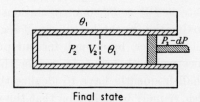

Final state

FIG. 22. Isothermal reversible expansion of a gas (schematic).

a pressure differing only infinitesimally from that of the gas, so that the change of volume is reversible or quasi-static. We can picture the gas as enclosed at pressure P in a cylinder by a piston on which the pressure is $P-dP$; and the cylinder as enclosed in a constant-temperature jacket from which heat is supplied. Suppose the initial state of the gas is characterized by the values P_1, V_1, θ_1, and the final by P_2, V_2, θ_1 (fig. 22). The work done by the gas in expansion (or compression) can be calculated in terms of the initial and final states as follows, introducing our knowledge step by step.

(i) By the First Law, the change in internal energy of the gas is given by $\Delta E = q - w$.

(ii) For perfect-gas behaviour, $(\partial E/\partial V)_\theta = 0$. Hence for expansion at constant temperature, $\Delta E = 0$. From the First Law equation, therefore, $q = w$.

(iii) The work done by the gas during a small change of volume dV is $dw = P\,dV$. In a reversible change such as the present one, all the work is used in pushing back the piston and none goes to increase the kinetic energy of gas or in frictional losses. For the complete change of volume from V_1 to V_2, we obtain by integrating,

$$w = q = \int_{V_1}^{V_2} P\,dV.$$

(iv) Assuming the equation of state $PV = R\theta$, so that $P_1 V_1 = R\theta_1$, and $P_2 V_2 = R\theta_1$, this gives

$$w = q = \int_{V_1}^{V_2} R\theta_1 \, dV/V$$

$$= R\theta_1 \int_{V_1}^{V_2} dV/V = R\theta_1 \int_{V_1}^{V_2} d\ln V = R\theta_1 \ln(V_2/V_1).$$

At constant temperature, $V_2/V_1 = P_1/P_2$, so that

$$\boxed{w = R\theta_1 \ln P_1/P_2.} \tag{1}$$

The work and heat of expansion are thus determined by the logarithm of the expansion ratio. This relation is worth noting as the source of many other logarithmic relations (cf., for example, section 5.15, p. 188). It could also be written in the exponential form $P_1 = P_2\,e^{w/R\theta_1}$.

3.52. *Work of reversible adiabatic expansion of a fixed quantity of a perfect gas*

Here a fixed mass of gas is supposed to be allowed to expand, without heat being supplied, by reducing the external pressure gradually. We must now picture the cylinder as enclosed in an insulating jacket (fig. 23). The pressure is opposed by a pressure only infinitesimally different.

For convenience we shall again assume that the mass of gas is one mole. Since the process is adiabatic, $q = 0$, and the First Law gives for an infinitesimal change

$$dE = -dw = -P\,dV. \tag{2}$$

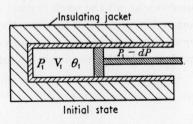

Initial state

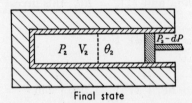

Final state

FIG. 23. Adiabatic reversible expansion of a gas (schematic).

We have to consider the variation of E with temperature and volume together. (The values of T, V, and P are related by the equation of state, so it is only necessary to consider two of these variables.) We therefore write quite generally

$$dE = \left(\frac{\partial E}{\partial \theta}\right)_V d\theta + \left(\frac{\partial E}{\partial V}\right)_\theta dV.$$

For a perfect gas, $(\partial E/\partial V)_\theta = 0$. For any substance (p. 53),

$$(\partial E/\partial \theta)_V = C_V.$$

Substituting these values,

$$dE = C_V\,d\theta. \tag{3}$$

Comparing equations 2 and 3,

$$C_V\,d\theta = -P\,dV. \tag{4}$$

Hence, by equation 2 the work done by the gas is

$$w = - \int_{\theta_1}^{\theta_2} C_V \, d\theta. \tag{5}$$

This is a function of temperature only, since C_V like E is independent of volume for a perfect gas.†

We can also obtain general relations between P, V, and θ in adiabatic change. For one mole of a perfect gas, $PV = R\theta$; substituting $P = R\theta/V$ in equation 4, we obtain

$$C_V \, d\theta/\theta = -R \, dV/V$$

or

$$C_V \, d\ln\theta = -R \, d\ln V. \tag{6}$$

We have already found (p. 93) from the First Law that for perfect-gas behaviour $C_P - C_V = R$, so that if we write γ for the ratio C_P/C_V of the heat capacities at constant pressure and at constant volume, then $C_V(\gamma-1) = R$. Substituting this in equation 6,

$$d\ln\theta = -(\gamma-1) \, d\ln V. \tag{7}$$

This equation is simple to integrate if $(\gamma-1)$ can be taken as constant, that is if γ is independent of volume and temperature. For a perfect gas, E is independent of V, and therefore so also is its derivative C_V; hence C_P is independent of V (since $C_P = C_V + R$), and therefore so also is γ. When the temperature varies, experiment shows that γ is strictly constant only for monatomic gases, as we have seen; for other gases, however, we can assume it to be constant as a first approximation. Equation 7 then integrates to

$$[\ln\theta] = -(\gamma-1)[\ln V].$$

Hence if the initial and final states are characterized by the values P_1, V_1, θ_1 and P_2, V_2, θ_2,

$$\ln(\theta_2/\theta_1) = (\gamma-1)\ln(V_1/V_2)$$

or

$$\theta_1 V_1^{\gamma-1} = \theta_2 V_2^{\gamma-1}. \tag{8}$$

This equation 8 at once gives the temperature-drop in terms

† The First Law equation for the internal energy of a closed system is $\Delta E = q - w$. We have now considered the special cases when for perfect gases (i) $w = q = 0$ (section 3.21); (ii) $\Delta E = 0$ (section 3.51); (iii) $q = 0$ (section 3.52).

of C_P/C_V and the pressure-drop. When, for instance, air ($\gamma = 1\cdot4$) expands from a pressure of 50 atm to 1 atm, θ_2/θ_1 is about $0\cdot5$.

Using the relations $P_1V_1 = R\theta_1$ and $P_2V_2 = R\theta_2$, equation 8 gives
$$P_1 V_1^\gamma = P_2 V_2^\gamma, \quad \text{or} \quad PV^\gamma = \text{constant}. \tag{9}$$

These important equations (8 and 9) state the relations between P, V, and T applicable to adiabatic expansion of a perfect gas when C_P/C_V is constant.

It is possible to determine the value of C_P/C_V, using equation 8, by experiments in which the temperature-drop is observed when a gas expands adiabatically, as in the method of Clément and Désormes. Since $C_P - C_V = R$, determination of C_P/C_V gives at once values for both C_P and C_V. (Correction may be made for deviations from perfect-gas behaviour.) These quantities are all of both practical and theoretical interest. More accurate experimental methods, based on the same equations, have been developed and we shall now outline these.

Adiabatic change during vibrations of a column of gas; determination of C_P/C_V. If rapid oscillations are set up in a column of gas, the compression and expansion of an element of gas occur faster than heat can be exchanged with the rest of the gas, and the conditions approach those of adiabatic change. The behaviour of the gas is then described by equation 8 or 9, with an accuracy depending on the departure of the gas from perfect-gas behaviour and from the condition that γ is independent of temperature. There are two different methods of determining γ, and hence C_P and C_V, based on this principle.

(i) *Velocity of sound.* The propagation of sound waves involves nearly adiabatic changes in a gas, and the velocity calculated in terms of γ and the molecular weight M is $v = (\gamma RT/M)^{\frac{1}{2}}$ for a perfect gas; corrections can be applied for deviations from perfect-gas behaviour. Measurements of the velocity of sound by means of Kundt's and similar methods have been used to obtain γ.† The method has been adapted to low temperatures

† Cf., for example, Partington, *Treatise on Physical Chemistry* (Longmans, 1949), vol. i, pp. 792 seq.

by applying an oscillator to a column of gas of known length in a thermostat, tuning to resonance, and measuring the frequency.†

(ii) *Oscillation of a piston.*‡ In a method suggested originally by Rüchhardt, a ball is allowed to oscillate vertically in a smooth tube connected to a vessel of gas (fig. 24 a). It may be shown that if equations 8 and 9 are correct, the motion will be simple-harmonic, with a period proportional to $1/\gamma^{\frac{1}{2}}$.

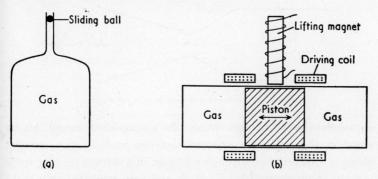

FIG. 24. Determination of C_P/C_V by oscillation of a piston.

The same principle has been used by Clark and Katz,§ in the most accurate method yet devised for determining C_P/C_V. A steel piston, whose weight is balanced by an electromagnet, divides the gas in a horizontal cylinder into two equal parts (fig. 24 b).‖ It is set into vibration along the cylinder by external coils in which an alternating current of variable frequency is maintained. At a particular frequency resonance occurs; this is detected by observing the amplitude of vibration with a micrometer eyepiece. Corrections are applied for friction, deviations from perfect-gas behaviour, and departure from adiabatic conditions; they amount to about 1 per cent. The ratio C_P/C_V for several gases has been determined at a series of pressures from 1 to 25 atm, and extrapolated to zero pressure. Some

† Cornish and Eastman, *J. Amer. Chem. Soc.*, 1928, **50**, 627.

‡ Cf. Zemansky, *Heat and Thermodynamics* (1943), pp. 106 seq.

§ Clark and Katz, *Canad. J. Res.* A, 1943, **21**, 1, and earlier papers.

‖ By permission from *Heat and Thermodynamics* by Zemansky. Copyright, 1943, McGraw-Hill Book Company, Inc.

results are given in Table 7, p. 67; in general they agree very well with the values calculated from statistical-spectroscopic values of C_P and the relation $C_P - C_V = R$ at $P = 0$.

3.53. *Work of irreversible adiabatic expansion; velocity of a jet of gas*†

In turbines and jet engines, a stream of gas passes from high to low pressure under nearly adiabatic conditions, and in doing

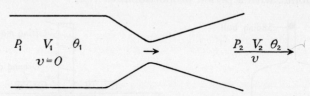

FIG. 25. Adiabatic expansion of a jet of gas.

so accelerates to a high speed. As a simplified model, let us consider the adiabatic expansion of one mole of gas, moving along a tube and out through a nozzle, in a stream passing from a state characterized by P_1, V_1, θ_1 and zero velocity, to a state characterized by P_2, V_2, θ_2 (where $\theta_2 < \theta_1$) and velocity v.

We wish to know how much work has gone to increase the kinetic energy of the jet; this will give us the velocity. The total work done by the gas (w_{total}) is made up of this work ($w_{\text{K.E.}}$) plus the work done on the surroundings (w_{surr}):

$$w_{\text{total}} = w_{\text{K.E.}} + w_{\text{surr}}. \tag{10}$$

The total work must, since $q = 0$, be numerically equal to the change in internal energy, by the First Law:

$$\Delta E = q_{\text{total}} - w_{\text{total}} = -w_{\text{total}}.$$

Since ΔE is a thermodynamic function, it depends only on P_1, V_1, θ_1 and P_2, V_2, θ_2, and will be the same whatever processes are used to bring the system from the first state to the second. We can settle its value by working it out for the particular case where the work is *all* done against the atmosphere, without any increase in kinetic energy. This would be so if the pressure

† Cf., for example, Ewing, *Thermodynamics for Engineers* (Cambridge, 2nd edn. 1936).

of the gas were opposed at every point by a pressure only in-finitesimally less. The work would then be $\int_{V_1}^{V_2} P\,dV$. This fixes ΔE and so w_{total}:

$$\Delta E = -w_{\text{total}} = -\int_{V_1}^{V_2} P\,dV. \tag{11}$$

The work done on the surroundings, w_{surr}, is the difference between the work done by the gas against the atmosphere on the low-pressure side $(P_2 V_2)$ and that done on the gas when it is expelled from the high-pressure side $(P_1 V_1)$. This may be written as follows:

$$w_{\text{surr}} = P_2 V_2 - P_1 V_1 = \int_{V_1}^{V_2} d(PV). \tag{12}$$

Substituting in equation 9 for w_{total} and w_{surr}, from equations 11 and 12, we find

$$w_{\text{K.E.}} = w_{\text{total}} - w_{\text{surr}} = \int_{V_1}^{V_2} P\,dV - \int_{V_1}^{V_2} d(PV) = -\int_{V_1}^{V_2} V\,dP. \tag{13}$$

This work has gone to accelerate one mole (M grammes) of gas to a velocity v, so that the kinetic energy is given by

$$w_{\text{K.E.}} = \tfrac{1}{2}Mv^2 = -\int_{V_1}^{V_2} V\,dP. \tag{14}$$

Using the relations $P_1 V_1 = R\theta_1$, $P_2 V_2 = R\theta_2$, and $P_1 V_1^\gamma = P_2 V_2^\gamma$ we obtain finally

$$v^2 = \left\{ \frac{2\gamma}{\gamma-1} \frac{R\theta_1}{M} \left[1 - \left(\frac{P_2}{P_1} \right)^{(\gamma-1)/\gamma} \right] \right\}. \tag{15}$$

This gives the velocity in terms of the initial temperature, the expansion ratio, and the ratio γ.

We have derived this relation not for the sake of the result but because several general comments may be made upon the method of derivation.

(i) We notice that the energy relations are here quite different from those when the gas remains at rest, the case considered in section 3.52 (p. 107). The assumption which we normally make

I

in chemical thermodynamics, that the kinetic energy of the system as a whole is zero relative to its surroundings, is thus an important one.

(ii) The First Law gives an exact result even for an irreversible process. We shall find that when the Second Law also is involved, we obtain an exact result only by considering reversible processes.

(iii) We can fix the value of the change in a thermodynamic function for a given change of state by working out the value when the change is brought about by a reversible process; this value, once fixed, can be used when dealing with irreversible processes. This is a useful device which we shall use in various connexions.

3.54. *Application of the First Law to heat engines: the reversible constant-pressure cycle for a monatomic perfect gas*

With the help of the relations for adiabatic change worked out in section 3.52, we can obtain a more exact result for the constant-pressure heat-engine cycle mentioned earlier (section 2.1).

Thermodynamically, the 'working substance' in the heat-engine is a closed system, exchanging heat and work with its surroundings. We shall assume that the pressure P of the system is always opposed by a pressure infinitesimally different, $P \pm dP$. We consider a completed cycle, after which the system has returned to its initial state and all the changes observable are in the surroundings alone. To simplify matters, we suppose the system to consist of one mole of a perfect gas; the results will thus be approximations to those for actual gases. We shall also assume that C_P and C_V can be taken as constant, as for a monatomic gas.

Suppose that the initial state of the system is represented on a P–V diagram by the point A, corresponding, say, to room temperature and pressure, P_1, V_1, θ_1. Suppose the gas is taken through the following cycle of changes.

(i) Compress adiabatically, to the state characterized by P_2, V_2, and θ_2, represented by point B. $(\theta_2 > \theta_1.)$

(ii) Arrange for heat to be supplied by the surroundings, and for the volume to be simultaneously increased so that the pressure remains constant, so that the state reached is characterized by P_2, V_3, and θ_3, represented by C. ($\theta_3 > \theta_2$.)

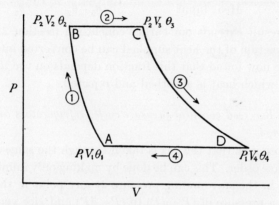

FIG. 26. Constant-pressure heat-engine cycle (schematic).

(iii) Expand the gas adiabatically until the initial pressure is reached, at point D, corresponding to P_1, V_4, and θ_4. ($\theta_4 < \theta_3$.)

(iv) Arrange for heat to be withdrawn to the surroundings, reducing the volume at the same time, so that the state represented by A is regained. ($\theta_1 < \theta_4$.)

From the perfect-gas equation of state and the relations $P_1 V_1^\gamma = P_2 V_2^\gamma$ and $P_1 V_4^\gamma = P_2 V_3^\gamma$, it is easy to show that

$$\theta_1/\theta_2 = \theta_4/\theta_3.$$

By the First Law, $\Delta E = 0$ for a completed cycle, so that the work done $w = q$, the net heat absorbed by the cycle. This is the difference between the heat absorbed from the surroundings in the higher temperature-range, which is $C_P(\theta_3 - \theta_2)$, and that rejected to the surroundings in the lower temperature-range, which is $C_P(\theta_4 - \theta_1)$. Thus:

$$w = q = C_P\{(\theta_3 - \theta_2) - (\theta_4 - \theta_1)\}.$$

It will later appear (section 4.42) that the ratio of the work done to the heat input in step (ii), a ratio known to engineers as the 'efficiency', is of more general thermodynamic interest. This quantity is

$$\frac{\text{Work done by system}}{\text{Heat input}} = 1 - \frac{\theta_4 - \theta_1}{\theta_3 - \theta_2} = 1 - \frac{\theta_4}{\theta_3}. \qquad (16)$$

This result extends our earlier conclusion (section 2.1) that only a fraction of the heat supplied can be converted into work. We have now found that this fraction depends on the temperatures at which heat is absorbed and rejected.

3.55. *Reversed constant-pressure cycle: refrigerators and heat-pumps*

Suppose now that the gas is taken through the same cycle in the reverse order. This can be done by making only infinitesimal changes in the surrounding pressure at any point in the cycle, altering a pressure of $(P+dP)$ to $(P-dP)$ and vice versa. We shall suppose (only for convenience; it is not essential) that the state of the gas at room temperature and pressure now corresponds to the point D, instead of A. Then suppose the cycle of operations is as follows (fig. 27):

(a) Compress the gas adiabatically (D to C; $\theta_3 > \theta_4$).

(b) Allow heat to pass to the surroundings so that the gas is cooled (C to B; $\theta_2 < \theta_3$).

(c) Expand the gas adiabatically to atmospheric pressure (B to A). This will bring the gas to below room temperature, since $\theta_1 < \theta_4$.

(d) Allow heat to pass from the surroundings (by suitably changing the environment), to bring the gas back to room temperature at constant pressure (A to D). These surroundings will thus lose heat.

In this cycle the system rejects heat at the *higher* temperature-range to its surroundings, and absorbs heat at the *lower* temperature-range. The net heat absorbed by the system is thus the negative of the heat absorbed in the heat-engine cycle of section 3.54, and as $q = w$ the work done by the system is

negative. That is, work is done *on* the system, by the surroundings. The result is, then, that *by expenditure of work* supplied from outside, heat is transferred from cooler bodies (step
(iv)) to hotter bodies (step (ii)). Heat has been made to 'flow
uphill', to pass in the direction opposite to that which it takes
when two bodies are simply brought into thermal contact; this

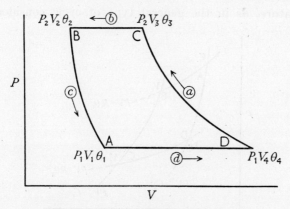

FIG. 27. Reversed constant-pressure cycle.

has been achieved through the expenditure of work. We shall
see that the Second Law (section 4.3) is much concerned with
the generalization of this result.

This type of cycle is put to practical use in two ways. (*a*) In
refrigeration we are interested in the bodies which are cooled
in step (iv), while the heat rejected in step (ii) is unimportant.
The working substance is commonly an easily-condensible gas
such as ammonia; the cycle is not unlike that of fig. 27, but the
constant-pressure lines correspond to evaporation and condensation of the gas. The work is supplied by a motor that drives
a pump to compress the gas. (*b*) In a *heat-pump*, which also
works by evaporation and condensation of a gas, the body which
is cooled in step (iv) is the external atmosphere, or sometimes
a lake or river, while the heat rejected at the higher temperature in step (ii) is used to heat air or water for the central-
heating system of a building. This is particularly advantageous
where electricity generated from water-power is available. It is

more economical to use a given amount of electrical energy to drive a motor to work a heat-pump that transfers heat from the cooler surroundings to the warmer building, than to use the same amount of electricity to warm the building directly.†

3.56. *Reversible Carnot cycle for a perfect gas*

In this cycle the heat transfers are conducted at constant temperature, as in the general type of cycle considered by

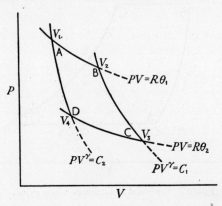

FIG. 28. Carnot cycle for a perfect gas (schematic).

Carnot in a paper published in 1824.‡ We again consider the limiting case of a monatomic perfect gas. The cycle, represented in fig. 28, is made up of parts of two isothermals, whose equations may be written $PV = R\theta_1$ and $PV = R\theta_2$; and parts of two adiabatics, whose equations may be written $PV^\gamma = c_1$ and $PV^\gamma = c_2$, where c_1 and c_2 are constants (cf. equation 9, p. 110).

Both for adiabatic and for isothermal changes, we can write down the heat absorbed by the gas, and the work done, using the expressions derived from the First Law and the definition of a perfect gas. For isothermal changes (section 3.51), such as that from A to B, $q = w = RT \ln(V_2/V_1)$. For adiabatic changes

† For a fuller account of refrigerators and heat-pumps see, for example, Zemansky, *Heat and Thermodynamics* (1943), chap. 12; S. J. Davies, *Heat Pumps* (Constable, 1950).

‡ Sadi Carnot, 'Réflexions sur la puissance motrice du feu, et sur les machines propres à développer cette puissance' (1824); extracts in Magie (ed.), *Source-book in Physics* (McGraw-Hill, 1935), p. 221.

(section 3.52), $q = 0$ and $w = -\int_{\theta_1}^{\theta_2} C_V\, d\theta$. For the cycle we may summarize the changes in a table as follows.

Change	Heat absorbed by gas	Work done by gas
(1) A → B, isothermal	$q_1 = w_1$	$w_1 = R\theta_1 \ln(V_2/V_1)$
(2) B → C, adiabatic	0	$w_2 = -\int_{\theta_1}^{\theta_2} C_V\, d\theta$
(3) C → D, isothermal	$q_2 = w_3$	$w_3 = -R\theta_2 \ln(V_3/V_4)$
(4) D → A, adiabatic	0	$w_4 = -\int_{\theta_2}^{\theta_1} C_V\, d\theta$

The net work done by the system at the end of the cycle is $(w_1+w_2+w_3+w_4)$, which is equal to (w_1+w_3) since w_2 and w_4 cancel. The heat input is q_1 which is equal to w_1. Hence the ratio

$$\text{(net work)/(heat input)} = (w_3+w_1)/w_1 = 1+w_3/w_1$$

$$= 1-\theta_2 \ln(V_3/V_4)/\theta_1 \ln (V_2/V_1). \quad (17)$$

From the equations of state and the equations for the adiabatics, it is easy to show that $(V_3/V_4) = (V_2/V_1)$, so that

$$\text{(net work)/(heat input)} = 1-(\theta_2/\theta_1) = (\theta_1-\theta_2)/\theta_1. \quad (18)$$

This equation refers to the efficiency of a reversible heat-engine working in such a cycle between temperatures θ_1 and θ_2.† Since the working substance is a (hypothetical) perfect gas, the result is an approximation for real gases. The conclusion is in itself of interest from the point of view of engineering, but for the purposes of chemical thermodynamics two of its consequences are more important as giving clues to more general relations between heat, work, and temperature.

(i) The first of these consequences is as follows. For a complete cycle, the net work done by a system is, by the First Law, equal to the algebraic sum of the heats absorbed by the system. Here this sum is q_1+q_2 (q_2 being negative). Substituting in

---

† The result may be shown to be true also when C_P and C_V vary with temperature, as with diatomic and polyatomic gases.

equation 18, we find for our reversible perfect-gas Carnot cycle:

$$\frac{q_1 + q_2}{q_1} = \frac{\theta_1 - \theta_2}{\theta_1}$$

or
$$\frac{q_1}{\theta_1} + \frac{q_2}{\theta_2} = \sum_{cycle} \frac{q}{\theta} = 0. \tag{19}$$

This will later be generalized, with the aid of the Second Law (section 4.44); the result will be found to be of great importance.

(ii) Suppose the system is brought from the state represented by A to that represented by C, reversibly as before, by one of the two paths ABC or ADC. For the first, the heat absorbed is q_1; for the second, it will be $q_2' = -q_2$, since the path ADC is the reverse of CDA, differing from it only infinitesimally if the change is done reversibly. The two heat changes are therefore related, according to equation 19, as follows:

$$\frac{q_1}{\theta_1} = \frac{q_2'}{\theta_2}. \tag{20}$$

Thus (q/T) is constant, independent of the path, provided that one of the two Carnot cycle paths is chosen. This result also will be generalized with the aid of the Second Law (section 4.44) and then has very important consequences.

THE SECOND LAW OF THERMODYNAMICS AND ITS CONSEQUENCES

WE have not yet paid any attention to the question of how the *direction* of a chemical or physical change is determined. The First Law is only concerned with the constant ratios between changes in amounts of heat, work, and material; whether the change in any of these is an increase or a decrease is not considered. Yet it is a matter of experience that the direction of a change that we can observe is fixed, under given conditions. For example, the First Law states that in the interconversion of heat and mechanical work, the ratio of heat to work is constant, but it says nothing about the direction of flow of heat. As far as the conservation of energy is concerned, there is no reason why one should not be able to construct a heat-engine that would take heat from the sea, leaving it colder, and turn all this heat into work. One could then arrange a heat-engine cycle in which mechanical work would be done, such as the raising of a weight, and the only other change would be the cooling of a heat reservoir. Experience shows that this cannot actually be done. In every heat-engine that has been realized, and every imaginable heat-engine that is in accord with the known behaviour of material systems, heat is absorbed by a working substance from a hot reservoir, some of it is converted into work, and the rest is given out to a cooler reservoir when the working substance returns to its original condition (cf. sections 3.54, 3.56). Heat will not pass spontaneously from a body at a lower temperature to one at a higher temperature. Such a process would not violate the First Law, but it does not happen. Normally, heat passes from a body at a higher temperature to one at a lower; water flows downhill; electricity passes from a higher potential to a lower; gas passes from a region of higher pressure to one of lower. Chemical reactions proceed in directions that we can predict as a result of experience, though either direction is compatible with the First Law. The direction of these changes in given circumstances is fixed. It would obviously be very interesting if we could find general criteria that would predict this direction. This is the concern of the present chapter.

The direction of the observed change can be altered if work is supplied from an external source. Heat can be made to flow from a body at a lower temperature to one at a higher, by expenditure of work, as we have seen from the example of refrigerators and heat-pumps (section 3.55). Again, a chemical reaction proceeding in a short-circuited galvanic cell can be stopped by balancing the e.m.f. of the cell by means of a potentiometer, and reversed by applying a contrary potential difference greater than the e.m.f. of the cell. Facts such as these must evidently be covered by any generalization about the direction of changes.

In chemical thermodynamics we are often interested in *equilibrium*—a state of affairs in which the rate of some change becomes zero. For instance, when pressures are equalized, as between a manometer and a vessel of gas, no further pressure change is observed; similarly temperature equilibrium, electrical equilibrium, and chemical equilibrium can be set up, and no observable change then occurs in either direction. Criteria for equilibrium are also the concern of the Second Law.

4.1. Intensity factors and the basic criteria for the direction of change and for equilibrium

We noted in section 2.3 that any of the terms contributing to a change in the internal energy E can be represented as the product of an intensity factor and the change in a capacity factor—$P\,dV$, $\mu\,dn$, and so on. For the general case we may write such a term as $I\,dC$, where I is any intensity factor and C the corresponding capacity factor.

A basic criterion for the direction of changes is derived directly from this conception. It is a matter of experience that, in simple cases where only one intensity factor is concerned, the direction of exchange of heat, work, or material between one system and another is determined by the values of the intensity factors of the two systems. Thus if one system consists of a fixed amount of gas at a certain pressure in a flask, and the other consists of gas at a lower pressure in a second flask connected to the first through a manometer or diaphragm, then the diaphragm or manometer-liquid separating the two systems will move towards the second system, until the pressures are equalized, when equilibrium is set up. Similarly, electric charge passes from a body at a higher potential to one of lower, and equilibrium will be set up when this process has resulted in the potentials being equalized, as for instance in the charging of a condenser by a battery. Heat flows from a reservoir at higher temperature to one at lower temperature, and equilibrium is set up when the temperatures are equalized, as for instance between a thermostat and its contents. The corresponding law for the transfer of material is not so obvious, but we shall later be able to show that any kind of material tends to pass from a system in which its chemical potential is higher to one in which it is lower, and that equilibrium is set up when the chemical potentials are equal (section 4.7). In general, then, we may say that if between two systems there is a difference in some one intensity factor I, then the direction of change will be such that the capacity factor C increases in the system in which I is lower; and that equilibrium will be set up when the values of I become equal. These are basic criteria for the direction of change and for equilibrium.

These criteria can only be used, however, when we know the whole path of the change. We could not tell whether a system in given surroundings would pass from a state A to a state B without knowing the temperatures, pressures, and chemical potentials at all stages during the change. Sometimes the problem is quite simple, as for the evaporation of a pure substance at constant temperature and pressure; but for a chemical reaction, for example, it may be very complex. It would be much simpler if we could find criteria that only needed a knowledge of the initial and final states, and not of the whole path in detail. We shall reach such criteria in the course of this chapter by combining the Second Law (section 4.3) with some general considerations about reversible and irreversible ways of carrying out changes (section 4.2), to which we now turn.

4.2. Reversible and irreversible changes

4.21. *Reversibility and the criteria for the direction of change and for equilibrium*

A reversible change, in the thermodynamic sense, is not merely one which can proceed in either direction, like the change ice $\rightleftharpoons$ water or $N_2O_4 \rightleftharpoons 2NO_2$. In the thermodynamic sense, a change is not of its nature either reversible or irreversible; it can be carried out in different ways, reversibly or irreversibly. Reversibility refers to a special way of carrying out a change. A reversible change is defined as a change carried out in such a way that if a system passes from a state A to a state B, and then back again to A, the state not only of the system but also of its surroundings is completely and exactly restored, leaving no permanent changes in either system or surroundings. *Complete restorability* is the essence of the reversible way of carrying out a change.

Such changes do not occur in nature; they are, however, the ideal limits of certain kinds of changes, as we may see by considering the following classification of actual observable changes into (i) intrinsically irreversible and (ii) conditionally irreversible.†

Intrinsically irreversible changes are processes such that after they have occurred it is not possible, even in principle, to restore both the system and its surroundings to their initial condition; if we restore the system exactly, we leave finite changes in the surroundings, and vice versa. In other words, the path of the change cannot be exactly retraced by both system and surroundings. An example is the generation of heat from mechanical work by friction. We cannot reverse the whole process exactly, converting all the heat back into mechanical work and leaving no changes anywhere; if we use the heat in a heat-engine, we can reconvert only part of it to work. Another example is the diffusion

---

† Cf. Partington, *Textbook of Thermodynamics* (Constable, 1913), chap. 3.

of one gas into another; after diffusion we cannot separate the gases again without leaving any other changes. We could indeed separate a mixture of hydrogen and nitrogen, for example, by making use of the fact that palladium is permeable to hydrogen but not to nitrogen; but, as the diagram (fig. 29) shows, to use this method we should have to do work in compressing the gas

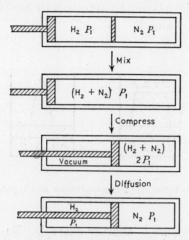

FIG. 29. Irreversible change: separation of gases after mixing
(schematic).

mixture, so that a change would be left in the surroundings, inasmuch as to do this work a weight would have descended or a spring uncoiled or something of the sort.

Conditionally irreversible changes are processes such that the changes left in the surroundings when the system is taken from state A to state B and back to A can be reduced indefinitely by control of the experimental conditions. Change of temperature is an example. Suppose that heat passes from system 1 at temperature t_1, to system 2 at temperature t_2, where $t_1 > t_2$. For instance, let system 1 be a thermostat at 25° and system 2 a piece of ice which is placed in a beaker in the thermostat; heat will flow from the thermostat and the ice will melt. To restore system 2, i.e. to refreeze the ice, we must make the heat flow in the opposite direction. We can only do this by decreasing the temperature of system 1—the thermostat—to a temperature t_2', below t_2, say $-5°$ C. Thus the operation as a whole leaves system 1 in a different condition, since it has lost heat proportional to $(t_1 - t_2')$. But we can reduce this heat-loss, and so the difference between the initial and final states, by reducing the temperature-intervals $(t_1 - t_2)$ and $(t_2' - t_2)$. The closer these temperatures, the smaller is $(t_1 - t_2')$ and so the smaller is the heat-loss, and the nearer the approach to complete restoration of both systems 1 and 2.

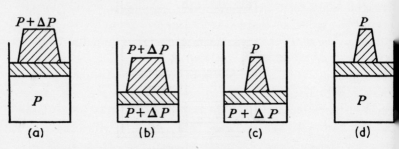

FIG. 30. Irreversible change: compression and expansion of a gas (schematic).

Change of pressure is another example. To compress a gas in a cylinder we have to apply a pressure greater than the initial pressure P of the gas, say $P + \Delta P$ (fig. 30 a). The compression will now go at a finite rate. Since there is a lag in the propagation of stresses, the pressure immediately under the piston will be higher than in the rest of the gas, and part of the work will be wasted in internal friction in the gas, before equilibrium is reached (fig. 30 b). If we now reduce the pressure on the gas (fig. 30 c), we can let it expand so that it reaches its original pressure (fig. 30 d), but the work which it does during expansion is less than was done during compression. If the pressure is exerted by weights, for instance, during compression a heavier weight will have descended the same distance that a lighter weight rises during expansion. Thus, when the gas has been restored to its original condition, the surroundings have not, and the process as a whole is irreversible. But we can reduce the change in the surroundings, by reducing the pressure-excess ΔP, and the smaller we make ΔP the closer will be the approach to complete restoration of both system and surroundings.

Chemical changes can be regarded in the same way. A discharging accumulator produces electrical energy through the occurrence of chemical reactions. If the accumulator is short-circuited, this energy is converted to heat. But if it is connected to an electric motor, the energy can be stored, for instance by raising a weight; the potential energy of the raised weight could then be used to drive a dynamo, whose output could be applied to charge the accumulator, and so reverse the original chemical changes. During charging and discharging, the potential difference across the terminals of the accumulator is commonly not exactly balanced, just as the pressures were not exactly balanced in the preceding example; some of the energy is wasted and the chemical system in the accumulator is not restored to exactly its original state. But the more exactly the potential difference is balanced, the more closely can complete restoration be approached.

The limiting case of conditionally irreversible changes is *reversible change*, or, as it is sometimes called, *quasi-static change*. If, in the above example, the differences of temperature, pressure, or potential could be made infinitesimal, then both the system and its surroundings would be restored completely; the differences between the initial and final states would become infinitesimal, and so indistinguishable from zero. A reversible change is thus the mathematical ideal limit of one of the conditionally irreversible processes that we can actually observe. It is an ideal limit both as regards the exact restorability of the system and its surroundings, and as regards the infinitesimal difference between the values of the relevant intensity factor in the system and its surroundings. It cannot, therefore, be realized exactly in practice. But experience shows that many laboratory processes—including, for example, manipulations of gases, phase changes, and chemical reactions in cells—can be made to differ so little from the corresponding ideally reversible processes that the equations derived below for reversible change may be applied without introducing errors greater than the experimental errors. We therefore often speak of reversible processes as if they were actually observable, although we really mean the ideal limit of observable processes.

Reversible processes have some very important characteristics. One which results immediately from the fact that the intensity factors between system and surroundings differ only infinitesimally is that the direction of the change may be reversed by an infinitesimal change in one of the intensity factors. If, for example, a gas at pressure P is enclosed by a piston on which the opposing pressure is $P-dP$, it will expand; if the opposing pressure is increased infinitesimally to $P+dP$, the gas will contract. Such a change of intensity factors involves work or heat changes which are only infinitesimal, and so indistinguishable from zero. Consequently the path on a P-V diagram representing the reversible process can be exactly retraced; both system and surroundings can be made to go through the exact sequence of changes in reverse order.

A second characteristic of a reversible change is that it is *indistinguishable from a series of states of equilibrium*. Reversible change is characterized by an infinitesimal difference of intensity factors between system and surroundings:

$$I_{\text{system}} - I_{\text{surr}} = \pm dI.$$

Equilibrium is defined by equality of these intensity factors:

$$I_{\text{system}} - I_{\text{surr}} = 0.$$

These two equations are indistinguishable. Reversible change will thus lead to the same results as a succession of states of equilibrium. *Any sufficient condition for reversibility is therefore also a sufficient condition for equilibrium.* This will be very important in the sequel (section 4.45).

A third related characteristic of a reversible change is that its rate is infinitesimal; it is the limiting case of a slow process. In general the rate of an ordinary observable process, which is irreversible, depends on the difference ΔI between the values of the relevant intensity factor in the system and in its surroundings. Heat is transferred faster the greater the difference of temperature, and so on. Whatever function of ΔI the rate may be, it will become infinitesimal for an infinitesimal value dI. A reversible process would therefore take an infinite time to complete. The most impressive approach to this in experimental work is provided by e.m.f. measurements. With a good potentiometer, we can balance the e.m.f. of a galvanic cell within 10^{-7} volts, and it has been estimated that with this difference of intensity factors, the process of charging an ordinary accumulator would take about a million years.

A process will have a finite rate only if ΔI is finite. It will then be irreversible. But only changes that proceed at a finite rate can be observed. Consequently *all observable processes are irreversible*. This conclusion also will prove to be of great importance. (Such statements as this are sometimes supposed to be equivalent to the Second Law of thermodynamics; but it is clear, from the reasoning given, that they depend solely on the notion of irreversibility).

TABLE 14

Equilibrium $\equiv$	Spontaneous Change $I_{syst} - I_{surr} = \pm\Delta I$ or $\pm dI$		
	Reversible change	Observable Change	
		Conditionally irreversible	Intrinsically irreversible
		Irreversible	
	$I_{syst} - I_{surr} = \pm dI$	$I_{syst} - I_{surr} = \pm\Delta I$	
$I_{syst} - I_{surr} = 0$	System and surroundings completely restorable	System and surroundings not completely restorable	
	Rate infinitesimal	Rate finite	

It may seem at first sight paradoxical to speak of reversible 'change' when the 'change' is infinitely slow and is indistinguishable from equilibrium. The solution of the paradox is that reversibility is an ideal limit, to which many actual changes, both physical and chemical, can be made to approximate. We therefore consider reversible changes, and compare them with other changes, even though they could never be exactly realized. The actual changes that we can observe in nature we shall call either *observable changes* or *irreversible changes*; these two classes of change are, as we have seen, coextensive.† To cover all processes, reversible or irreversible, that occur or could in principle occur as natural processes in inanimate nature—as distinct from changes effected by men or organisms—we shall use the term *spontaneous change*.

We have summarized the distinctions, relations, and definitions that we have been discussing in Table 14.

4.22. *Work done by a system during reversible and irreversible changes*

From the general properties of reversible and irreversible changes just discussed, we can deduce an important proposition about the difference in the work done when a given change in a system is effected reversibly and irreversibly.

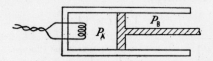

FIG. 31. Expansion of a gas at constant temperature and pressure.

We consider a system that can do mechanical work against its surroundings—for instance, a gas enclosed in a cylinder. Let us call the gas A and surroundings B, and the corresponding pressures P_A and P_B. Suppose for example that the gas is being electrically heated in such a way that it expands at constant temperature and pressure against the external pressure.

(i) Suppose first that the expansion is done *irreversibly*, with $P_A > P_B$; let $P_A = P_B + \Delta P$. The work done on the surroundings is
$$(w)_{\text{irrev}} = P_B \Delta V = (P_A - \Delta P) \Delta V.$$

(ii) Suppose now that the same expansion is effected *reversibly*, with $P_A = P_B + dP$. The work done on the surroundings is now
$$(w)_{\text{rev}} = P_B \Delta V = (P_A - dP) \Delta V.$$

† They have also been called 'natural' changes, by Guggenheim, following Planck.

This is greater than the corresponding work done in the irreversible expansion, $(w)_{\text{irrev}}$, by the finite amount $\Delta V \Delta P$.

Thus the work done on the surroundings is a maximum for the reversible way of carrying out the expansion at constant temperature and pressure; and the work dissipated as heat is then infinitesimal. *For the irreversible way, the work done on the surroundings is less than the maximum*, and the difference appears as heat. If the change is in the reverse direction, so that work is done *on* the system, this work is again a maximum for reversible change. As a general statement we can say that the numerical value of the work done on the surroundings, whether positive or negative, is a maximum in reversible change.

These conclusions can be generalized for any kind of work (section 2.3) and for any path. They are important in formulating the conditions of equilibrium (section 4.45).

Since only irreversible processes are observable, it follows that *all observable processes yield less than the maximum work, and lead to the dissipation of work as heat*. This has sometimes been expressed in picturesque language in such statements as 'Energy tends to become degraded'. The generalization is not, it should be noted, equivalent to the Second Law in the form given below.

4.3. The Second Law of Thermodynamics

At this point we must state the Second Law, which is a generalization about the direction of changes of the kinds relevant to thermodynamics, that is, exchanges of heat, work, or material, in inanimate nature. A general form of the law†

states that *the direction of spontaneous change in an inanimate system is such that the system can be made to do work on its surroundings*. It is perhaps easier to grasp the equivalent converse statement, that *spontaneous processes in a system can only be reversed by supplying work from the surroundings*.

It should be noted that the law does not state that work *must* be obtained if the change is spontaneous; only that it *can* be

† Butler, *Chemical Thermodynamics* (Macmillan, 1946), p. 32; *Commentary on the Works of Willard Gibbs* (Yale University Press, 1936), vol. i, p. 64.

obtained in suitable circumstances. An accumulator does practically no work if it is discharged on short circuit, but it can
be made to do work if connected to an electric motor. So also
an expanding gas does no useful work if it expands into a
vacuum, but if it is made to push out a piston it can be made to
do work; and similarly with other systems. We have seen in
section 4.22, independently of the Second Law, that the work
will be a maximum if the change is carried out reversibly.

The above statement of the law places no restrictions on the
type of thermodynamic change concerned; it refers equally to
exchanges of heat, work, or material. The Second Law in a
form relating to heat and work only was stated in 1850 by
Clausius, as a result of an examination of Carnot's paper of
1824 on the motive power of heat. Clausius's version was 'It
is impossible for a self-acting machine, unaided by any external
energy, to convey heat from one body to another at a higher
temperature'. Planck† gives the similar version 'It is impossible
to construct an engine that will work in a complete cycle and
produce no effect except the raising of a weight and the cooling
of a reservoir'. Such an engine would be able to extract heat
from the sea (leaving it cooler), turn some of the heat into work,
and reject it at a higher temperature; the direction of the heat
flow would be the contrary of the observed direction of spontaneous change, and we should have a heat-transfer process
that would yield work although it would be the converse of
the spontaneous process. The statement that this never happens implies that spontaneous heat transfers are those which
can yield work. This is generalized in our first statement above
to include all thermodynamic changes.

The evidence for the Second Law comes from different sources
for the different types of thermodynamic change. For sources of
work, it is obvious. For heat transfer, it is not self-evident that
transfer in the spontaneous direction (from bodies at higher to
bodies at lower temperature) can be made to do work, or that its
reversal requires work. Direct evidence comes from the invariable

† Planck, *Treatise on Thermodynamics* (Eng. trans. Ogg, Longmans, 1903),
pp. 81 seq.

rules encountered when working with heat-engines and refrigerators (section 3.55). Indirect evidence comes from comparisons between experiment and the consequences of the Second Law, some of which are to be deduced in the remainder of this book; no discrepancy attributable to inaccuracy of the Second Law has ever been established. For transfer of materials, this indirect verification appears to be the only kind available. From the point of view of scientific methodology, the Second Law is thus an unusual kind of statement; it is an empirical generalization, rather than an explanatory theory such as the atomic theory, but it is so broad a generalization that it is supported largely by the agreement of its consequences with experiment. Incidentally the Second Law as stated refers to the changes natural to inanimate systems; whether the law applies to changes in organisms may still be debated.†

We can summarize the Second Law, together with the conclusion of section 4.22, in the following table, which may be combined with Table 14 (p. 129).

TABLE 15

Spontaneous change in a system
Can be made to do work on surroundings, and reversed only by supplying work from surroundings.

Reversible path	Irreversible path
Work done by system numerically a maximum.	Work done by system numerically less than maximum.

4.4. Thermodynamic functions based on the Second Law, and criteria for the direction of change and for equilibrium in closed systems

4.41. *Need for criteria in terms of thermodynamic functions*

We have now to see how the Second Law enables us to understand the direction of changes and the conditions for equilibrium.

† Cf., for example, Ubbelohde, *Man and Energy* (Hutchinson, 1954), chap. 13.

The criteria in terms of reversibility that we formulated in section 4.21, using the basic criteria in terms of intensity factors, are not very useful as they stand. Their greatest limitation is that we cannot apply them to a particular process without a detailed knowledge of the way in which it is carried out. Another is that they give only a qualitative criterion of the direction of a change, and no quantitative measure of the 'tendency of the change to occur'. It would be a great advance if we could find a criterion in terms of some thermodynamic function. Such a criterion would be of the form 'Changes in a system occur in a direction such that the value of the thermodynamic function X increases (or decreases)'. This would enable us to predict whether a system would pass from a state A to a state B in given conditions from a knowledge of the states A and B alone, irrespective of the paths between them. It would also allow us to express in quantitative form such imprecise notions as 'chemical affinity', which force themselves upon our attention and demand precise definition.

A criterion of this type, which however proved unsuccessful, was the hypothesis underlying the thermochemical work of Thomsen (1854 onward) and of Berthelot, namely, that all chemical changes occur in the direction such that heat is evolved, i.e. H for the system decreases. Since H is a thermodynamic function, this would be a criterion of the type we are seeking. It has a certain range of usefulness, as we shall see, but it cannot be generally true, as is shown by the occurrence of endothermic reactions, and of chemical equilibria, in which one of the two balanced reactions must be endothermic.†

Another candidate for consideration is a criterion in terms of work, suggested by our findings in section 4.22 (p. 130). The condition for equilibrium is the same as the condition for reversible change (p. 128), and reversible changes are characterized by the maximum work. Observable changes are always irreversible (p. 129) and in irreversible changes a system always does less than the maximum work (p. 131). A criterion of

† For restricted conditions in which it is correct, see section 4.45, p. 148.

equilibrium is, then, that any change would lead to the maximum work being done by the system; correspondingly in any observable change, the work is less than this maximum. Apart from difficulties of application, this criterion has the limitation that the work done when a system passes from state A to state B is not in general fixed by the specifications of A and B alone, but also by the path between A and B, and by the degree of irreversibility in the way the change is carried out. Even when the change is carried out reversibly, so that the work done is the maximum for a given path, it still depends on the path. Suppose the work concerned is mechanical work due to expansion of a gas against an external pressure; the work is then $w = \int_A^B P \, dV$. Here P is a function of temperature t as well as of volume, so that $w = \int_A^B f(V, t) \, dV$, and the maximum work is not fixed unless we know the variation of t. Suppose, however, that t is fixed, i.e. that the change is done isothermally. The maximum work is now given by $w = \int_A^B f(V) \, dV$, which can be integrated and is uniquely determined by the volume in states A and B. Thus at constant temperature, and only at constant temperature, the maximum work that could be done by the system is independent of the path and depends only on the initial and final states of the system. In this special case of isothermal change, the maximum work has the properties of a thermodynamic function, and could be used as a criterion of the kind we are seeking. But for a general criterion, applicable to all changes, we must look farther.

This general criterion will turn out to be a statement in terms of a new thermodynamic function called the *entropy*, defined in virtue of certain consequences of the Second Law. To reach it we must first derive from the Second Law a general equation for the ratio of heat to work in reversible changes (section 4.42), then define a thermodynamic temperature scale (section 4.43), and finally apply these results to define the new thermodynamic function (section 4.44).

4.42. *Carnot's theorem; heat and work in reversible cycles*

We wish to find out the relation of work to heat in reversible changes. To do this we consider in the first place a complete cycle of changes; this simplifies matters, because at the end of the cycle the system is in its original condition and only the heat and work changes need be considered. A system going through such a cycle is functioning as a heat-engine (section 3.54 seq.), though we are not at present interested in it from the engineer's point of view.

For simplicity, we first consider reversible heat-engines in which the input of heat occurs all at one temperature t_1 and the rejection of heat all at one other temperature t_2. (We use the symbol t because the results of this section will be found to be true whatever scale of temperature we use; they do not require the perfect-gas scale.) We have already met a hypothetical heat-engine of this kind, in which the system is a perfect gas (section 3.56); but here we wish to consider real systems which might actually be made to undergo cycles of isothermal and adiabatic changes. All the changes are supposed to be done reversibly. Any system that can undergo work and heat changes reversibly will do. Some examples are:†

(i) *Real gases.* The $P–V$ diagram (fig. 32 a) will be similar to that for a perfect gas. If we start at A, we compress the gas adiabatically (AB), add heat at constant temperature t_1 (BC), expand adiabatically (CD), and remove heat at constant temperature t_2 (DA).

(ii) *Liquid and vapour.* The $P–V$ diagram is shown in fig. 32 b. Starting at A with a mixture of liquid and vapour, we compress adiabatically with rise of temperature (AB), vaporize at constant pressure and temperature t_1 (BC), expand adiabatically with fall of temperature (CD), and condense at constant pressure and temperature t_2 (DA).

(iii) *Stretched rubber, wire, or fibre.* The relations between tension and length are shown in fig. 32 c. At constant temperature, tension is proportional to extension, so that the isothermals

† For other examples see Zemansky, *Heat and Thermodynamics* (McGraw-Hill, 1943), chap. 9.

BC and AD would pass through the origin if projected. Starting at A, we extend the elastic body adiabatically (AB), then isothermally at temperature t_1 (BC); after this we allow it to contract adiabatically (CD), then isothermally at temperature t_2 (DA).

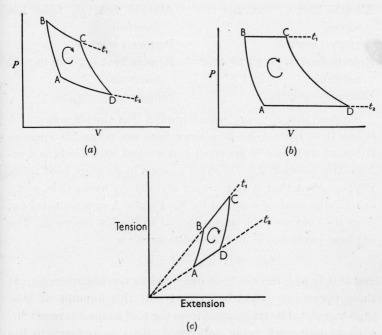

Fig. 32. Carnot cycles for (a) a gas, (b) liquid and vapour, (c) stretched rubber, wire, or fibre.

What these cycles have in common is that, whatever the system or the kind of work concerned, each of the heat changes is done at constant temperature, and all of the changes are supposed to be done reversibly. *Carnot's theorem* states that all heat-engines using cycles of this type, working between the same temperature limits, have the same efficiency (work/heat absorbed). This may be proved with the aid of the Second Law, as follows.

Imagine any two such reversible engines, A and B, each taking in heat from the same hot reservoir at temperature t_1

and rejecting heat to the same cold reservoir at temperature t_2. Suppose that it is possible to arrange that they absorb different amounts of heat, yet perform the same amount of work w. Their operations may then be summarized:

Engine A	Engine B
Absorbs heat q_A from hot reservoir	Absorbs heat q_B from hot reservoir
Performs work w	Performs work w
Rejects heat $(q_A - w)$ to cold reservoir	Rejects heat $(q_B - w)$ to cold reservoir
Efficiency $= w/q_A$	Efficiency $= w/q_B$

Suppose that $q_A > q_B$, which implies that the efficiency of A is less than that of B. Now since both are reversible engines, either of them can be reversed and worked backwards as a refrigerator (section 3.55) without change in its work/heat ratio. Suppose then that A is reversed and driven backwards, using exactly the work w supplied by B. Engine A now *extracts* heat from the cold reservoir and rejects it to the hot reservoir. The net heat extracted from the cold reservoir is

$$(q_A - w) - (q_B - w) = q_A - q_B$$

and this is also the net heat delivered to the hot reservoir. If these operations could be carried out, this amount of heat $(q_A - q_B)$ would be transferred from the cold to the hot reservoir, without any work being performed. This is contrary to the Second Law, according to which the spontaneous direction of flow of heat could only be reversed if work were supplied. Given the Second Law, therefore, the original supposition must be false, namely that it is possible for q_A to be greater than q_B if the engines work between the same two temperatures and deliver the same amount of work. Clearly the supposition $q_A < q_B$ can be similarly disproved. It follows then by the Second Law that $q_A = q_B$. Consequently *the efficiencies w/q of all such engines are equal*. This is Carnot's theorem. The proof is obviously applicable to all systems, and to all kinds of work, provided the changes are carried out reversibly. It is moreover independent of any particular scale of temperature.

4.43. *The thermodynamic scale of temperature*

As we have just seen, a Carnot engine working between two given temperatures has an efficiency determined by those two temperatures alone, and not by any of the particular characteristics of the system undergoing the Carnot cycle. Temperatures may therefore be *defined* on a new scale by the efficiency of the Carnot engine working between them. Suppose the heat absorbed is q_1, and the heat rejected q_2; then the work done is $w = q_1 - q_2$ and the efficiency is w/q_1. We now define a new temperature-scale such that the temperature T_1 at which heat is absorbed is related to the temperature T_2 at which heat is rejected by the relation

$$\frac{w}{q_1} = \frac{T_1 - T_2}{T_1} = 1 - \frac{T_2}{T_1}, \tag{1}$$

whence

$$\frac{q_1}{T_1} = \frac{q_2}{T_2}. \tag{2}$$

This temperature-scale, based on heat and work changes, has the advantage that it is independent of the individual properties of any particular substance, and yet is experimentally accessible. We can compare it with the perfect-gas scale, by referring to our result for the efficiency of a reversible Carnot cycle in terms of that scale (section 3.56). The result was derived for a particular system, but as we have just seen (section 4.42) it will be true for all Carnot cycles. The result was:

$$w/q_1 = 1 - (\theta_2/\theta_1).$$

Comparing this with equation 1, we find:

$$\frac{T_2}{T_1} = \frac{\theta_2}{\theta_1}, \tag{3}$$

so that the temperature T on the thermodynamic scale is proportional to the temperature θ on the perfect-gas scale. We now complete the definition† of the thermodynamic scale in such a way as to make it *identical with the perfect-gas scale*.

† For a fuller argument see Zemansky, *Heat and Thermodynamics* (1943), chap. 9.

This is done by defining the temperature-interval between the ice-point and the steam-point as 100 degrees, just as on the perfect-gas scale. Our result for the ice-point on the perfect-gas scale, $\theta_i = 273\cdot2°$, will now apply also to T_i. The identification of the thermodynamic scale T with the perfect-gas scale θ is very convenient wherever the latter scale can be established; it relates T to the readings of gas-thermometers and any other thermometers calibrated by means of them. But the thermodynamic scale is independent of the properties of any particular system, requiring only that it shall be capable of undergoing reversible work and heat changes. At very low temperatures, for instance, it has been established by means of the cooling effects in the demagnetization of paramagnetic substances.†

4.44. *Definition of the thermodynamic function entropy*

Using the temperature-scale just defined, equation 2 (p. 139) tells us that in any closed system, for any reversible cycle of changes in which heat q_1 is absorbed at one constant temperature T_1 and heat q_2 rejected at another constant temperature T_2, the exact relation holds:

$$\frac{q_1}{T_1} - \frac{q_2}{T_2} = 0, \quad \text{or} \quad \sum_{\text{cycle}} \frac{q}{T} = 0. \tag{4}$$

This will be true for any of the Carnot cycles represented in fig. 32 (p. 137), in which heat q_1 is absorbed along BC and heat q_2 rejected along DA. Now, using the diagrams of fig. 32, let us consider the change of any of these systems from the state represented by A to the state represented by C. Two paths from A to C are represented. One is the path ABC, in which heat q_1 is absorbed at temperature T_1. The other is the path ADC, which is the exact reverse of CDA, and therefore involves the absorption of heat q_2 at temperature T_2.‡ Hence the heats

---

† Fowler and Guggenheim, *Statistical Thermodynamics* (Cambridge, 1939), pp. 662 seq.; Taylor and Glasstone, *Treatise on Physical Chemistry* (van Nostrand, 1942), vol. i, p. 642.

‡ Formally, if we define q_{CDA} and q_{ADC} as the heats *absorbed* by the system in passing along the paths CDA and ADC, $q_{\text{CDA}} = -q_2$ (since q_2 is defined as the heat *rejected* along CDA); and $q_{\text{CDA}} = -q_{\text{ADC}}$ since the path ADC is the reverse of CDA; hence $q_{\text{ADC}} = q_2$.

absorbed in the two different paths from A to C are related to
the corresponding temperatures by the equation

$$\frac{q_1}{T_1} = \frac{q_2}{T_2}.$$

Thus q/T for the change of any closed system from one state
to another is *independent of the path*, provided that the change

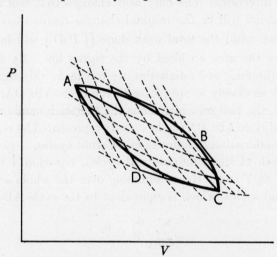

FIG. 33. Resolution of a cycle into Carnot cycles.

can be effected by a combination of one adiabatic process and
one isothermal process. We must next generalize this result to
cover *any* reversible path.

Suppose we consider a system—a gas, for example, undergoing changes of pressure, volume, and temperature—that can
pass from a state represented by A in fig. 33 to a state represented by C, by either of two reversible paths ABC and ADC.
It can therefore undergo the reversible cycle ABCDA. Suppose
that heat is absorbed (and rejected) over a *range* of temperatures, so that the paths cannot be reduced as in the preceding
case to one adiabatic step and one isothermal step.

We can cross the paths, as represented in fig. 33, by a number
of sections of curves representing adiabatic and isothermal
changes. (We are considering a gas, but the argument can be

applied equally to any other system.) These curves describe a series of imaginary Carnot cycles. Suppose we imagine the system to traverse a set of Carnot cycles in the same direction, say clockwise. Then all the heat changes corresponding to the parts of the isothermals common to two cycles will cancel, since the system will traverse the same path twice in opposite directions. The only heat changes that will need to be considered will be the residual changes represented by the zigzag line. And the total work done $\left(\int P \, dV \right)$ will be represented by the area enclosed by the zigzag line. By drawing more isothermals and adiabatics, we can make this zigzag line approach as closely as we please to the cycle ABCDA; and in the limit, the two coincide. Thus the thermodynamic changes in the real cycle ABCDA can be exactly represented by regarding it as a combination of infinitesimal Carnot cycles.

For each of these infinitesimal cycles, equation 4 (p. 140) holds: $\sum dq/T = 0$. Hence summing over the whole set of infinitesimal cycles, which is equivalent to the cycle ABCDA,

$$\sum_{\text{ABCDA}} \frac{dq}{T} = 0. \tag{5}$$

We can now argue as at the start of this section, but more generally, as follows. We first split the cycle into two parts, ABC and CDA. Then, by equation 5,

$$\sum_{\text{ABC}} \frac{dq}{T} + \sum_{\text{CDA}} \frac{dq}{T} = 0. \tag{6}$$

Suppose now that the system passes reversibly along CDA in the reverse direction, i.e. along ADC; then all the heat changes will have their signs changed, so that

$$\sum_{\text{CDA}} \frac{dq}{T} = - \sum_{\text{ADC}} \frac{dq}{T}. \tag{7}$$

Combining equations 6 and 7,

$$\sum_{\text{ABC}} \frac{dq}{T} = \sum_{\text{ADC}} \frac{dq}{T}. \tag{8}$$

This means that for each of the paths ABC and ADC, the sum of the changes $(\sum dq/T)$ is the same. This sum is thus independent of the path, and therefore depends only on the initial and final states. Since ABC and ADC may be any paths whatever, this result is true for *all* paths from A to C, provided only that the changes are carried out reversibly. Thus we conclude that for any given change $\sum dq_{rev}/T$ is independent of the path, and depends only on the initial and final states of the system. This result has now been shown to be true not only for any type of closed system, using any type of work and any working substance, but also for any variation in temperature.

When any system undergoes any reversible change, then, the quantity $\sum dq_{rev}/T$ is determined only by the initial and final states of the system. It is, moreover, an extensive quantity, since in any such change the heat absorbed is proportional to the amount of material. It is therefore a thermodynamic function and is called the *entropy*. It is usually designated by S, and is defined for an infinitesimal change by

$$dS = dq_{rev}/T, \tag{9}$$

where dS is a perfect differential (section 2.4). Thus for a finite change of a system from state A to state B, the entropy difference is

$$S_B - S_A = \Delta S = \sum_{A \to B} dq_{rev}/T. \tag{10}$$

It is important that while the entropy difference between two states of a system is fixed, it is equal to $\sum dq/T$ only if the change is done reversibly. Incidentally equation 10 shows that we can determine only differences of entropy, not absolute values.

It is also noteworthy that the entropy can be defined in this way only if we adopt the thermodynamic scale of temperature, since the argument makes use of equation 4 which is not true for any other temperature scale. Entropy and the thermodynamic scale thus enter thermodynamics together. The arguments leading up to both conceptions depend on the Second Law. Some indeed would prefer to regard the equation 9 as a statement, rather than as a consequence, of the Second Law. On this view the Second Law states that there is a thermodynamic function S, and a thermodynamic temperature T which is a function only of the empirical temperature t, such that $dS = dq_{rev}/T$. The evidence for the truth of these statements would then be the agreement of their consequences with experiment. The advantage of such a version, from the mathematical physicist's point of view, is that it makes no reference to heat-engines and appears to emancipate thermodynamics from its engineering origins. However, the behaviour of heat-engines remains among the phenomena which have to be compared with the consequences of equation 9 and which lend it indirect support; the evidence for equation 9 is ultimately the same as for the Second Law in the form we used in section 4.3. Which form we adopt appears to affect only the order of the exposition, and to be mainly a matter of taste. Our procedure in this chapter has been adopted because it brings out the relation between the definition of entropy and a variety of experimental facts.†

Determination of entropy changes. When heat changes alone are concerned, as in the heating of a solid, there is only one possible path for the change and no difficulty arises; the entropy change is simply $\int C_S \, dT/T$ or $\int C_S \, d \ln T$. When both heat and work changes are involved, the entropy change can be determined directly only when the physical or chemical change undergone by the system can be made to occur reversibly, or rather to approach reversibility closely enough for the error to be negligible. Whether a change carried out in a given way is nearly reversible can only be determined by experiment, either by finding whether the results are altered by carrying out the change at a different rate, or by seeing whether the experimental results agree with certain relations which will be deduced for reversible change in later sections. Thus in ordinary measurements of the pressure of a gas, equilibrium is reached, but this is not the case for the acceleration of a jet of gas, discussed in section 3.53 above. Chemical reactions, as

† We have also passed over the axiomatic approach of Carathéodory, for which see Hinshelwood, *The Structure of Physical Chemistry* (Oxford, 1951), pp. 55–60; Born, *Natural Philosophy of Cause and Chance* (Oxford, 1949).

ordinarily carried out, are far from being reversible; as we saw in section 2.63, the heat evolved when a reaction is carried out in a calorimeter at constant pressure is equal to $-\Delta H$, whereas the heat evolved in reversible change is $-T\Delta S$. (We shall later define the difference $\Delta H - T\Delta S$ as the 'free energy' of the reaction.) Similarly, reactions that occur in galvanic cells (section 6.21), proceed irreversibly if they occur at an appreciable rate, as in the discharge of an accumulator, and the heat evolved is then $-\Delta H$. But if the rate is made negligible, by balancing the e.m.f. of the cell with an opposing e.m.f., the heat evolved will approximate closely to $T\Delta S$. It cannot then be directly measured, however, because it is evolved too slowly. Various indirect means of determining the entropy changes in chemical reactions, which are of great interest, have therefore been devised (sections 5.46, 6.22, Chap. VIII).

Entropy changes are commonly expressed in calories per degree per mole (cal deg^{-1} $mole^{-1}$); this is often (but illogically) written 'entropy units', or in shortened form 'e.u.'

Statistical interpretation of entropy. It is shown in statistical mechanics that the entropy of an assembly of molecules forming a thermodynamic system is given by $S = k \ln W$.[†] Here k is Boltzmann's constant and W is the number of complexions of the assembly, i.e. the number of possible ways of distributing the molecules, among the various positions and energy-levels available, that will lead to the observed state of the system. W is thus affected by two important factors. (i) It is greater, the larger the volume available to any molecule, since a given number of molecules can then be spatially distributed in a greater number of ways. This factor we shall find to give rise to an entropy change in, for example, the isothermal expansion of gases (section 5.14) and in the mixing at constant temperature and pressure of gases or liquids (sections 5.33, 10.2). (ii) W is greater, the more widely the molecules are spread among the available energy-levels, since this increases the number of ways in which a given total energy may be made up. This is the

[†] Cf., for example, Butler, *Chemical Thermodynamics* (1946), Appendix; Rushbrooke, *Introduction to Statistical Mechanics* (Oxford, 1949).

factor responsible for the increase in the entropy of solids with temperature (section 5.21); the molecules do not change position but more of them pass into states of higher vibrational energy. The same factor is responsible in part for the increase of entropy with temperature in gases; as more of the molecules pass into higher vibrational energy-levels, the term in C_i increases (section 5.22, p. 204). The equation $S = k \ln W$ is thus of great importance in interpreting entropy changes. We shall later (section 4.53) be able to relate the entropy to the partition functions, which express W exactly.

4.45. *Criteria for the direction of change and for equilibrium in terms of entropy, internal energy, and heat content*

We have seen that the entropy change ΔS when the state of a closed system undergoes a given change is q_{rev}/T if the change is carried out *reversibly*, supposing for the moment that the temperature is constant. If the change is carried out *irreversibly*, the work w_{irrev} done by the system is less than the work w_{rev} done in the reversible process (section 4.22). Now by the First Law, $(q-w)$ is equal to ΔE, which for a given change in the system is fixed and independent of the way the change is carried out. Hence the heat absorbed in the irreversible change, q_{irrev}, is less than q_{rev}. Hence q_{irrev}/T is less than q_{rev}/T, and is therefore less than ΔS. We can remove the restriction to changes at constant temperature by considering infinitesimal changes; the result is then:

$$\text{For reversible processes,} \quad (đq/T) = dS. \qquad (11)$$

$$\text{For irreversible processes,} \ (đq/T) < dS. \qquad (12)$$

We now recall that a reversible process is indistinguishable from *equilibrium*, and that all *observable* changes are irreversible (section 4.21, pp. 128, 129). From equations 11 and 12 we thus obtain as criteria for equilibrium and for the direction of observable changes:

$$\boxed{\begin{aligned} \text{For equilibrium,} &\qquad (đq/T) = dS \\ \text{For observable changes,} &\ (đq/T) < dS \end{aligned}} \qquad \begin{aligned} (13) \\ (14) \end{aligned}$$

The converse expression, $(đq/T) > dS$, corresponds to imaginary changes occurring in the opposite direction to that which is actually observed.

The criteria 13 and 14 are fundamental. They are true for all processes, subject only to the restriction that the system must be a closed one; this restriction will later be removed (section 4.61). But since they contain q, these criteria are not expressed entirely in terms of quantities defined by the state of a system; that is, by thermodynamic functions and the variables of state such as P, V, and T. Our next step, therefore, is to use these fundamental criteria to formulate the conditions for equilibrium and for observable change in terms of thermodynamic functions and variables of state.

The most general way of doing this is to combine our present criteria with the First Law, which for a closed system is

$$dE = đq - đw. \qquad (15)$$

To show that this refers to closed systems, for which all the dn's in the general equation for dE (p. 29) are zero, it may be written $(dE)_{n_i} = đq - đw$. In many systems of interest to chemists, the only work done is that against the pressure of the surroundings, which we will write P_{surr} to distinguish it from the pressure P of the system. Then $đw = P_{surr} dV$, and equation 15 becomes

$$dE = đq - P_{surr} dV. \qquad (16)$$

Criteria in terms of entropy.† Consider an adiabatic change. Here $đq = 0$, so that the criteria stated in equations 13 and 14 for equilibrium and for observable change become $dS = 0$ and $dS > 0$ respectively. Also equation 16 becomes $dE = -P_{surr} dV$. If the *volume* is kept constant during the change, $dV = 0$, and therefore $dE = 0$. In this case, therefore, the volume and energy of the system are both constant—that is, the system is isolated —and the direction of change is such that the entropy increases, towards a maximum; when there is equilibrium, the entropy is constant. The criteria may be expressed for these conditions as follows:

For equilibrium, $(dS)_{E,V,n_i} = 0$. $\qquad (17)$

For observable change, $(dS)_{E,V,n_i} > 0$. $\qquad (18)$

† On the criteria of equilibrium, cf. Guggenheim, *Thermodynamics* (1957), pp. 34–40.

If the pressure P of the system is kept constant during the adiabatic change (instead of V), and is made to differ only infinitesimally from that of the surroundings, equation 16 becomes $dE = -P\,dV = -d(PV)$. Then by the definition of H (p. 35) we find $dH = dE + d(PV) = 0$. In this case, therefore, H and P are constant, and the criteria are:

$$\text{For equilibrium, } (dS)_{H,P,n_i} = 0. \tag{19}$$

$$\text{For observable change, } (dS)_{H,P,n_i} > 0. \tag{20}$$

Thus the entropy again tends to a maximum at equilibrium. This is true only under restricted conditions (constant E and V, or constant H and P); and so such statements as 'the entropy of the universe tends to a maximum' depend on assumptions that may not be fulfilled.

Criteria in terms of E and H. It may be shown (see Appendix, p. 408) that the corresponding conditions at constant entropy and volume are:

$$\text{For equilibrium, } (dE)_{S,V,n_i} = 0. \tag{21}$$

$$\text{For observable change, } (dE)_{S,V,n_i} < 0. \tag{21a}$$

At constant entropy and pressure, they are:

$$\text{For equilibrium, } (dH)_{S,P,n_i} = 0. \tag{22}$$

$$\text{For observable change, } (dH)_{S,P,n_i} < 0. \tag{22a}$$

Since (p. 35) $\Delta H = (q)_P$, it follows that the direction of observable change is such that heat is evolved, if the entropy and pressure are constant. This restricted criterion is the correct form of one used by Thomsen and Berthelot (pp. 134, 248).

Fundamental equations for E and H for a closed system.

We can derive some important relations between the properties of a closed system from equation 15. The work done by the system against the pressure of the surroundings varies from zero for the expansion of a gas into a vacuum, to $P\Delta V$ when the opposing external pressure is effectively equal to the pressure P of the system, as in reversible change; for an infinitesimal reversible change, it is $P\,dV$. The heat absorbed in such a change is $T\,dS$. Substituting in equation 15, we obtain the following

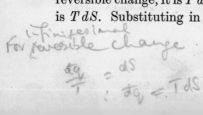

relation between E and S, in which the essential results of the First and Second Laws are combined:

$$(dE)_{n_i} = T\,dS - P\,dV.$$ (23)

If other kinds of work are involved, besides that done against the pressure of the surroundings, the corresponding terms must be added in addition to $P\,dV$; the extension of an elastic body for example, is considered in section 5.16 below.

Equation 23 is a fundamental relation which is very important in what follows (section 4.51). Although it has been derived by consideration of a reversible change, it is true generally, however the change is conducted. This follows from the fact that it contains only quantities characteristic of the state of the system (T, P, and V because they describe the state, E and S because they are thermodynamic functions); it contains no terms such as w or q which depend on the history of the system. Consideration of a reversible change is merely a convenient way of reaching a result which applies generally (cf. p. 114).

The corresponding relation between H and S is obtained as follows. Since $H = E + PV$ by definition,

$$dH = dE + P\,dV + V\,dP,$$

and substitution for dE in equation 23 gives:

$$(dH)_{n_i} = T\,dS + V\,dP.$$ (24)

This equation also will be true generally, for any closed system capable of P–V work only.

In passing, it may be noted that the conditions for equilibrium are always *equations*, such as 13, 17, 19, 21, while conditions for observable change are always *inequalities*, such as 14, 18, 20, 21 a, the magnitude of the inequality depending on how far the change departs from reversibility. This explains the preference shown in classical thermodynamics for equilibrium and reversible change; for equations are easier to handle and give us more precise information than do inequalities. In recent years, however, a body of theory concerning irreversible processes has been developed, largely by the Brussels and Netherlands schools.†

† Cf., for example, de Groot, *Thermodynamics of Irreversible Changes* (North Holland Publishing Co., 1951); I. Prigogine, *Introduction to the Thermodynamics of Irreversible Processes* (Blackwell, 1955).

4.46. *Criteria for the direction of change and for equilibrium in terms of free energy functions*

Definitions of free energy functions. In practice it is often convenient to conduct chemical reactions, phase changes, and so on, at constant temperature, and either at constant pressure (say one atmosphere) or at constant volume in a closed vessel. None of our criteria of equilibrium in terms of S, E, and H apply to experiments done under these conditions. To find criteria that do apply to them, we now define two other functions, known for historical reasons as the *Helmholtz free energy*, written A, and the *Gibbs free energy*, or often simply the *free energy*, written G.[†] The definitions are

$$A \equiv E - TS, \tag{25}$$

$$G \equiv H - TS \equiv E + PV - TS. \tag{26}$$

It will be seen that each term on the right-hand side is extensive and is determined solely by the state of the system, so that A and G are thermodynamic functions.[‡] The definition given for G is adapted to the common case where the only kind of work that need be considered is P–V work; if another kind is important in a given problem, a suitable function similar to G must be defined (see, for example, section 5.16).

Before applying these definitions to the statement of new criteria of equilibrium, we must note in passing that in special cases both A and G can be related directly to the work done in a reversible change, as follows.

A and reversible work. The change in A resulting from an infinitesimal change of any kind in the state of any system is, by general differentiation of equation 25,

$$dA = dE - T\,dS - S\,dT.$$

For any change at constant temperature, therefore:

$$dA = dE - T\,dS. \tag{27}$$

† Though many authors use the symbol G for the Gibbs free energy, others use F. But since some use F as the symbol for the Helmholtz free energy, it seems best to avoid confusion by not using F at all.

‡ For their statistical significance, and relation to partition functions, see section 4.53, p. 161.

By the First Law, any change in a closed system leads to an internal energy change given by:

$$dE = dq - dw.$$

If the change is carried out reversibly, $dq = T\,dS$, and so

$$dE = T\,dS - dw_{\text{rev}}. \tag{28}$$

Substituting this value for dE in equation 27, we obtain:

$$dA = -dw_{\text{rev}}. \tag{29}$$

Therefore, for a finite change under similar conditions,

$$\Delta A = -w_{\text{rev}}. \tag{30}$$

This equates the change in A in a closed system with the work done, provided that the temperature is constant, and that the process is carried out reversibly. (It will be remembered that in adiabatic change, by contrast, the work done is equal to $-\Delta E$, cf. p. 39.)

The role of the entropy as *a measure of the non-availability of the energy* of a chemical reaction in this special case may be noted. The energy decrease of the reacting system, $-dE$, is by equation 28 equal to $(dw_{\text{rev}} - T\,dS)$, or for a finite change at constant temperature $(w_{\text{rev}} - T\Delta S)$. Here ΔS is the change of entropy of the system; for the surroundings, if the process is reversible, the entropy change will be $-\Delta S$. Thus the energy decrease of the system will be equal to the work done on the surroundings plus their entropy increase multiplied by T. So $T\Delta S$ represents the difference between the energy output and the maximum work that can be extracted from the reaction at constant temperature, and is therefore a measure of the energy that is not available for doing work under these conditions.

G and reversible work. The change in G resulting from an infinitesimal change in the state of any system is, by general differentiation of equation 26:

$$dG = dE + P\,dV + V\,dP - T\,dS - S\,dT. \tag{31}$$

For a change at constant temperature and pressure, therefore,

$$dG = dE + P\,dV - T\,dS. \tag{32}$$

If the system is closed, and the change is carried out reversibly, equation 28 is again applicable and substitution in equation 31 gives:

$$dG = P\,dV - đw_{\text{rev}}. \tag{33}$$

For a finite change under similar conditions,

$$\Delta G = P\,\Delta V - w_{\text{rev}}. \tag{34}$$

This equates the change in G in a closed system with the 'net work'—the total work less the work $P\,\Delta V$ done against the atmosphere—provided the temperature and pressure are both constant, and that the process is carried out reversibly. This 'net work' is evidently zero for any change in which the only work is that done against the pressure of the surroundings; it is of interest only when some other kind of work can be done, as for instance by a galvanic cell in driving an electric motor (section 6.2). These conclusions, it should be noted, are true only for closed systems; the role of G in open systems is rather different (section 4.61).

Equilibrium and the direction of change. The criteria for equilibrium and for the direction of change in terms of A and G may be found as follows. Consider a closed system undergoing a change at constant temperature. From equation 27, we have

$$(dA)_{T,n_i} = dE - T\,dS. \tag{35}$$

But by the First Law, $dE = đq - đw$, so that

$$(dA)_{T,n_i} = đq - đw - T\,dS. \tag{36}$$

Suppose that the system can do work only against the pressure of the surroundings. If the *volume* is kept constant, the work $đw$ will be zero, and so

$$(dA)_{T,V,n_i} = đq - T\,dS. \tag{37}$$

Applying the fundamental conditions 13 and 14 (p. 146) to equation 37, we obtain the criteria in terms of A:

$$\text{For equilibrium,} \qquad (dA)_{T,V,n_i} = 0. \tag{38}$$

$$\text{For observable change,} \ (dA)_{T,V,n_i} < 0. \tag{39}$$

Thus at constant T and V, the value of A tends to a minimum as equilibrium is approached.

If the *pressure* of the surroundings is kept constant, instead of the volume, and if it differs only infinitesimally from the pressure P of the system, then:

$$\mathit{d}w = P\,dV = d(PV) = d(G-A)_{T,P,n_i} = (dG)_{T,P,n_i}-(dA)_{T,P,n_i}.$$

Substitution in equation 36 gives

$$(dG)_{T,P,n_i} = \mathit{d}q-T\,dS, \tag{40}$$

which with the conditions 13 and 14 gives the criteria in terms of G:

$$\text{For equilibrium,} \qquad (dG)_{T,P,n_i} = 0. \tag{41}$$

$$\text{For observable change,} \quad (dG)_{T,P,n_i} < 0. \tag{42}$$

At constant temperature and pressure, therefore, the value of G tends to a minimum as equilibrium is approached. These criteria in terms of G are widely applicable, because many processes are most easily conducted at constant temperature and pressure. We shall meet many examples of such processes, including reactions, phase changes, and the phenomena of solutions. It is often of interest to consider ΔG for such a process as made up of two terms, a heat content term and an entropy term, since from the definition (equation 26) at constant temperature

$$\Delta G = \Delta H - T\Delta S.$$

In chemical reactions, either of these two terms may be dominant (p. 248).

Fundamental equations for A and G for a closed system. If we differentiate equations 25 and 26 generally, and restrict ourselves to the consideration of closed systems capable of doing P–V work only, we obtain:

$$(dA)_{n_i} = dE-T\,dS-S\,dT,$$

$$(dG)_{n_i} = dE+P\,dV+V\,dP-T\,dS-S\,dT.$$

Combining these expressions with the fundamental relation $dE = T\,dS-P\,dV$ (equation 23), we obtain for closed systems:

$$(dA)_{n_i} = -P\,dV-S\,dT, \tag{43}$$

$$(dG)_{n_i} = V\,dP-S\,dT. \tag{44}$$

These relations are true generally, like equation 23, whether the change in question is reversible or not. We return to them in section 4.51.

4.47. *Summary of thermodynamic criteria for changes in a closed system, and fundamental equations*

The criteria for equilibrium and for the direction of change in a closed system obtained in sections 4.45 and 4.46 are summarized in the following table, which may be combined with Tables 14 and 15 (pp. 129, 133). The fundamental equations, relating the entropy to other thermodynamic functions, are also shown; these, as we have noted, are true generally, whether the change in question is reversible or not.

TABLE 16

Function	Equilibrium and reversible change	Observable change
dS	$= đq/T$	$> đq/T$
Process at constant		
$E, V, n_i:$ $(dS)_{E,V,n_i}$	$= 0$	> 0
$S, V, n_i:$ $(dE)_{S,V,n_i}$		
$S, P, n_i:$ $(dH)_{S,P,n_i}$	$= 0$	< 0
$T, V, n_i:$ $(dA)_{T,V,n_i}$		
$T, P, n_i:$ $(dG)_{T,P,n_i}$		
$dE - T\,dS + P\,dV$		
$dH - T\,dS - V\,dP$	$= 0$	$= 0$
$dA + P\,dV + S\,dT$		
$dG - V\,dP + S\,dT$		

Where the work $P\,dV$ done against the atmosphere is not the only kind of work involved, appropriate work terms must be inserted in the equations.

The reasoning by which we have reached these extremely useful results may be summarized as follows. We began with criteria of equilibrium and of the direction of observable change in terms of intensity factors (section 4.1). Reversible and irreversible ways of carrying out a change in a system were then distinguished (section 4.21); and we noted that any criterion for reversible change is also a criterion for equilibrium, and any criterion for irreversible change is a criterion for observable change. The consequences of carrying out processes reversibly and irreversibly were examined, using the intensity-factor criterion, and it was found in particular that in reversible changes a system performs the maximum work possible for a given change in its state, while in irreversible change the work done is less (section 4.22). But general criteria depending only on the states of the system before and after the change could not yet be found. The Second Law was next introduced (section 4.3), stating that the direction of spontaneous change in a system is such that the system can be made to do work on its surroundings; it led to definitions of the thermodynamic temperature scale (section 4.43) and the thermodynamic function called entropy (section 4.44). The definition of entropy was combined with the principle that only reversible changes give the maximum work, to obtain criteria for reversible and irreversible processes in terms of the relation of the heat absorbed to the entropy change (section 4.45). These were identified with criteria for equilibrium and for observable change. Conditions in terms of E, H, A, and G were then derived, and the fundamental equations (sections 4.45, 4.46).

4.5. Thermodynamic relations derived from the fundamental equations for closed systems

4.51. *The Gibbs–Helmholtz relation and Maxwell's relations*

The fundamental set of equations expressing the variation of E, H, A, or G, for a small change of conditions in a closed system, undergoing only P–V work, may be written (cf. pp. 149, 153):

$$(dE)_{n_i} = T\,dS - P\,dV, \tag{1}$$

$$(dH)_{n_i} = T\,dS + V\,dP, \tag{2}$$

$$(dA)_{n_i} = -P\,dV - S\,dT, \tag{3}$$

$$(dG)_{n_i} = V\,dP - S\,dT. \tag{4}$$

It is important that these fundamental equations are true whether the change is reversible or not, since they contain only quantities characteristic of the state of the system. The only restriction is that the system must be in a definite state; that is, it must have uniform temperature and pressure, and be in chemical equilibrium. Such a system is said to be in internal equilibrium.

If now we suppose the system to be partially restricted, by putting one of the differentials at a time equal to zero, we obtain the following set of equations:

$$\left(\frac{\partial E}{\partial S}\right)_{V,n_i} = T, \qquad \left(\frac{\partial E}{\partial V}\right)_{S,n_i} = -P. \qquad (6)$$

$$\left(\frac{\partial H}{\partial S}\right)_{P,n_i} = T, \qquad \left(\frac{\partial H}{\partial P}\right)_{S,n_i} = V. \qquad (7)$$

$$\left(\frac{\partial A}{\partial T}\right)_{V,n_i} = -S, \qquad \left(\frac{\partial A}{\partial V}\right)_{T,n_i} = -P. \qquad (8)$$

$$\left(\frac{\partial G}{\partial T}\right)_{P,n_i} = -S, \qquad \left(\frac{\partial G}{\partial P}\right)_{T,n_i} = V. \qquad (9)$$

We notice that the free energy of a pure substance decreases with increase of temperature at constant pressure, and increases with pressure at constant temperature; we shall later have examples of this behaviour (sections 5.15, 5.2).

Gibbs–Helmholtz relation. If we combine the expression, $(\partial G/\partial T)_{P,n_i} = -S$, just obtained with the general definition $H = G + TS$, the result is

$$\boxed{H = G - T\left(\frac{\partial G}{\partial T}\right)_{P,n_i}} \qquad (10)$$

This is called the Gibbs–Helmholtz relation, and it applies to any closed system capable of P–V work.† Since differentiation of G/T gives

$$\frac{d}{dT}\left(\frac{G}{T}\right) = -\frac{G}{T^2} + \frac{1}{T}\left(\frac{dG}{dT}\right),$$

it may also be written

$$\left(\frac{\partial}{\partial T}\left(\frac{G}{T}\right)\right)_{P,n_i} = -\frac{H}{T^2}. \qquad (11)$$

Integrating, we find, for constant-pressure changes,

$$G = -T \int \frac{H}{T^2}\, dT + \text{const.} \qquad (11\,a)$$

† If work of another kind is involved, as in elastic extension (section 5.16), the relevant intensity-factor (tension in this case) must be constant, as well as P, when $(\partial G/\partial T)_{P,n_i}$ is evaluated.

If we apply equation 10, 11, or 11 a to the initial and final states of a process occurring at constant temperature and pressure, and take the difference, we obtain:

$$\Delta H = \Delta G - T\left(\frac{\partial(\Delta G)}{\partial T}\right)_{P,n_i}, \tag{12}$$

$$\left(\frac{\partial}{\partial T}\left(\frac{\Delta G}{T}\right)\right)_{P,n_i} = -\frac{\Delta H}{T^2}, \tag{13}$$

$$\Delta G = -T\int \frac{\Delta H}{T^2}\,dT + \text{const.} \tag{13a}$$

Thus the temperature-coefficient of ΔG or $\Delta G/T$ in a change at constant temperature and pressure is related to ΔH.

Similarly, the definition $A = E - TS$ combined with the relation $(\partial A/\partial T)_{V,n_i} = -S$ gives us the corresponding relations for changes in a closed system at constant temperature and volume:

$$\Delta E = \Delta A - T\left(\frac{\partial(\Delta A)}{\partial T}\right)_{V,n_i}, \tag{14}$$

$$\left(\frac{\partial}{\partial T}\left(\frac{\Delta A}{T}\right)\right)_{V,n_i} = -\frac{\Delta E}{T^2}. \tag{15}$$

$$\Delta A = -T\int \frac{\Delta E}{T^2}\,dT + \text{const.} \tag{15a}$$

Maxwell's equations. Suppose we take the two equations 8 above,

$$(\partial A/\partial T)_{V,n_i} = -S \quad \text{and} \quad (\partial A/\partial V)_{T,n_i} = -P,$$

and differentiate the first with respect to V at constant T, and the second with respect to T at constant V. We obtain

$$\left(\frac{\partial^2 A}{\partial T \partial V}\right)_{n_i} = -\left(\frac{\partial S}{\partial V}\right)_T, \tag{16}$$

$$\left(\frac{\partial^2 A}{\partial V \partial T}\right)_{n_i} = -\left(\frac{\partial P}{\partial T}\right)_V. \tag{17}$$

Since A is a thermodynamic function, dA is an exact differential, and the order of differentiation does not matter; the above expressions may therefore be equated, and so

$$\left(\frac{\partial P}{\partial T}\right)_V = \left(\frac{\partial S}{\partial V}\right)_T. \tag{18}$$

Similar treatment of equations 6, 7, and 9 gives

$$\left(\frac{\partial T}{\partial V}\right)_S = -\left(\frac{\partial P}{\partial S}\right)_V, \tag{19}$$

$$\left(\frac{\partial T}{\partial P}\right)_S = \left(\frac{\partial V}{\partial S}\right)_P, \tag{20}$$

$$\left(\frac{\partial V}{\partial T}\right)_P = -\left(\frac{\partial S}{\partial P}\right)_T. \tag{21}$$

These equations 18 to 21 are called Maxwell's equations. They have many applications, especially the first of them. Like the equations from which they are derived, they apply to any closed system doing P–V work only.

Equation 20 may be expanded thus:

$$\left(\frac{\partial T}{\partial P}\right)_S = \left(\frac{\partial V}{\partial S}\right)_P = \left(\frac{\partial V}{\partial T}\right)_P \left(\frac{\partial T}{\partial S}\right)_P. \tag{22}$$

A vast number of such relations could be derived by manipulation of the four Maxwell's equations; it is possible to give rules for the systematic derivation of 10^{10} equations in this way.†
Equation 22 has been chosen as an illustration because it can be easily related to experiment. For a reversible change at constant pressure, $(dS)_P = đq/T = C_P\,dT/T$, so that

$$\left(\frac{\partial T}{\partial S}\right)_P = \frac{T}{C_P}.$$

Substituting in equation 22,

$$\left(\frac{\partial T}{\partial P}\right)_S = \frac{T}{C_P}\left(\frac{\partial V}{\partial T}\right)_P. \tag{23}$$

All the quantities in this equation can be measured; $(\partial V/\partial T)_P$ represents the thermal expansion of a body at constant pressure

† Cf., for example, Margenau and Murphy, *The Mathematics of Physics and Chemistry* (van Nostrand, 1943), chap. 1.

(say atmospheric), and $(\partial T/\partial P)_S$ represents the temperature increase on adiabatic reversible compression (for which the entropy change is zero because $dS = đq/T$ and $đq = 0$). Experiments have been carried out in which (dT/dP) has been found for various organic liquids by measuring the temperature-rise produced when a hydrostatic pressure is applied to the liquid (fig. 34). Using the known coefficient of thermal expansion,

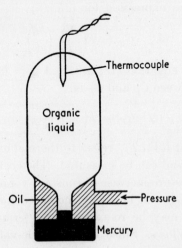

Fig. 34. Apparatus for measuring the temperature-rise when a liquid is adiabatically compressed (diagrammatic).

C_P was calculated. The values agreed with those determined by other methods.†

4.52. *General relation between C_P and C_V*

An interesting application of the first of Maxwell's equations (18) is to make more explicit the relation between the heat capacities at constant volume and constant pressure, for any substance. In section 2.72 we showed from the First Law alone that

$$C_P - C_V = \left(\frac{\partial V}{\partial T}\right)_P \left[P + \left(\frac{\partial E}{\partial V}\right)_T\right]. \qquad (24)$$

† Richards and Wallace, *J. Amer. Chem. Soc.*, 1932, **54**, 2705; Burlew, ibid., 1940, **62**, 681, 690, 696; Joule, *Phil. Mag.*, 1859, **17**, 364.

We now use the results of the Second Law, in the form of the equation (p. 149) for a closed system in terms of E,

$$dE = T\,dS - P\,dV.$$

Putting the temperature constant, and dividing through by dV, we obtain:

$$\left(\frac{\partial E}{\partial V}\right)_T = T\left(\frac{\partial S}{\partial V}\right)_T - P. \tag{25}$$

Substituting this expression for $(\partial E/\partial V)_T$ in equation 24, we find:

$$C_P - C_V = T\left(\frac{\partial V}{\partial T}\right)_P\left(\frac{\partial S}{\partial V}\right)_T. \tag{26}$$

Now Maxwell's equation (18) is $(\partial S/\partial V)_T = (\partial P/\partial T)_V$, so that the relation between C_P and C_V is:

$$C_P - C_V = T\left(\frac{\partial V}{\partial T}\right)_P\left(\frac{\partial P}{\partial T}\right)_V. \tag{27}$$

The coefficient $(\partial V/\partial T)_P$ refers to thermal expansion at constant pressure, and can be measured. The coefficient $(\partial P/\partial T)_V$ refers to the pressure-increase at constant volume with increase of temperature; it can be easily measured for a gas, but not for a solid. It may be re-expressed in terms of measurable quantities as follows. Since P is a single-valued function of V and T,

$$dP = \left(\frac{\partial P}{\partial T}\right)_V dT + \left(\frac{\partial P}{\partial V}\right)_T dV.$$

Hence for changes at constant pressure, putting $dP = 0$ and dividing through by dT,

$$\left(\frac{\partial P}{\partial T}\right)_V = -\left(\frac{\partial P}{\partial V}\right)_T\left(\frac{\partial V}{\partial T}\right)_P.$$

Substituting in equation 27,

$$C_P - C_V = -T\left(\frac{\partial P}{\partial V}\right)_T\left(\frac{\partial V}{\partial T}\right)_P^2. \tag{28}$$

Since the compressibility $\kappa = -(\partial V/\partial P)_T/V$ and the coefficient of cubical expansion $\beta = (\partial V/\partial T)_P/V$,

$$C_P - C_V = \beta^2 V T/\kappa. \tag{29}$$

This expresses $C_P - C_V$ in terms of measurable properties of any material.

For perfect gases, equation 29 takes a specially simple form (p. 93). The equation is important for solids and liquids. C_V for solids cannot be directly measured, because the pressures required to keep the volume constant as the temperature rises would be enormous; yet it is C_V rather than C_P which can be compared with the predictions of molecular theories, such as the classical theory of Dulong and Petit which predicted a constant value of $3R$ cal mole^{-1} deg^{-1}, or the quantum theory of Debye which predicts a value increasing from zero at $0°$ K to a limiting value.[†] In Table 5 (p. 62) are given measured values of C_P for aluminium, with the values of C_V calculated using equation 29, and a comparison of these with the values calculated from the Debye theory, which is seen to be fairly closely followed.

4.53. *Statistical relations for A and G for gases*

We have seen in section 3.11 (p. 69) that the internal energy E of a perfect gas, which may be described in statistical terms as a system composed of independent (i.e. non-interacting) non-localized particles, may be expressed in terms of the partition function f, defined as $\sum e^{-\epsilon_i/kT}$, by the equation

$$E - E_{(0)} = N^0 \sum \epsilon_i e^{-\epsilon_i/kT} \Big/ \sum e^{-\epsilon_i/kT} \tag{30}$$

$$= nRT^2(\partial \ln f/\partial T)_V. \tag{31}$$

It is further shown in statistical mechanics[‡] that for n moles of such a gas, in which the number of molecules is N $(= nN^0)$ the Helmholtz free energy is given by the expression:

$$A - A_{(0)} = -nRT(\ln f - \ln N + 1), \tag{32}$$

and consequently, since $G = A + PV = A + nRT$,

$$G - G_{(0)} = A - A_0 + nRT = -nRT \ln(f/N). \tag{33}$$

---

† On the quantum theory of solids see, for example, Rushbrooke, *Introduction to Statistical Mechanics* (1949), chap. 2; Ubbelohde, *Modern Thermodynamics* (Oxford, 2nd edn. 1952), chap. 7; Fowler and Guggenheim, *Statistical Thermodynamics* (Cambridge, 1939), chap. 4.

‡ See e.g. Taylor and Glasstone, *Treatise on Physical Chemistry*, vol. i (1942) pp. 504 seq.

M

Equation 33 may be put into the following form, by taking antilogarithms,

$$e^{-(G-G_{(0)})/nRT} = f/N = \sum e^{-\epsilon_i/kT}/N. \tag{34}$$

Comparison of equations 30 and 34 shows that G and E both represent the results of averaging the energy of the molecules of the system, but that different averaging processes are concerned.[†] We note also that A and G are very directly related to the partition function (equations 32 and 33) and do not involve its temperature-coefficient; from the molecular point of view they are thus simpler quantities than E.

The entropy also can now be expressed in terms of partition functions. Since $A = E - TS$, we find for gases:

$$S - S_{(0)} = nR\{\ln f - \ln N + 1 + T(\partial \ln f/\partial T)_V\}. \tag{35}$$

Thus, whenever the partition function is known, we can compute A, G, and S, relative to their values at $0°$ K.

4.6. Open systems

As far as closed systems are concerned, we have already reached the objective with which we started this chapter, namely to find criteria for equilibrium and for the direction of change in terms of thermodynamic functions. It only remains to extend the treatment to open systems, those which can exchange material with their surroundings.

4.61. *Fundamental equations for an open system*

We define the function *entropy* for open systems exactly as for closed ones (section 4.44), by the equation:

$$dS = dq_{rev}/T. \tag{36}$$

The justification of this definition is the agreement of its consequences with experiment.

We have already defined the internal energy for an open system, in section 2.25, by the equation

$$dE = dq - dw + \sum \mu_i dn_i, \tag{37}$$

† Cf. Bell, *Acid-base Catalysis* (Oxford, 1941), p. 182.

where $\sum \mu_i \, dn_i$ is the sum of terms such as $\mu_1 \, dn_1$, one for each of the chemical species 1, 2, etc., transferred to or from the surroundings. For a reversible change, we insert $dq = T \, dS$. If the only kind of work involved is P–V work, $dw = P \, dV$. Under these conditions, the change in internal energy for a small change in the system is given by equation 38 below; combined with the definitions of H, A, and G, this gives the expressions 39, 40, 41, which are the fundamental equations for an open system:

$$dE = T \, dS - P \, dV + \sum \mu_i \, dn_i, \qquad (38)$$

$$dH = T \, dS + V \, dP + \sum \mu_i \, dn_i, \qquad (39)$$

$$dA = -S \, dT - P \, dV + \sum \mu_i \, dn_i, \qquad (40)$$

$$dG = -S \, dT + V \, dP + \sum \mu_i \, dn_i. \qquad (41)$$

These four fundamental equations differ only in the term $\sum \mu_i \, dn_i$ from the corresponding relations for closed systems (p. 155). Like them, they must be true generally, although derived by consideration of the particular case of reversible change, since they contain only terms characteristic of the state of the system, and not of its history. The only condition is that each phase shall be in internal equilibrium, with definite temperature, pressure, and chemical potentials.

If we suppose all possible changes in the system to be prevented, putting all the differentials on the right-hand side of these equations equal to zero, we obtain:

$$(dE)_{S,V,n_i} = 0, \qquad (dH)_{S,P,n_i} = 0,$$

$$(dA)_{T,V,n_i} = 0, \qquad (dG)_{T,P,n_i} = 0. \qquad (42)$$

We obtain some important results if we partly restrict the changes in the system, but allow it to exchange chemical species with its surroundings. This gives the equations:

$$(dE)_{S,V} - \sum \mu_i \, dn_i, \qquad (dH)_{S,P} - \sum \mu_i \, dn_i,$$

$$(dA)_{T,V} = \sum \mu_i \, dn_i, \qquad (dG)_{T,P} = \sum \mu_i \, dn_i. \qquad (43)$$

Suppose we now allow the system to exchange only one species at a time with its surroundings, assuming that semi-permeable membranes can be arranged for this purpose. For any species i we obtain from equations 43 the following relations, in which the subscript j indicates that the amounts of all species except i are being kept constant:

$$\mu_i = \left(\frac{\partial E}{\partial n_i}\right)_{S,V,n_j} = \left(\frac{\partial H}{\partial n_i}\right)_{S,P,n_j} = \left(\frac{\partial A}{\partial n_i}\right)_{T,V,n_j} = \left(\frac{\partial G}{\partial n_i}\right)_{T,P,n_j}. \quad (44)$$

The most useful of these relations is the last,

$$\mu_i = (\partial G/\partial n_i)_{T\,P,n_j}. \quad (45)$$

For the special case of a single pure substance, this may be written $\mu = (\partial G/\partial n)_{T,P}$ and the free energy change associated with a gain of dn moles at constant temperature and pressure is given by $dG = \mu\, dn$. Thus if we build up a finite quantity, n moles, of a pure substance, at constant T and P, we find that

$$G = \mu n. \quad (46)$$

For one mole of a pure substance, therefore, $G = \mu$. Since G is a thermodynamic function, this result must be generally true, whatever the history of the system. Thus the chemical potential of a pure substance under given conditions is equal to the Gibbs free energy per mole.

There is an important difference between the roles of G in open and in closed systems. For reversible changes at constant temperature and pressure, involving only P–V work, the change in the free energy of the system is:

$dG = 0$ for closed systems (section 4.46, p. 153),

$dG = \sum \mu_i\, dn_i$ for open systems (equation 43, p. 163).

Thus for closed systems at constant T and P, ΔG is zero in reversible changes—except where other kinds of work are done, as by a galvanic cell; while for open systems at constant T and P, such as an evaporating liquid, ΔG is not zero but is related to the nature and amount of material exchanged between system and surroundings. (If an open system is considered together with its surroundings—for example, an evaporating liquid and its vapour—then the composite system-and-surroundings constitute a closed system, for which as a whole $dG = 0$, that is $dG_{\text{syst}} + dG_{\text{surr}} = 0$.) The criterion of equilibrium in terms of G must therefore be used with care.

The fundamental equations relating to changes in open systems are summarized in the following table, which may be added to that given earlier for closed systems (p. 154). Closed systems can now be regarded as a special case in which all the dn_i's are zero.

TABLE 17

Summary of fundamental equations for changes in
open systems

Function	Equilibrium and reversible change	Observable change
dS	$= dq/T$	$> dq/T$
$dE - T\,dS + P\,dV - \sum \mu_i\,dn_i$ $dH - T\,dS - V\,dP - \sum \mu_i\,dn_i$ $dA + P\,dV + S\,dT - \sum \mu_i\,dn_i$ $dG - V\,dP + S\,dT - \sum \mu_i\,dn_i$	$= 0$	$= 0$

It will be noticed that in this section on open systems we are mainly concerned with the fundamental equations and their consequences, which are true for any type of change, rather than with conditions of equilibrium. The most useful criterion of equilibrium between a system and its surroundings is actually in terms of intensity-factors: both must have the same temperature, pressure, and chemical potentials (cf. section 4.7).

4.62. *Some general thermodynamic relations in open systems*

Let us imagine that we build up a quantity of some phase of a pure substance, say one mole, starting with an infinitesimal amount, dn moles, and adding successive infinitesimal amounts, maintaining constant temperature and pressure. Since the composition of the phase is the same throughout the process, μ will also be constant. All the thermodynamic functions for the phase will be proportional to n. Consequently the equations for E, A, G, and H—equations 38 to 41 of section 4.61,

p. 163—will give on integration:†

$$E = \mu n + TS - PV, \tag{47}$$

$$H = \mu n + TS, \tag{48}$$

$$A = \mu n - PV, \tag{49}$$

$$G = \mu n \quad \text{(cf. p. 164)}. \tag{50}$$

Suppose we build up in the same way a homogeneous mixture—whether a gaseous mixture, a liquid solution, or a solid solution such as an alloy. We keep the proportions of the constituents 1, 2, etc., constant as we build up the system by successive additions at constant temperature and pressure. We then obtain, on integrating equations 38 to 41 as before, the following expressions connecting the thermodynamic functions of the mixture:

$$E = \sum \mu_i n_i + TS - PV, \tag{51}$$

$$H = \sum \mu_i n_i + TS, \tag{52}$$

$$A = \sum \mu_i n_i - PV, \tag{53}$$

$$G = \sum \mu_i n_i. \tag{54}$$

The most applicable of these results is the last (54). It is important that, although we derived this by a particular process at constant temperature and pressure, it must be true generally, since G is a thermodynamic function. It must remain true when P and T vary (the effect of P and T on G will be reflected in changes in the μ's and n's). We can therefore differentiate it generally, without restriction on the type of process that the result applies to. We obtain

$$dG = \sum \mu_i dn_i + \sum n_i d\mu_i. \tag{55}$$

This result will be true generally, the effect of all changes of conditions being reflected in the μ's and n's. But we can also express dG for any system in internal equilibrium in terms of T, P, and the μ's and n's, by equation 41 (p. 163):

$$dG = -S\,dT + V\,dP + \sum \mu_i dn_i.$$

† Mathematically, the four equations are all homogeneous and of the first degree in all the capacity factors, and so can be integrated provided that all the intensity factors are constant.

Comparing this with equation 55, we obtain the relation:

$$S\,dT - V\,dP + \sum n_i\,d\mu_i = 0. \tag{56}$$

This is a *general intensity-factor relation*, connecting any possible variations of the intensity factors T, P, and μ's within a phase in internal equilibrium. In equation 56, the values of S and V refer to $\sum n_i$ moles of the mixture; if we wish them to refer to *one* mole, we must divide through by $\sum n_i$ and obtain

$$S\,dT - V\,dP + \sum x_i\,d\mu_i = 0, \tag{57}$$

where $x_i = n_i/\sum n_i =$ mole fraction of species i.

An interesting special case of the intensity-factor relation 56 is the equation for processes at constant temperature and pressure. Putting $dT = 0$ and $dP = 0$, we find for such processes

$$\sum n_i\,d\mu_i = n_1\,d\mu_1 + n_2\,d\mu_2 + \ldots = 0. \tag{58}$$

Dividing each term in the sum by $\sum n_i$, we obtain:

$$\sum x_i\,d\mu_i = x_1\,d\mu_1 + x_2\,d\mu_2 + \ldots = 0. \tag{59}$$

This is a general relation for the variations of the chemical potentials of the various species present in a phase in internal equilibrium, when the composition of the phase is varied at constant temperature and pressure. It is called the *Gibbs–Duhem relation*, and is especially useful in the treatment of mixtures.†

4.63. *The law of mass action*

The condition for equilibrium in a reaction occurring in a homogeneous mixture, at constant temperature and pressure, can now be put in terms of chemical potentials. Suppose first that the stoichiometric equation for the reaction has the form

$$A + B \rightleftharpoons C + D,$$

as, for example, in the water-gas equilibrium,

$$CO + H_2O \rightleftharpoons CO_2 + H_2.$$

---

† If we wished only to derive the Gibbs–Duhem equation, we could put $dT = dP = 0$ in equation 41, obtaining $(dG)_{T,P} = \sum \mu_i\,dn_i$, and compare with the general equation 55.

Suppose that an infinitesimal amount of reaction occurs, in which the amounts of A and B decrease by dn_A and dn_B moles respectively, while dn_C moles of C and dn_D moles of D make their appearance. Then:

$$dn_C = dn_D = -dn_A = -dn_B = dn \quad \text{(say)}. \tag{60}$$

The effect of this change on G must in general be given by the expression:

$$dG = \left(\frac{\partial G}{\partial n_A}\right)_{T,P,n_j} dn_A + \left(\frac{\partial G}{\partial n_B}\right)_{T,P,n_j} dn_B +$$
$$+ \left(\frac{\partial G}{\partial n_C}\right)_{T,P,n_j} dn_C + \left(\frac{\partial G}{\partial n_D}\right)_{T,P,n_j} dn_D.$$

Since $\mu_i = (\partial G/\partial n_i)_{T,P,n_j}$ (equation 44, p. 164), this may be written:

$$dG = \mu_A\, dn_A + \mu_B\, dn_B + \mu_C\, dn_C + \mu_D\, dn_D.$$

Using equation 60, this becomes:

$$dG = dn(\mu_C + \mu_D - \mu_A - \mu_B). \tag{61}$$

Now the condition for equilibrium, for changes in a closed system at constant temperature and pressure, is $dG = 0$ (section 4.46). Hence if our reaction mixture is at equilibrium, equation 61 gives

$$\mu_A + \mu_B = \mu_C + \mu_D. \tag{62}$$

This is the *law of mass action* for this type of reaction. A similar treatment applied to the generalized stoichiometric equation

$$aA + bB + \ldots \rightleftharpoons mM + nN + \ldots$$

gives the general form of the law of mass action for any reaction:

$$a\mu_A + b\mu_B + \ldots = m\mu_M + n\mu_N + \ldots. \tag{63}$$

The same result is reached if we consider reactions at constant temperature and volume, using the criterion of equilibrium $dA = 0$ (section 4.46). The close relation of the form of equation 63 to that of the stoichiometric reaction makes it easy to remember.

This expression for the law of mass action is still quite indeterminate; to make contact with experimental results, we have to express the chemical potentials in terms of the partial pressures in the case of gas reactions (section 5.42), or of concentrations in the case of reactions in solution (section 6.1).

If the substances concerned in the reaction are mixed in non-equilibrium proportions, reaction will tend to occur in one direction or the other until the μ's have adjusted themselves to the equilibrium relation 62 or 63. The direction of change is thus dependent upon the chemical potentials (cf. p. 52). The law of mass action tells us nothing about the rate of reaction, however; a mixture such as hydrogen and oxygen in the absence of catalysts may remain indefinitely in a state far removed from thermodynamic equilibrium.

4.7. Equivalence of conditions of equilibrium in terms of thermodynamic functions and of intensity factors

Our criteria of equilibrium in terms of thermodynamic functions have been derived ultimately from the criteria in terms

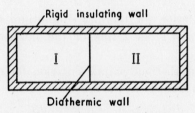

FIG. 35. Thermal equilibrium.

of intensity factors (section 4.1), with the help of the Second Law. It is of interest to show that we can reverse the reasoning and deduce the intensity-factor criteria from the thermodynamic ones.† This will also throw light on the role of the chemical potential.

Thermal equilibrium. To investigate thermal equilibrium, we imagine a system which is kept at constant volume by a rigid container, and is isolated from its surroundings as regards the transfer of energy. Let the system be composed of two sub-systems, I and II, which are in thermal contact but otherwise isolated from each other (fig. 35).

† The following treatment is based on that of Guggenheim in *Modern Thermodynamics* (Methuen, 1933), pp. 20–24.

The appropriate condition of reversible change or equilibrium, since the system as a whole is closed and is kept at constant energy and volume, is (p. 154):

$$(dS)_{E,V} = 0. \tag{1}$$

Thus for any possible change conducted reversibly, if we denote the entropies of I and II by S_I and S_{II} respectively, we have

$$dS_I + dS_{II} = 0. \tag{2}$$

But for reversible change,

$$dS_I = dq/T_I$$

if the sub-system I is at temperature T_I and absorbs heat dq. Now the heat absorbed by sub-system II must be $-dq$, and so:

$$dS_{II} = -dq/T_{II}.$$

Inserting for dS_I and dS_{II} in equation 2, we find for reversible change or equilibrium:

$$T_I = T_{II}. \tag{3}$$

This is the criterion for thermal equilibrium with which we started (section 4.1) in terms of the intensity-factor temperature.

Similarly, our thermodynamic criterion for the irreversible transfer of heat from II to I is

$$(dS)_{E,V} > 0, \quad \text{i.e. } dS_I + dS_{II} > 0.$$

If all the internal changes in I and II are reversible, the entropy changes will be the same as in the reversible transfer of the same amount of heat, so that we shall still have $dS_I = dq/T_I$ and $dS_{II} = -dq/T_{II}$. Hence:

$$\frac{dq}{T_I} - \frac{dq}{T_{II}} > 0$$

so that

$$T_I < T_{II}. \tag{4}$$

The direction of flow of heat is thus from higher to lower temperature, in agreement with our original intensity-factor criterion.

Mechanical (pressure) equilibrium. We again imagine a system composed of two sub-systems I and II—two gases, for instance —either of which can change its volume at the expense of the other, while the total volume, and the temperature and composition, remain constant and uniform (fig. 36).

The criterion of reversible change for the system as a whole, which is at constant temperature and volume, is (p. 154)

$$(dA)_{T,V} = dA_{\mathrm{I}} + dA_{\mathrm{II}} = 0. \tag{5}$$

For such a change in a closed system, we have the general relation (p. 153)

$$dA = -S\,dT - P\,dV = -P\,dV \quad \text{when } T \text{ is constant.}$$

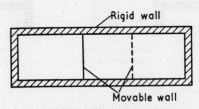

FIG. 36. Mechanical equilibrium.

Thus if the pressures in the sub-systems I and II are P_{I} and P_{II}, and I is reversibly enlarged by a volume dV while II decreases correspondingly by dV,

$$dA_{\mathrm{I}} = -P_{\mathrm{I}}\,dV \quad \text{and} \quad dA_{\mathrm{II}} = P_{\mathrm{II}}\,dV.$$

Equation 5 then gives, for reversible change or equilibrium,

$$-P_{\mathrm{I}}\,dV + P_{\mathrm{II}}\,dV = 0,$$

whence
$$P_{\mathrm{I}} = P_{\mathrm{II}}. \tag{6}$$

If I increases in volume irreversibly at the expense of II, all internal changes in I and II being reversible so that we still have $dA_{\mathrm{I}} = -P_{\mathrm{I}}\,dV$ and $dA_{\mathrm{II}} = P_{\mathrm{II}}\,dV$, the criterion $(dA)_{T,V} < 0$ leads to the conclusion that

$$P_{\mathrm{I}} > P_{\mathrm{II}}. \tag{7}$$

These conclusions agree with our original criteria in terms of the intensity-factor pressure.

Chemical equilibrium and chemical potentials. Suppose now that the two sub-systems are kept at constant and uniform temperature and pressure, while some chemical species can pass from one to the other through a semi-permeable membrane (fig. 37).

The criterion for equilibrium or reversible change at constant temperature and pressure is (p. 154)

$$(dG)_{T,P} = dG_{\mathrm{I}} + dG_{\mathrm{II}} = 0. \tag{8}$$

Suppose dn moles of some substance pass reversibly from I to II. According to the general equation, $dG = \mu\, dn$ (section 4.61,

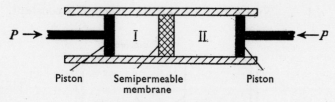

FIG. 37. Chemical equilibrium.

p. 164), so the change in the free energy of I is $dG_{\mathrm{I}} = \mu_{\mathrm{I}}\, dn$, and that of II is $dG_{\mathrm{II}} = \mu_{\mathrm{II}}(-dn)$. Then equation 8 gives

$$\mu_{\mathrm{I}} = \mu_{\mathrm{II}}. \tag{9}$$

For equilibrium as regards the given chemical substance, therefore, its chemical potential must be uniform throughout the system. If the substance migrates irreversibly from II to I, all internal changes in I and II being reversible so that we still have $dG_{\mathrm{I}} = \mu_{\mathrm{I}}\, dn$ and $dG_{\mathrm{II}} = -\mu_{\mathrm{II}}\, dn$, the criterion $(dG)_{T,P} < 0$ leads to the conclusion:

$$\mu_{\mathrm{II}} > \mu_{\mathrm{I}}. \tag{10}$$

These relations 9 and 10 imply that *a chemical species will migrate from a region where its chemical potential is higher to one where it is lower, other intensity factors being constant* (cf. section 2.71). Similarly it will tend to reduce its chemical potential by reacting. The chemical potential of a species under given conditions of temperature, pressure, etc., thus represents quantitatively the tendency of the species to migrate from one phase to another, or to react. Chemical equilibrium in a reaction at constant temperature and pressure is set up when the change in G due to the disappearance of a small amount of reactants is exactly counterbalanced by the change due to the corresponding

appearance of products, and these changes in G are determined
by the chemical potentials of the species concerned. Chemical
potentials are thus extremely important in dealing with chemical change and equilibrium. Fortunately it is often possible to
express the chemical potential simply in terms of pressure for
gases (section 5.15) or of concentration for solutions (section
6.1).

4.8. The Phase Rule: a qualitative treatment of systems in equilibrium

Besides the exact thermodynamic conditions for equilibrium
that we have derived in sections 4.4, 4.5, and 4.6, there is also
a qualitative treatment of systems in equilibrium which is useful as a preliminary to the exact treatment and to experimental
investigation. It leads to the 'Phase Rule', which expresses a
consequence of the criteria of equilibrium, in a form which
enables us to predict in general terms the conditions that must
be satisfied for a given system to be in equilibrium, and the
relations that may be expected among the variables defining
its state.

4.81. *Statement and definitions*

The Phase Rule states that, *for systems in complete internal
equilibrium*, in which the phases can exchange material, heat,
and P-V work, the following relation holds:

$$P+F = C+2, \tag{1}$$

where P is the number of phases, C is the 'number of components', and F is the number of degrees of freedom of the
system. These terms may be defined as follows.

A phase is a homogeneous part of a system. A gas or gaseous
mixture is always homogeneous and constitutes a single phase;
so does a pure solid, a pure liquid, or a solution. A mixture of
two solids constitutes two phases unless a solid solution is
formed.

The '*number of components*' C is equal to the minimum
number of concentrations that must be known in order to fix
the composition of any phase (i.e. the concentrations of all
the species present in the phase) at equilibrium, For a pure

substance, this is simply 1; thus for a gaseous phase consisting of pure hydrogen chloride, only one concentration need be specified, and so $c = 1$. For a mixture of two substances, benzene and toluene for example, we must specify two concentrations, so that $c = 2$. In such simple cases, c is equal to the number of chemical species present. But this is true only when no chemical reaction occurs. If some species can be formed from others, by a reaction of some kind, the number c is less than the number of species. For instance, in a mixture of hydrogen and iodine at equilibrium there are present three species— hydrogen, iodine, and hydrogen iodide. But the three concentrations are not independent. They are related by the law of mass action, and more specifically by the expression for the equilibrium constant, which we shall derive in section 5.42 (p. 227); its simplest form is $K = [HI]^2/[H_2][I_2]$. To fix the concentrations of all three species, we need only specify two of them; the third will be fixed by virtue of the equilibrium. Hence for this system $c = 2$, which is one less than the number of species. Thus the 'number of components' c is not always equal to the number of chemical species. If there are s species and R independent mass-action equilibrium relations, it follows from the definition of c that $c = s - R$. Incidentally c is the same for each phase in a system, since at equilibrium there must be some of each species in each phase.

The number of degrees of freedom F is the number of variables of state that can be *independently* varied, when the system is kept in equilibrium. The variables concerned are temperature, pressure, and the composition of each phase, which may be expressed in terms of the concentrations of the various chemical species.

4.82. *Derivation of the Phase Rule*

Suppose we have a system composed of P phases, each phase in internal equilibrium, and also in complete equilibrium with the neighbouring phases constituting its surroundings. Its temperature and pressure will then be uniform throughout. Suppose the number of chemical species in each phase is s. For generality we will suppose that the number of components, C, is less than S. Then, as we have just seen, there must be $R = S - C$ independent mass-action relations governing chemical equilibrium between the species.

In considering the factors that fix the state of the system, we will neglect variations in the amounts of the several phases, and concentrate on the essentials—their temperatures, their pressures, and the concentrations of the various species. The state of every phase of the system will then be completely specified by (a) the two common properties, temperature and pressure; and (b) the concentration of each species in each phase, to specify which, since there are P phases and S species in each, requires SP quantities. Thus the total number of quantities required to specify the state of the system is

$$SP + 2. \tag{2}$$

Not all of these quantities are independent, however; there are restricting conditions, of three types.

(i) There are $S - C$ relations for chemical equilibria.

(ii) In each phase, the mole fractions of the various species must add up to unity; there will be P relations of the type $x_1^\alpha + x_2^\alpha + \ldots = 1$, where x_1^α is the mole fraction of species 1 in phase α.

(iii) Complete equilibrium between phases requires that the chemical potential of each species be the same in each phase. Thus for each species there will be $P - 1$ equations of the type $\mu_1^\alpha = \mu_1^\beta = \ldots$, and so in all there will be $S(P - 1)$ relations of this type.

The total number of restricting conditions is thus

$$S - C + P + S(P - 1), \quad \text{or} \quad (P + SP - C). \tag{3}$$

The difference between the number of quantities required to specify the state of the system, and the number of restricting relations due to their interdependence, is evidently to be identified with the number of degrees of freedom, F. Hence subtracting expression 3 from expression 2, we obtain:

$$F = SP + 2 - (P + SP - C) = 2 - P + C,$$

or, putting the equation into the more familiar form,

$$P+F = C+2. \tag{4}$$

This is the Phase Rule, due to Willard Gibbs. Its form shows that it is not S but C that is relevant to the equilibrium state of the system; S has dropped out of the final equation. The number 2 appears because two variables only—T and P—have been considered in addition to those defining the compositions of the phases. This implies that only P–V work has been considered; if the system undergoes other kinds of work also, the number is different.†

To show the way in which the factors considered in the derivation of the Phase Rule determine the state of a system in equilibrium, consider a pure liquid in equilibrium with its vapour. The temperature and pressure must be uniform; let us call them simply T and P. If there were no other restricting conditions, we could vary T and P independently. At equilibrium we have, however, a restriction of type (iii), namely $\mu^\alpha = \mu^\beta$. This is connected with T and P, because there is a relation of the form of equation 56 (section 4.62, p. 167) for each phase; denoting gas and liquid by subscripts G and L, the relations are:

$$S_G\,dT - V_G\,dP + d\mu_G = 0, \tag{5}$$

and

$$S_L\,dT - V_L\,dP + d\mu_L = 0. \tag{6}$$

The condition $\mu_G = \mu_L$ implies that $d\mu_G = d\mu_L$ and hence equations 5 and 6 give:

$$dT(S_G - S_L) = dP(V_G - V_L). \tag{7}$$

Thus the restricting condition leads to a relation between P and T. This implies that the pressure and temperature of the system cannot both be varied independently; one can be varied at a time, but the other is then fixed. The number of degrees of freedom will thus be one.

Significance of the Phase Rule. The Phase Rule allows us, if we know the number of phases and the number of components

† The Phase Rule as stated applies to systems in complete equilibrium. For systems in partial equilibrium such as those exhibiting osmotic pressure, it must be modified. Cf. Guggenheim, *Modern Thermodynamics* (1933), p. 27.

in a system, to predict the number of degrees of freedom F, and hence the relations to be expected, when the system is in equilibrium. For instance, for the case considered above of a pure liquid and its vapour, $P = 2$ and $C = 1$, so that for equilibrium the Phase Rule predicts $F = 1$. The possible variables are temperature and pressure, and since $F = 1$ we shall be able to vary only one of these independently; thus if we fix T, P will be automatically fixed when equilibrium is set up, and vice versa. We shall therefore expect a constant vapour pressure at a given temperature, and a relation between vapour pressure and temperature (cf. equation 7 above). Experiment confirms this prediction (section 7.1).

The Phase Rule thus provides a rapid method of predicting which quantities will be related. This is a useful preliminary to the derivation of the exact relations. In the rest of this book we shall often begin the inquiry into a new system in this way. For this reason, we shall not here go into further details of the application of the Phase Rule. Nor have we room to discuss its application to many important systems such as hydrates and alloys; these topics are well treated in standard textbooks and in several well-known monographs.†

† For example, Bowden, *The Phase Rule and Phase Reactions* (Macmillan, 1938); Ricci, *The Phase Rule and Heterogeneous Equilibrium* (van Nostrand, 1951); Findlay, *The Phase Rule* (9th edn. revised by Campbell and Smith, Dover Publications, 1951).

V

APPLICATIONS OF THE SECOND LAW TO GASES

THE Second Law and the relations deduced from it enable us to extend the study of gases beyond the results obtained with the aid of the First Law alone. The properties of gases, as we noticed at the beginning of Chapter III, fall into two classes, which we may now distinguish generally as (i) those that depend on the variation of the thermodynamic functions with temperature, and (ii) those that depend on their variation with volume or pressure. Of the second class, we have dealt separately with $(\partial E/\partial V)_T$ and similar properties in section 3.2, and with equations of state in sections 3.3 and 3.4; we can now, with the aid of the Second Law, show that $(\partial E/\partial V)_T$ is related to the equations of state (section 5.1). We have also to discuss the variation of the entropy and free energy with pressure (section 5.1). Of the first class, we have already dealt in section 3.1 with the temperature-variation of the first-law functions E and H; we have still to discuss the Second Law functions such as S and G (section 5.2). After this we shall be in a position to deal with gas mixtures (section 5.3) and gas reactions (section 5.4).

The application of the Second Law to predict exact relations between the properties of a gas is possible because in ordinary laboratory manipulations of gases internal equilibrium (p. 155) is generally effectively reached and in practice may be assumed to hold. This is an important presupposition of the thermodynamic treatment which follows; it will be found to be justified by the experimental evidence for the phenomena to which it is applied.

5.1. The variation of the thermodynamic functions of a gas with V and P

5.11. *The relation of $(\partial E/\partial V)_T$ to equations of state; perfect-gas behaviour*

We begin with perfect-gas behaviour, the limiting behaviour of gases at low pressures (section 3.34). The general equations derived with the aid of the Second Law allow us to show that the limiting equation of state, $PV = nRT$, implies that $(\partial E/\partial V)_T = 0$.

The variation of the internal energy of a given mass of gas, in any small change in which the only work done is that due to change of volume against atmospheric pressure, is given by the fundamental equation, obtained by combining the First and Second Laws (p. 149):

$$dE = T\,dS - P\,dV.$$

Dividing by dV, $\dfrac{dE}{dV} = T\dfrac{dS}{dV} - P.$

This equation is a general one; for the particular case of changes at constant temperature, we can write:

$$\left(\frac{\partial E}{\partial V}\right)_T = T\left(\frac{\partial S}{\partial V}\right)_T - P.$$

But one of Maxwell's equations (p. 158) is

$$(\partial S/\partial V)_T = (\partial P/\partial T)_V.$$

Hence, $\left(\dfrac{\partial E}{\partial V}\right)_T = T\left(\dfrac{\partial P}{\partial T}\right)_V - P.$ (1)

This equation relates $(\partial E/\partial V)_T$ to the equation of state of the gas, from which $(\partial P/\partial T)_V$ is easily derived. If the equation of state is that of a perfect gas, namely $PV = nRT$, then

$$(\partial P/\partial T)_V = nR/V,$$

and on substituting in equation 1 we find that $(\partial E/\partial V)_T$ is zero:

$$(\partial E/\partial V)_T = (nRT/V) - P = P - P = 0.$$

A similar treatment may be applied to find $(\partial H/\partial P)_T$. Starting with the general Second Law equation for a closed system (p. 149),

$$dH = T\,dS + V\,dP,$$

dividing by dP, taking T as constant, and using the Maxwell relation $(\partial S/\partial P)_T = -(\partial V/\partial T)_P$ (p. 158), we obtain $(\partial H/\partial P)_T$ in terms of P, V, and T:

$$\left(\frac{\partial H}{\partial P}\right)_T = -T\left(\frac{\partial V}{\partial T}\right)_P + V. \qquad (1\,\text{a})$$

If the equation of state is $PV = nRT$, $(\partial V/\partial T)_P = nR/P$ and it then follows from equation 1a that $(\partial H/\partial P)_T = 0$.

Conversely, we can show that the equation of state must be $PV = nRT$ if $(\partial E/\partial V)_T$ and $(\partial H/\partial P)_T$ are both zero, that is if E and H are both functions of temperature alone. When $(\partial E/\partial V)_T = 0$, equation 1 gives:

$$P/T = (\partial P/\partial T)_V,$$

so that for changes at *constant volume*,

$$dP/P = dT/T, \quad \text{or} \quad d\ln P = d\ln T.$$

Integrating this for the change from the state characterized by P_1 and T_1 to that characterized by P_2 and T_2, at constant volume,

$$T_2/T_1 = P_2/P_1.$$

Similarly, when $(\partial H/\partial P)_T = 0$, equation 1a gives

$$V/T = (\partial V/\partial T)_P,$$

so that for changes at *constant pressure*,

$$dV/V = dT/T, \quad \text{or} \quad d\ln V = d\ln T,$$

and therefore $\qquad T_2/T_1 = V_2/V_1.$

Since one proportionality holds for constant volume and the other for constant pressure, they may be combined into a general equation $\qquad PV = \lambda T,$

where λ is a constant independent of P, V, and T. We then reach the general perfect-gas equation $PV = nRT$, exactly as in section 3.33.

We conclude, therefore, that the two tendencies found experimentally in the behaviour of gases at low pressures—namely $PV \rightarrow nRT$, and $(\partial E/\partial V)_T$ and $(\partial H/\partial P)_T \rightarrow 0$—are related through the Second Law. Both can be derived statistically from the model of a gas as consisting of small non-interacting non-localized particles.

5.12. *The relation of $(\partial E/\partial V)_T$ to equations of state for imperfect gases*

For actual gases at ordinary pressures, the value of $(\partial E/\partial V)_T$ is not zero. It can be related to quantities such as the second virial coefficient B, or the van der Waals constants a and b (section 3.42), by using equation 1 and inserting the value of $(\partial P/\partial T)_V$ from the corresponding equation of state. For example, the van der Waals equation may be written for one mole of gas as:

$$P = \frac{RT}{V-b} - \frac{a}{V^2}. \tag{2}$$

If a and b are assumed independent of temperature, we obtain on differentiating with respect to temperature at constant volume:

$$(\partial P/\partial T)_V = R/(V-b). \tag{3}$$

Substituting in equation 1,

$$\left(\frac{\partial E}{\partial V}\right)_T = \frac{RT}{V-b} - P = \frac{a}{V^2}. \tag{4}$$

The corresponding expression in terms of the second virial coefficient B is easily shown to be:

$$\left(\frac{\partial E}{\partial V}\right)_T = \frac{RT^2}{V^2}\left(\frac{dB}{dT}\right). \tag{5}$$

Values of $(\partial E/\partial V)_T$, which depends on the intermolecular forces, may thus be obtained from equations of state alone, though the results appear to be rather less accurate than those obtained from Joule–Kelvin coefficients in the way described in section 3.22. As a test of the van der Waals equation, the predictions of equation 4 may be compared with the experimental results for helium, given in Table 11 above (p. 83). If a is constant, the value of $(\partial E/\partial V)_T$ at constant temperature should vary as P^2, and this is approximately true. But at constant pressure it should vary as T^{-2}, whereas it actually increases with T. The numerical values of $(\partial E/\partial V)_T$ and a/V^2 also differ considerably.

5.13. *Application of the Second Law to the Joule and Joule–Kelvin effects*

For the *Joule effect* (section 3.21), we obtained from the First Law alone the equation:

$$\left(\frac{\partial T}{\partial V}\right)_E = -\frac{1}{C_V}\left(\frac{\partial E}{\partial V}\right)_T.$$

If we introduce the value of $(\partial E/\partial V)_T$ given by equation 1 of section 5.11 (p. 179), we obtain

$$\left(\frac{\partial T}{\partial V}\right)_E = \frac{1}{C_V}\left\{P - T\left(\frac{\partial P}{\partial T}\right)_V\right\}. \tag{6}$$

This equation contains only quantities determined by the state and not the history of the gas, and must therefore hold for all paths, whether reversible or not. Since all the quantities on the right-hand side are accessible by experiment, we can compute $(\partial T/\partial V)_E$ without carrying out the Joule experiment. The accuracy is not high, because the quantity in brackets is a small difference between large quantities, vanishing for a perfect gas.

For the *Joule–Kelvin effect* (section 3.22), the First Law alone gave us a relation between the Joule–Kelvin coefficient and $(\partial E/\partial V)_T$:

$$\left(\frac{\partial T}{\partial P}\right)_H = -\frac{1}{C_P}\left(\frac{\partial H}{\partial P}\right)_T = -\frac{1}{C_P}\left\{\left(\frac{\partial E}{\partial V}\right)_T\left(\frac{\partial V}{\partial P}\right)_T + \left(\frac{\partial(PV)}{\partial P}\right)_T\right\}.$$

We can however, alternatively, substitute for $(\partial H/\partial P)_T$ the value found with the help of the Second Law, in terms of P, V, and T only (equation 1 a, p. 179). If we do this, we obtain for the Joule–Kelvin coefficient:

$$\left(\frac{\partial T}{\partial P}\right)_H = \frac{1}{C_P}\left\{T\left(\frac{\partial V}{\partial T}\right)_P - V\right\}. \tag{7}$$

This expression contains only terms characteristic of the state of the system, and therefore holds for all paths, whether reversible or not. Since it contains only measurable quantities, such as the coefficient of thermal expansion, it can be tested directly by experiment. Such tests are successful.†

The equation just derived is important for the *fixing of the absolute thermodynamic scale of temperature* defined in section 4.43, since the Joule–Kelvin effect provides a means of relating that scale to experimental data. We wish to relate the readings of some convenient practical thermometer—for instance, a

† e.g. Roebuck, *Phys. Rev.*, 1934, **45**, 335. In this paper the equation is verified for helium by using Joule–Kelvin and P–V–T data to compute V, the molar volume, by equation 7, and comparing with the observed value.

constant-pressure nitrogen thermometer—to the absolute thermodynamic scale. The temperature t measured on the scale of the nitrogen thermometer is related to the volume of the gas in the bulb (V) and to its volume at the ice-point (V_i) and at the steam-point (V_s) by equation 4 of section 3.23 (p. 87):

$$t/100 = (V-V_i)/(V_s-V_i).$$

This may be rewritten as:

$$V = V_i(1+\alpha t),$$

where $\alpha = (V_s-V_i)/100V_i$, which is the mean coefficient of thermal expansion of the gas over the 100 degrees between the ice-point and steam-point, and can be measured with high accuracy.

We now rewrite equation 7 (p. 182) in terms of this empirical temperature-scale and of (dT/dt), which depends only on the characteristics of the two scales and not on P, V, H, etc. We must notice that the apparent heat capacity of the gas as measured on the empirical t-scale is not $C_P = (\partial H/\partial T)_P$, but $C'_P = (\partial H/\partial t)_P = C_P(dT/dt)$. Thus we obtain:

$$\left(\frac{\partial t}{\partial P}\right)_H \frac{dT}{dt} = \frac{1}{C'_P}\left(\frac{dT}{dt}\right)\left\{T\left(\frac{\partial V}{\partial t}\right)_P\left(\frac{dt}{dT}\right)-V\right\}.$$

Cancelling (dT/dt) and separating the variables so that both terms in T are on the left, we obtain:

$$\frac{dT}{T} = \frac{(\partial V/\partial t)_P\, dt}{V+C'_P(\partial t/\partial P)_H}.$$

Integrating between the ice-point and the steam-point,

$$\ln\frac{T_s}{T_i} = \int_{t_i}^{t_s} \frac{(\partial V/\partial t)_P}{V+C'_P(\partial t/\partial P)_H}\, dt.$$

If the Joule–Kelvin coefficient $(\partial t/\partial P)_H$ is that for nitrogen (or whatever other gas is used in the constant-pressure gas thermometer), we can substitute $V = V_i(1+\alpha t)$ and $(\partial V/\partial t)_P = V_i\alpha$. Then

$$\ln\frac{T_s}{T_i} = \int_{t_i}^{t_s} \frac{\alpha\, dt}{1+\alpha t+(C'_P/V_i)(\partial t/\partial P)_H}.$$

Thus the ratio T_s/T_i can be evaluated, by graphical integration of the right-hand side, if we know the mean coefficient of expansion α and the heat capacity and Joule–Kelvin coefficient of the gas on the t-scale between the ice-point and the steampoint. Also, since the difference $(T_s - T_i)$ is defined as 100 degrees, to make a centigrade scale, we have a second equation in T_i and T_s. Hence both T_i and T_s can be determined. No measurements below 0° C are needed. The value for T_i obtained by Roebuck,[†] using helium, was $273 \cdot 18 \pm 0 \cdot 03°$ K, in good agreement with the value determined from gas thermometry alone (p. 90). If the term in $(\partial t/\partial P)_H$, which would be zero for a perfect gas, were omitted, the value obtained would be $273 \cdot 32°$ K; this illustrates the size of the correction for gas imperfection. The corrections to gas thermometers at temperatures between 0° and 100° C can be similarly determined; they amount to a few hundredths of a degree.

5.14. *The entropy of a gas at constant temperature*

We now turn to the Second Law functions, entropy (S) and Gibbs free energy (G), to see how they depend on the pressure, for a gas at constant temperature.

The entropy of any substance varies with pressure and temperature in a way which must in general terms be given by:

$$dS = (\partial S/\partial T)_P \, dT + (\partial S/\partial P)_T \, dP. \tag{8}$$

Since we are taking the temperature as constant, the first term is here zero; it will be further considered in section 5.2. For the second term, we use the Maxwell relation

$$(\partial S/\partial P)_T = -(\partial V/\partial T)_P,$$

giving $\qquad\qquad dS = -(\partial V/\partial T)_P \, dP.$

Thus the change of entropy with pressure depends on the coefficient of thermal expansion; it is very small for a solid, but considerable for a gas. For one mole of a *perfect gas*, $(\partial V/\partial T)_P = R/P$, so that

$$dS = -R \, d\ln P,$$

[†] Roebuck, *Proc. Amer. Acad. Arts Sci.*, 1925, **60**, 537. Cf. Hoxton in Glazebrook's *Dictionary of Applied Physics* (Macmillan, 1922), vol. i, art. 'Thermodynamic scale of temperature'.

and on integration we obtain for such a gas

$$S = -R \ln P + \text{constant.}$$

If S^0 is the value of S when the gas is at unit pressure (at the given temperature), then the constant in this equation is evidently S^0, and

$$S - S^0 = -R \ln P.$$

To show plainly that this refers to a gas, and to a definite temperature T, it is convenient to write it as follows:

$$S_{G(T)} - S^0_{G(T)} = -R \ln P, \tag{9}$$

or in terms of the volume,

$$S_{G(T)} - S^0_{G(T)} = R \ln V - R \ln RT. \tag{9a}$$

These equations state the variation with pressure and volume of the entropy at temperature T of one mole of a perfect gas, relative to the standard state in which $P = 1$. $S^0_{G(T)}$ is called the *standard entropy* of the gas at temperature T. In giving a numerical value to the standard entropy of a gas, we must evidently specify the unit of pressure; commonly the pressure adopted for the standard state is one atmosphere. For real *imperfect gases*, the corresponding relation can be found by using an appropriate value for $(\partial V / \partial T)_P$, derived from the equation of state or from the coefficient of thermal expansion. For gases at ordinary pressures, it suffices to apply a small correction, calculated from the equation of state, to the perfect-gas expression 9.†

† The correction is calculated as follows. One of Maxwell's relations is $(\partial S / \partial P)_T = -(\partial V / \partial T)_P$. Hence for a real gas, the entropy S at 1 atmosphere is given by

$$S_{1\,\text{atm}} - S_{\text{low}\,P} = -\int_{\text{low}\,P}^{1\,\text{atm}} (\partial V / \partial T)_P \, dP.$$

If the gas were ideal, its entropy would be S', given by

$$S'_{1\,\text{atm}} - S'_{\text{low}\,P} = -\int_{\text{low}\,P}^{1\,\text{atm}} (\partial V / \partial T)_P \, dP = -\int_{\text{low}\,P}^{1\,\text{atm}} (R/P) \, dP.$$

At low pressure the behaviour of the gas will approach that of an ideal gas, so we can identify $S_{\text{low}\,P}$ for the real gas with $S'_{\text{low}\,P}$ for the ideal gas. Hence the correction to S is:

$$S_{1\,\text{atm}} - S'_{1\,\text{atm}} = \int_{\text{low}\,P}^{1\,\text{atm}} [R/P - (\partial V / \partial T)_P] \, dP.$$

The right-hand side can be evaluated graphically from P–V–T data or from the equation of state.

The relation between entropy and pressure for a perfect gas is thus logarithmic. This is the source of a number of relations in which pressure is related logarithmically to thermodynamic functions. Examples are the free-energy relation and the chemical-potential relation given below, the expression for the equilibrium constant in gas reactions (p. 229), and the vapour-pressure equation (p. 277).

The logarithmic relation between S and P at constant temperature for perfect gases has a very simple statistical interpretation, in terms of the effect on the entropy of the larger volume available to each molecule as the pressure decreases. At constant temperature, the distribution of molecules among the possible vibrational, rotational, and electronic energy-states is fixed and independent of pressure, so that the only source of entropy change is the variation with volume or pressure of the number of positions in space and of the number of possible translational energy-levels open to each molecule. For a system of independent non-localized particles, these are affected by change of volume in precisely the way required to give the logarithmic equation 9 for the entropy, and therefore also the logarithmic relations derived from it. This may be seen by combining the partition function for translation (p. 69, note) with the general relation between the partition function and the entropy (p. 162).†

This statistical interpretation also throws light on the pressure-volume relations of gases. For the changes on expansion of a gas, the general relation (p. 149) may be applied:

$$dE = T\,dS - P\,dV.$$

For changes at constant temperature, therefore,

$$P = T\left(\frac{\partial S}{\partial V}\right)_T - \left(\frac{\partial E}{\partial V}\right)_T. \tag{10}$$

For a perfect gas, $(\partial E/\partial V)_T = 0$, and so

$$P = T\left(\frac{\partial S}{\partial V}\right)_T. \tag{10a}$$

† See also, for example, Rushbrooke, *Introduction to Statistical Mechanics* (Oxford, 1949), chap. 3.

Thus the pressure of a perfect gas is related very simply to the increase of entropy on expansion at constant temperature, $(\partial S/\partial V)_T$. Now the statistical calculation of the increase of entropy with volume in a system of independent non-localized particles leads to equations 9 and 9 a. Differentiation of equation 9 a gives $(\partial S/\partial V)_T = R/V$, which on substituting in 10 a gives $PV = RT$. The perfect-gas equation of state may thus be regarded as a consequence of the fact that when the volume of an assembly of non-interacting non-localized particles is increased, at constant temperature, there is no change in internal energy, but an increase in entropy, related simply to the increase in volume. Real gases approximate to this behaviour.

5.15. *The free energy and chemical potential of a gas at constant temperature. The fugacity of a gas*

The Gibbs free energy G is related to the pressure by a general relation derived from the fundamental equation for G (p. 156):

$$(\partial G/\partial P)_T = V.$$

For changes at constant temperature, therefore, $dG = V\,dP$, and on integration we obtain:

$$\int dG = \int V\,dP.$$

To obtain a definite integral, we can write G^0 for the value of G when $P = 1$ (commonly one atmosphere); this is called the *standard Gibbs free energy* of the gas at temperature T. Then:

$$G - G^0 = \int\limits_1^P V\,dP. \tag{11}$$

For n moles of a *perfect gas*, $V = nRT/P$, so that, since T is constant,

$$G - G^0 = nRT \int\limits_1^P \frac{dP}{P} = nRT \int\limits_1^P d\ln P = nRT \ln P. \tag{12}$$

For one mole, therefore, the value of $G - G^0$ is:

$$G - G^0 = RT \ln P. \tag{13}$$

This equation expresses a logarithmic relation between the pressure, at a fixed temperature, and the value of G for a perfect gas, relative to the standard free energy G^0 at unit pressure. (G^0 will depend on the temperature—see section 5.2—and on the nature of the gas.) The same equation can be deduced from the entropy-pressure relation (9, p. 185), together with the fact that H is independent of P for a perfect gas, and the definition $G = H - TS$. The statistical interpretation of the G–P relation 13, is therefore the same as that of the S–P relation 9, and is to be found in the properties of a system of non-interacting gas molecules.

It is interesting to derive this relation 13 between G and P at constant temperature from the expression for the work of reversible isothermal expansion of one mole of a perfect gas (p. 107). For expansion from P_1 to P_2, this work is

$$w = -RT \ln P_1/P_2.$$

This is related to the change in the Helmholtz free energy A by the equation $\Delta A = -w$ (p. 151). If expansion takes place reversibly from unit pressure to P (so that $P_1 = 1$, $P_2 = P$), we may write:

$$\Delta A = A - A^0 = -w = RT \ln P. \tag{14}$$

Hence, using the relation $G = A + PV = A + RT$ for one mole,

$$G = (A^0 + RT) + RT \ln P,$$

which is equivalent to equation 13, with $G^0 = A^0 + RT$. This illustrates the use of the maximum work function.

The chemical potential μ of a perfect gas is likewise related logarithmically to the pressure. We have shown in section 4.61 (p. 164) that for a pure substance μ is simply equal to the free energy per mole, that is to G in equation 13. For the particular case of unit pressure, $G^0 = \mu^0$ where μ^0 is the chemical potential at unit pressure. Hence for a perfect gas we obtain, using equation 13, the following relation between the pressure and the chemical potential μ, relative to its value μ^0 in the standard state in which $P = 1$:

$$\mu - \mu^0 = RT \ln P. \tag{15}$$

This equation is of great importance in dealing with equilibria involving gases, such as evaporation and chemical equilibrium.

For an *imperfect gas*, it would be possible to derive the corresponding more complex equations by substituting in equation 11 an appropriate value of V derived from the equation of state. However, the form of equation 15 suggests another way of expressing deviations from perfect-gas behaviour, in terms of a new function, called the fugacity.

The fugacity of a gas. Corresponding to equation 15 for a perfect gas, we may write for an imperfect gas the equation:

$$\mu - \mu^0 = RT \ln P^*, \tag{16}$$

where P^* is called the fugacity of the gas under the given conditions of temperature and pressure. This function was introduced as a measure of the 'escaping tendency' of real gases.† It is analogous to the function 'activity' used in the study of solutions (sections 6.1, 9.2). For perfect-gas behaviour, it is equal to the pressure, and since all gases tend to perfect-gas behaviour at low pressures, $P^* \to P$ as $P \to 0$. Values of P^* for a given gas must be determined by experiment, using the same P–V–T data that determine the equation of state. The use of the fugacity, therefore, does not as such advance our understanding of imperfect gases, but it has sometimes advantages of mathematical simplicity, particularly in dealing with equilibria in gaseous reactions (section 5.44).

The fugacities of gases under given conditions may be empirically determined as follows. Differentiating equation 16 with respect to pressure at constant temperature, we obtain:

$$RT(\partial \ln P^* / \partial P)_T = (\partial \mu / \partial P)_T = V,$$

where V is the molar volume. Thus for changes at constant temperature, $V dP = RT d \ln P^*$, and integration gives:

$$\int V \, dP = RT \int d \ln P^*.$$

Suppose we take P as one of the limits of integration, and as the other some very low pressure P' at which $P^* = P'$ within

† Lewis and Randall, *Thermodynamics* (McGraw-Hill, 1923), chap. 10.

experimental error. Then:

$$RT \ln(P^*/P') = \int_{P'}^{P} V\, dP.$$

Adding to both sides $RT \ln(P'/P)$, we find

$$RT \ln(P^*/P) = \int_{P'}^{P} V\, dP - RT \ln P + RT \ln P'$$

$$= \int_{P'}^{P} (V - RT/P)\, dP = \int_{P'}^{P} \alpha\, dP. \qquad (17)$$

The function $\alpha = (V - RT/P)$, which is zero for a perfect gas, can be computed for any given gas at any pressure if P–V data are available, and the integral can then be found graphically. The plot is usually such that the integration can be carried to zero pressure, so that we can put $P' = 0$ and obtain a true value for the fugacity.

The deviations of the fugacity from the pressure increase as the pressure increases, and are greater the larger the van der Waals constants, as the following data show.†

TABLE 18

Fugacities of gases

P atm	Oxygen at 0° C			Carbon dioxide at 60° C		
	P^* atm	$\dfrac{P^*}{P}$	$\dfrac{P}{P_{\text{p.g.}}}$	P^* atm	$\dfrac{P^*}{P}$	$\dfrac{P}{P_{\text{p.g.}}}$
50	48·0	0·960	0·961	42·8	0·86	0·83
100	92·5	0·925	0·929	70·4	0·70	0·51
200	174	0·87	0·91	91	0·45	0·43

Although the fugacity enters equation 16 in the same way as the pressure enters equation 15, the equation of state of an imperfect gas is not simply $P^*V = RT$, as it would be if we could simply write P^* in place of P in the relation $PV = RT$. We can show this by relating P^* to equations of state, by means

† Data from Lewis and Randall, *Thermodynamics* (1923), pp. 196–7.

of equation 17. Suppose we choose the equation in terms of the second virial coefficient (p. 102):

$$PV = RT + BP.$$

This gives for the term in the integral in equation 17:

$$(V - RT/P) = B.$$

Hence equation 17 gives:

$$RT \ln(P*/P) = \int_0^P B \, dP = BP. \qquad (18)$$

This equation relates the fugacity to the second virial coefficient, which of course can be determined from P–V–T experiments.[†] The equation will be valid so long as the pressure is not high enough for the term involving the third virial coefficient to be appreciable. At pressures up to, say, 50 atmospheres for permanent gases, $(P*/P)$ is close enough to unity for us to use the approximation $\ln(1+x) = x$, and rewrite equation 18 as follows:

$$BP = RT \ln(P*/P) = RT \ln(1 + [P*/P - 1]) = RT(P*/P - 1).$$

It follows that:

$$P*/P = 1 + BP/RT = [(RT + BP)/RT] = PV/RT. \qquad (19)$$

We now find $P*V$ from equation 19:

$$P*V = (PV)^2/RT = (RT + BP)^2/RT,$$

or approximately,

$$P*V = RT(1 + 2BP). \qquad (20)$$

This puts the relation between the fugacity and B in a form from which we see that we cannot simply write $P*V = RT$. The values of B for permanent gases are, however, such that this will be a good approximation at ordinary pressures. The fugacity may be similarly related to other equations of state; for instance it may be calculated from the critical constants by means of the Berthelot equation (p. 101).

One further result may be noted. The pressure which a perfect gas would exert if under the same conditions as the

† As an example, cf. the measurement of the fugacity and second virial coefficient of benzene, Baxendale and Enüstün, *Phil. Trans. Roy. Soc.* A, 1951, **243**, 176; cf. Allen, Everett, and Penney, *Proc. Roy. Soc.* A, 1952, **212**, 159.

imperfect is (RT/V). If we call this $P_{p.g.}$, equation 19 gives $P^*/P = P/P_{p.g.}$ so that the geometric mean of the fugacity and $P_{p.g.}$ is the actual pressure. This relation is verified when the pressure is not too high (as is shown in Table 18 above); it may be used to give a useful approximation to the fugacity.

5.16. *The thermodynamics of the stretching of rubber*

The discussion in section 5.14 shows that when a perfect gas is compressed at constant temperature, its internal energy is unchanged, but that there is an entropy decrease, which may be attributed to the smaller volume available to each molecule. Real gases at moderate pressures approximate to this behaviour, and the entropy change is much more marked than the energy change. This is also true for the stretching of rubber, which shows some remarkable analogies with the compression of gases. The general thermodynamic theory of the extension of elastic substances (such as metal wires, fibres, and rubber) also presents interesting analogies with the thermodynamics of gases.†

In experiments on elastic extension, the measurable quantities are tension (t), and length (l). In the thermodynamic treatment, we must therefore use the variables t, l, and T, in place of P, V, and T which we have used almost exclusively hitherto. The equation for reversible change, obtained by combining the First and Second Laws, is as always

$$dE = T\,dS - dw.$$

In the reversible compression or expansion of a gas, the work done by the gas against the surroundings is $dw = P\,dV$ and the equation takes the familiar form (p. 149):

$$dE = T\,dS - P\,dV. \tag{21}$$

In the stretching of elastic bodies, however, the volume change is generally small, and therefore at atmospheric pressure the work $P\,dV$ is negligible compared to the work done by the stretching force. When Hooke's law is obeyed, this work is $t\,dl$,

† On the thermodynamics of elastic extension see, for example, Gee, *Quart. Rev. Chem. Soc.*, 1947, **1**, 265; P. J. Flory, *Principles of Polymer Chemistry* (Cornell University Press, 1953), chap. 11; Ubbelohde, *Modern Thermodynamics* (Oxford, 1952), chap. 16; L. R. G. Treloar, *The Physics of Rubber Elasticity* (Oxford, 1949).

where t is the tension and l the length. Thus inserting $dw = -t\,dl$ as the work done by the system, we obtain the fundamental equation for elastic stretching:

$$dE = T\,dS + t\,dl. \qquad (22)$$

This is analogous in form to equation 21; P is replaced by t and dV by $-dl$. (The negative sign enters because an increase of tension leads to increase of length, whereas increasing the pressure of a gas leads to decrease of volume.) Dividing by dl, and inserting the condition that T is kept constant, we obtain:

$$t = \left(\frac{\partial E}{\partial l}\right)_T - T\left(\frac{\partial S}{\partial l}\right)_T. \qquad (23)$$

This equation relating to the extension of an elastic body at constant temperature is the analogue of that for the expansion of a gas (equation 10, p. 186).

From the fundamental equation 22 we obtain equations analogous to the standard relations used in gas thermodynamics. We define the Helmholtz free energy A and the Gibbs free energy for elastic systems, G', as:

$$A = E - TS, \qquad G' = E - TS - tl. \qquad (24)$$

The function A is the same as that defined in section 4.46; but the definition of G' has $-tl$ where that of G has PV. If we differentiate and combine with equation 22, we obtain the fundamental equations in terms of A and G':

$$dA = -S\,dT + t\,dl, \qquad (25)$$

$$dG' = -S\,dT - l\,dt. \qquad (26)$$

From these equations we can find the relations corresponding to the usual Maxwell relations (p. 158) as follows. Equation 25 gives

$$(\partial A/\partial l)_T = t, \qquad (\partial A/\partial T)_l = -S.$$

Differentiating the first of these with respect to T at constant l, and the second with respect to l at constant T,

$$\left(\frac{\partial}{\partial T}\left(\frac{\partial A}{\partial l}\right)_T\right)_l = \left(\frac{\partial t}{\partial T}\right)_l; \qquad \left(\frac{\partial}{\partial l}\left(\frac{\partial A}{\partial T}\right)_l\right)_T = -\left(\frac{\partial S}{\partial l}\right)_T.$$

Since the order of differentiation for an exact differential does not matter, these may be equated, and we obtain:

$$\left(\frac{\partial S}{\partial l}\right)_T = -\left(\frac{\partial t}{\partial T}\right)_l. \tag{27}$$

This equation relates the *entropy change* on extension at constant temperature, $(\partial S/\partial l)_T$, to the experimentally observable quantity $(\partial t/\partial T)_l$, which represents the variation of the tension required to maintain constant the length of a wire or fibre as the temperature changes. It is analogous to Maxwell's relation $(\partial S/\partial V)_T = (\partial P/\partial T)_V$ for systems doing work against atmospheric pressure.

We can find the corresponding *energy change* on extension at constant temperature, by using equation 23 and substituting from 27. We find

$$\left(\frac{\partial E}{\partial l}\right)_T = t - T\left(\frac{\partial t}{\partial T}\right)_l. \tag{28}$$

Thus $(\partial E/\partial l)_T$ is related to the experimentally accessible quantities T, t, and l. The relation 28 is analogous to the expression for $(\partial E/\partial V)_T$ for the expansion of a gas (equation 1, p. 179).

Using equations 27 and 28 we can find experimentally how the entropy and energy of a body vary when it is stretched. With rubber, it is found that the tension required to keep a sample at constant length is approximately proportional to the absolute temperature; thus $t = aT$, where a is a constant. This is analogous to Charles' law for perfect gases. Taking $(\partial t/\partial T)_l = a$, and substituting this in equations 27 and 28, we obtain as approximate results for rubber:

$$(\partial S/\partial l)_T = -a \tag{29}$$

and
$$(\partial E/\partial l)_T = 0, \tag{30}$$

whence by equation 23,

$$t = -T(\partial S/\partial l)_T. \tag{31}$$

These equations mean that on stretching rubber at constant temperature, there will be very little change in energy (equation 30), but there will be a change in entropy (equation 29), which accounts for nearly the whole of the tension (equation 31). The interpretation is that in the extension of rubber no chemical bonds are appreciably stretched, so that the energy change is small; but that the rubber molecules, which consist of long chains made up of isoprene units, are coiled in unstretched rubber and uncoil when it is stretched, becoming oriented along the direction of extension; since this is a more ordered state, the entropy is decreased. This behaviour is in contrast with that of steel or wool, for which the energy change is more important than the entropy change.

The results for rubber are closely analogous to those for the compression of a perfect gas (section 5.14, p. 186), for which $(\partial E/\partial V)_T = 0$ (cf. equation 30) and $P = T(\partial S/\partial V)_T$ (cf. equation 31). The similarity arises from the fact that in both processes the energy changes are small compared with the entropy changes; the difference lies in the different ways in which the entropy is increased.

5.2. The variation of the entropy and free energy of a gas with temperature

The entropy of a gas at 25° C and one atmosphere pressure can in principle be determined, like its internal energy and heat content (section 3.12, p. 72), in two ways. (i) We may conduct calorimetric experiments at a pressure of one atmosphere; then at low temperature the gas will have condensed. This procedure is considered in section 5.21. (ii) Alternatively we may keep the pressure always below the vapour pressure of the condensed form, down to temperatures low enough to make possible an extrapolation to 0° K. Calorimetric experiments cannot conveniently be carried out under these conditions, but we can use the spectroscopic values of the heat capacities (p. 70). This method is outlined in section 5.22. These two methods should give the same result, since the entropy is a thermodynamic function and does not depend on the history of the gas.

Since we have already worked out the way in which the entropy varies with pressure (section 5.14), and are here concerned only with the variation with temperature, we shall consider the standard entropy $S^0_{G(T)}$ of the gas, which is independent of the pressure (p. 185).

5.21. *Calorimetric determination of the standard entropy and free energy of a gas at one atmosphere pressure*

Just as in the determination of E or H at one atmosphere, we begin with the substance in the solid state at a low temperature, supply energy to it, and measure the heat capacity at a series of temperatures up to, say, 25° C, and the heats and temperatures of fusion and evaporation. From these data the entropy of the gas can be found as follows. The change in entropy of any substance due to small changes of T and P is expressed generally by the equation:

$$dS = dT\left(\frac{\partial S}{\partial T}\right)_P + dP\left(\frac{\partial S}{\partial P}\right)_T. \tag{1}$$

For processes at constant pressure, the second term on the right becomes zero and may be omitted; we have seen in section 5.14 that when the pressure varies this term gives rise to a term $(-R\ln P)$ in the entropy of a perfect gas. The first term on the right is independent of pressure, and will give us the pressure-independent term $S^0_{G(T)}$, i.e. the standard entropy of the gas.

Suppose that the mass of the substance is one mole. For any reversible change in such a closed system, $dS = dq/T$ (section 4.44); hence at constant pressure $dS = C_P dT/T$, so that $(\partial S/\partial T)_P = C_P/T$. Substituting this in equation 1, we have

$$dS^0 = C_P dT/T = C_P d\ln T. \tag{2}$$

We now apply this to the changes in the entropy of the substance as heat is supplied to it at constant pressure. Suppose that initially the substance is in the solid state at 0° K. We represent the heat capacity of the solid at temperature T by C_S, and the entropy of the solid at temperature T by $S_{S(T)}$ and at 0° K by $S_{S(0)}$. (The effect of pressure on the entropy of the solid —and liquid—is so small that the superscripts indicating unit pressure can be omitted.) Equation 2 then gives

$$dS_{S(T)} = C_S d\ln T \tag{3}$$

and on integrating

$$S_{S(T)} - S_{S(0)} = \int\limits_{0}^{T} C_S \, d\ln T. \tag{4}$$

The entropy of a solid at a temperature T, relative to its value at $0°$ K, can thus be found from a knowledge of the heat capacity between $0°$ and $T°$. A typical plot of heat capacity

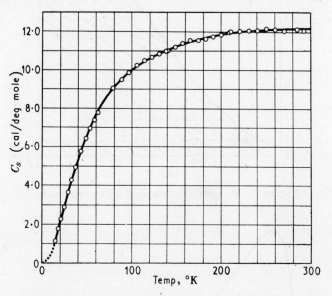

FIG. 38 (a). Plot of C_S against T for silver chloride.

against temperature for a solid is shown in fig. 38 a.† The solid concerned is silver chloride; similar curves are given by the solid forms of ordinary gases, up to their melting-points.

The choice of $0°$ K as the reference temperature for a solid requires some comment. If C_S were constant down to the lowest temperatures attainable, we could not conveniently take $T = 0$ as the reference temperature, since at $0°$ the integral in equation 4 would then become $C_S \ln 0$, which is $-\infty$. Actually, at low enough temperatures the heat capacity decreases with T,

† Data of Eastman and Milner, *J. Chem. Phys.*, 1933, **1**, 444. Fig. 38 a by permission from *Principles of Chemical Thermodynamics* by Paul. Copyright, 1951, McGraw-Hill Book Company, Inc.

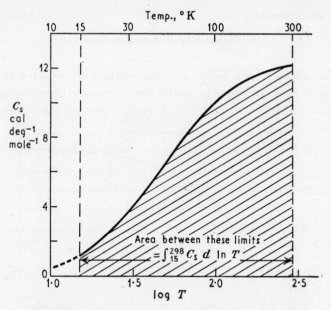

FIG. 38 (b). Plot of C_S against $\log T$ for silver chloride.

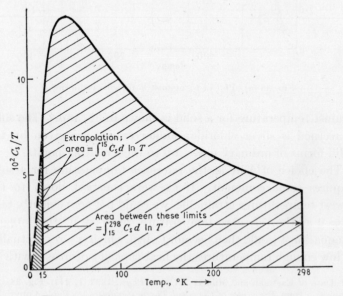

FIG. 38 (c). Plot of C_S/T against T for silver chloride.

and more rapidly than T (the Debye theory of solids suggests the law $C_S \propto T^3$). The integral in equation 4 then becomes zero at $T = 0$, and has a finite value at all temperatures. In practice, heat capacities are seldom measured below about $15°$ K. The value of $\int_{15}^{T} C_S\, d\ln T$ may be found from the area under a plot of C_S against $\ln T$ (fig. 38b) or of C_S/T against T (fig. 38c). The value of $\int_{0}^{15} C_S\, d\ln T$ may be found by an extrapolation using the Debye formula; this introduces no great uncertainty. The entropy change of a solid when its temperature is raised from $0°$ K can thus be evaluated within about 0·2 cal deg^{-1} mole^{-1}.

As the temperature of a solid is increased, then, up to the melting-point T_f, the increase of entropy will be $\int_{0}^{T_f} C_S\, d\ln T$. When the substance melts, the entropy of fusion will be L_f/T_f. On heating the liquid at a pressure of one atmosphere to its boiling-point T_e, the increase of entropy will be $\int_{T_f}^{T_e} C_L\, d\ln T$, where C_L is the heat capacity of the liquid. The entropy of evaporation at one atmosphere will be L_e/T_e. The entropy increase on bringing the gas to some temperature T from T_e at one atmosphere pressure will be $\int_{T_e}^{T} C_G\, d\ln T$, where C_G is the heat capacity of the gas at constant pressure. For the substance in the gaseous state at temperature T and at one atmosphere, then, the entropy, which by definition is the standard entropy $S^0_{G(T)}$ at this temperature, is given, relative to that of the solid at $0°$ K, by the equation:

$$S^0_{G(T)} - S_{S(0)} = \int_{0}^{T_f} C_S\, d\ln T + L_f/T_f + \int_{T_f}^{T_e} C_L\, d\ln T + L_e/T_e +$$
$$+ \int_{T_e}^{T} C_G\, d\ln T. \quad (5)$$

This equation relates the standard entropy to the temperature. It may be written for short as follows:

$$S^0_{G(T)} - S_{S(0)} = [\text{thermal terms for } S]. \qquad (6)$$

If the substance undergoes transitions in the solid or liquid state, these will give rise to additional thermal terms.

As an example, the experimental results for nitrogen† are given in Table 19 and plotted in fig. 39. Data for various gases at various temperatures are given in Table 20.‡

When temperature and pressure both vary, the entropy of a perfect gas is given by a combination of equation 6 with equation 9 of section 5.14 (p. 185) as follows:

$$S_{G(T)} - S_{S(0)} = [\text{thermal terms for } S] - R \ln P. \qquad (7)$$

TABLE 19

Calorimetric determination of the standard entropy of nitrogen at various temperatures

Temperature range in °K	Contribution to entropy cal deg^{-1} mole^{-1}	Total $S^0_{G(T)} - S_{S(0)}$ cal deg^{-1} mole^{-1}
0 to 10. Debye extrapolation . . .	0·46	0·46
10 to 35·61. Graphical integration of C_S curve	6·03	6·49
35·61. Transition; heat 54·71 cal	1·54	8·03
35·61 to 63·14. Graphical integration .	5·59	13·62
63·14. Fusion; heat 172·3 cal . . .	2·73	16·35
63·14 to 77·32. Graphical integration .	2·73	19·08
77·32. Evaporation at 1 atm; heat 1,333 cal	17·24	36·32
77·32 to 298·1 at 1 atm . . .	9·36	45·68
Correction for non-ideality . . .	0·22	..
Total for $(S_{G(T)} - S_{S(0)})$ at 298·1 . . .	..	45·90
,, ,, ,, 400 . . .	..	47·83
,, ,, ,, 600 . . .	..	50·70
,, ,, ,, 800 . . .	..	52·82
,, ,, ,, 1,000 . . .	..	54·53
,, ,, ,, 1,500 . . .	..	57·81

† The data given are calorimetric up to 77·32° K; above this, values from spectroscopy and statistical mechanics have been taken, but in principle calorimetric values could be used.

‡ The values given in Tables 20 and 22 were calculated by the methods outlined in section 5.22; no account is taken of dissociation, etc., at a higher temperature. They are reproduced by permission from chapter 5 by L. Brewer, in *Chemistry and Metallurgy of Miscellaneous Materials: Thermodynamics*, ed. Quill. (Copyright, 1950, McGraw-Hill Book Company, Inc.)

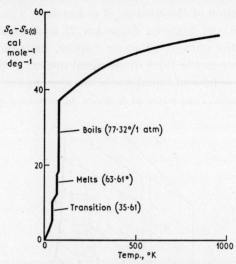

FIG. 39. Standard entropy of nitrogen, at one atmosphere pressure, as a function of temperature.

TABLE 20

Standard entropies of gases at various temperatures

Standard state: 1 atm pressure. Entropy in cal mole^{-1} deg^{-1}. Corrected for deviations from the perfect-gas laws.

Gas	Molal entropy, $S_{G(T)}^0 - S_{S(0)}$				
	298° K	500° K	1,000° K	1,500° K	2,000° K
H_2	31·23	34·83	39·72	42·74	45·03
N_2	45·79	49·40	54·53	57·81	60·25
O_2	49·02	52·74	58·21	61·68	64·23
F_2	48·58	52·64	58·58	62·09	64·64
Cl_2	53·31	57·65	63·74	67·37	70·03
Br_2	58·63	63·15	69·36	73·03	75·68
I_2	62·29	66·89	73·11	76·80	79·44
CH_4	44·54	49·54	59·24	66·97	73·18
NH_3	46·03	50·76	58·76	64·67	69·43
H_2O	45·13	49·37	55·63	59·91	63·30
HF	41·53	45·13	50·01	53·03	55·31
HCl	44·66	48·25	53·23	56·41	58·82
HBr	47·48	51·09	56·17	59·42	61·85
HI	49·36	53·04	58·20	61·51	63·97
CO	47·32	50·94	56·13	59·46	61·92
CO_2	51·08	56·09	64·39	69·87	73·95
SO_2	59·24	64·56	72·93	78·28	82·20

The variation of the entropy of one mole of a gas with both temperature and pressure (equation 7) is illustrated by the values for the entropy of water vapour, represented by the surface shown in the three-dimensional diagram, fig. 40.† The surfaces for solid and liquid water are also shown. The variation of S with T at each of a series of constant pressures is

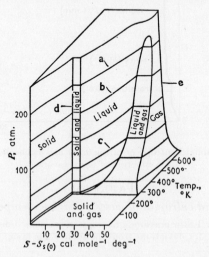

FIG. 40. Entropy of water as a function of temperature and pressure.

shown by the lines a, b, c, etc., along which the surface is cut by constant-pressure planes. The variation with P at constant temperature is given by the line along which the surface is cut by a constant-temperature plane; hence in the solid and liquid regions, where S varies very little with P, these lines, such as d, are almost vertical; while a line such as e shows the nearly logarithmic variation of the entropy of the gas with pressure. The discontinuities at the phase changes, corresponding to the entropies of fusion and evaporation, are clearly seen. We note a certain resemblance between this S–P–T diagram for water and the V–P–T diagram for water given in fig. 20 (p. 98);

† Figs. 40 and 41 are by permission from *Introduction to Chemical Physics*, by Slater. Copyright, 1937, McGraw-Hill Book Company, Inc.

both S and V show discontinuities at the phase changes, and both increase with increase of temperature or decrease of pressure.

The Gibbs free energy of a gas in relation to temperature. The same calorimetric measurements that determine the entropy of a gas suffice also to determine its *heat content* under standard conditions, relative to the solid at $0°$ K, as was shown in section 3.12 (p. 75). Equation 5 of that section may be written:

$$H^0_{G(T)} - H_{S(0)} = [\text{thermal terms for } H]. \tag{8}$$

Combining this with equation 6 (p. 200), and the general relation $G = H - TS$, we find for the *standard Gibbs free energy* (p. 187) of the gas at temperature T and unit pressure:

$$G^0_{G(T)} = H^0_{G(T)} - TS^0_{G(T)} \tag{9}$$

$$= H^0_{G(T)} - TS_{S(0)} - T[\text{thermal terms for } S] \tag{10}$$

$$= H_{S(0)} - TS_{S(0)} + [\text{thermal terms for } H] - \\ - T[\text{thermal terms for } S]. \tag{11}$$

The *Helmholtz free energy* may be found from the same experimental data, since $A = G - PV$ (p. 150), so that for a perfect gas $A^0_{G(T)} = G^0_{G(T)} - RT$, and may be found from equation 9.

To obtain the Gibbs free energy at any pressure other than unity, we must use equation 13 of section 5.15 (p. 187); for a perfect gas at pressure P,

$$G_{G(T)} = G^0_{G(T)} + RT \ln P. \tag{12}$$

Equations 11 and 12 together express the free energy of a gas as a function of temperature and pressure. The variation of the free energy with pressure and temperature simultaneously is illustrated for water vapour by the surface shown in the three-dimensional diagram, fig. 41, which also includes the surfaces for solid and liquid water. This diagram differs from that for the entropy of water (fig. 40), in that there are no discontinuities at the phase changes. This is because μ and therefore G for two pure phases in equilibrium must be equal (p. 172). The surface is not discontinuous but simply folded along the lines a and b, which separate the solid, liquid, and gaseous regions. (C is the critical point.) The variation of G with temperature at constant pressure is shown by such horizontal lines as d, e, f. The variation with pressure alone is given by the intersection of vertical constant-temperature planes with the surface. For the condensed phases (solid and liquid) G

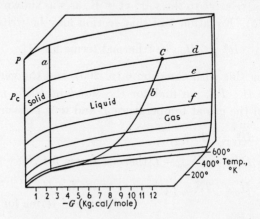

FIG. 41. Gibbs free energy of water as a function of temperature and pressure.

varies little with pressure, as is shown by the nearly vertical line a. For the gas, the variation is nearly logarithmic, but this is not shown explicitly in the diagram.

5.22. *The standard entropy and free energy of a gas, from statistical mechanics and spectroscopy*

We now turn to the alternative method of determining the entropy of a gas (p. 195), in which it is supposed that the pressure is kept always below the vapour pressure of the condensed form, so that the substance remains gaseous down to a temperature low enough to allow extrapolation to absolute zero. Calorimetric measurements of the heat capacities of gases are not usually available at pressures much below the normal boiling-point (that is, below a pressure of one atmosphere), but the heat capacities can be calculated by statistical methods (p. 70). The results refer to perfect-gas behaviour, and a correction must be applied for deviations, but at ordinary pressures this correction is small (p. 185, note).

We consider the standard entropy, as in section 5.21, and start with equation 2 of section 5.21 (p. 196):

$$dS_G^0 = C_P \, d\ln T. \tag{13}$$

For a monatomic gas, C_P at low pressures is experimentally found to be independent of T and nearly equal to $\frac{5}{2}R$ cal mole^{-1} deg^{-1} (p. 66), the value predicted by statistical mechanics for an assembly of independent particles whose energy is entirely translational. Then equation 13 becomes:

$$dS_G^0 = \tfrac{5}{2}R \, d\ln T. \tag{14}$$

Integration of this is straightforward, and we obtain for the standard entropy at temperature T,

$$S_{G(T)}^0 = \text{constant} + \tfrac{5}{2}R\ln T. \tag{15}$$

The constant has the dimensions of entropy and may be written S_G^*. It is known as the *entropy constant* and is characteristic of the particular gas. (For one mole of a monatomic gas, to which equation 15 refers, it is seen to be the value of S when $P = 1$ and $T = 1$.) Thus:

$$S_{G(T)}^0 = S_G^* + \tfrac{5}{2}R\ln T. \tag{16}$$

The entropy constants S_G^* are important in dealing with equilibrium constants in gas reactions (section 5.48) and with vapour pressure (section 7.24). At the moment, however, we simply use them as a stepping-stone in the calculation of the standard entropy of a gas relative to that of the solid at 0° K.

So far we have used statistical mechanics only in the assumption that, for a monatomic perfect gas, $C_P = \frac{5}{2}R$ down to the lowest temperatures. We now make use of a further statistical calculation which gives a value for the entropy constant S_G^*, relative to $S_{S(0)}$ the entropy of the solid at 0° K. The basis of the calculation is that, compared with a perfectly ordered state with every molecule in its lowest energy-level, a state which it is natural to identify with that of the solid form at 0° K,† a

† Cf. below, pp. 211, 212, and section 8.3, p. 303, on perfect crystals; and p. 207 on the effects of the presence of isotopes. See Rushbrooke, *Introduction to Statistical Mechanics* (1949), chap. 9.

gas has additional entropy, for two reasons; its molecules can distribute themselves (i) in various positions about the volume which the gas occupies and (ii) among various energy-levels, which arise because the translational energy is quantized. The result is the equation due to Sackur and Tetrode:[†]

$$S^*_G - S_{S(0)} = R\ln[(2\pi M/N^0 h^2)^{\frac{3}{2}} k^{\frac{5}{2}}] + \tfrac{5}{2}R. \qquad (17)$$

Here M is the molecular weight of the gas, h is Planck's constant, and k is Boltzmann's constant. Combining with equation 16, we obtain for the gas at one atmosphere:

$$S^0_{G(T)} - S_{S(0)} = \tfrac{5}{2}R\ln T - 2\cdot 314 + \tfrac{3}{2}R\ln M. \qquad (18)$$

This gives the standard entropy of the gas at temperature T, relative to the entropy of the solid at $0°$ K. The equation applies to a hypothetical perfect gas, but the correction for the deviation of a real gas from perfect-gas behaviour can be calculated and is not important at ordinary pressures. The standard entropy of a monatomic gas at a given temperature, relative to that of its solid form at $0°$ K, thus depends only on the molecular weight. It increases with the mass of the molecule, because a greater mass implies that the energy-levels of the translational motion are closer together, so that for a given energy more possibilities are open to the molecules (p. 69); this increases W, and hence $k\ln W$, which is equal to S (p. 145).

The values obtained by equation 18 for the standard entropy of a monatomic gas may be compared with the calorimetric values dealt with in section 5.21. Since the entropy of a sample of gas does not depend on its history, but only on its state, the two sets of values should agree, if we are correct in identifying the state of the solid at $0°$ K with a state of perfect order, that is, if the solid at $0°$ K is a 'perfect crystal'. The comparison is in fact satisfactory, as the following table shows.

† For the statistical derivation of the Sackur–Tetrode equation see, for example, Rushbrooke, *Introduction to Statistical Mechanics* (Oxford, 1949), chap. 3; Hinshelwood, *The Structure of Physical Chemistry* (Oxford, 1951), chap. 7; Butler, *Chemical Thermodynamics* (Macmillan, 1946), appendix. The results are compared with those from a method involving vapour pressures in section 7.25.

Standard entropies of monatomic gases at $298 \cdot 1^\circ$ *K and*
1 *atmosphere*

Gas	$S^0_{G(298)} - S_{S(0)}$, cal deg^{-1} mole^{-1}	
	Calorimetric	Statistical
He	30·4	30·1
A	36·9	37·0
Hg	42·2	41·8
Na	37·2	36·7

It may be asked why, if the solid at 0° K is in a state of
perfect order, we do not put $S_{S(0)} = k \ln 1 = 0$, and omit it from
the equations. One reason is that there are interesting cases
when the experimental results indicate that the solid at 0° K
is not a perfect crystal, so that $S_{S(0)}$ is not zero (pp. 211, 303).
Another is that even in a solid substance at 0° K there is
necessarily some disorder if (as is usual) the substance, though
chemically pure, contains different isotopes of the various
atoms, distributed at random. These isotopic atoms are inter-
changeable, and the number of complexions W of the system
is greater than one (we calculate the 'entropy of mixing' later,
in section 5.33) so that $S_{S(0)}$ is not equal to 1. There may also
be molecules differing only in nuclear spin, such as those of
ortho- and para-hydrogen. Again, the transmutation of elements implies that their entropies cannot all be independent.
Thus we cannot in general put $S_{S(0)} = 0$. However, considerations based on the Third Law of thermodynamics (section 8.3)
suggest that it is *a legitimate convention for certain purposes* to
suppose that $S_{S(0)} = 0$ and omit it from thermodynamic equations. Because of the risk of confusion, we shall generally avoid
using this convention.

For a diatomic gas, there are contributions to C_P from the
rotation and internal vibrations of the molecules as well as
from translation. It is then convenient (p. 73) to write

$$C_P = C_i + \tfrac{7}{2}R, \tag{19}$$

where the term $\tfrac{7}{2}R$ arises from translation and rotation and is
the same for all diatomic gases, while the term C_i arises from

the internal vibrations and depends on the gas. C_i decreases with temperature and tends to zero at $0°$ K. Substituting for C_P in equation 13 (p. 205), we find:

$$dS_G^0 = \tfrac{7}{2}R\,d\ln T + C_i\,d\ln T. \qquad (20)$$

Integrating, and leaving the integral in T as an indefinite integral,

$$S_{G(T)}^0 = \text{constant} + \tfrac{7}{2}R\ln T + \int^{T} C_i\,d\ln T. \qquad (21)$$

The value of the integration constant depends on the reference temperature chosen as the lower limit in the integral. It is legitimate and convenient to choose $T = 0°$ K, since C_i decreases with temperature and tends asymptotically to zero at $0°$ K, so that $\int_0^T C_i\,d\ln T$ can be determined from a plot of C_i against $\log T$, which has a form similar to that in fig. 38 b. Writing S_G^* for the constant so determined, equation 21 becomes

$$S_{G(T)}^0 = S_G^* + \tfrac{7}{2}R\ln T + \int_0^T C_i\,d\ln T. \qquad (22)$$

This may be compared with equation 16 for a monatomic gas. S_G^* is again known as the *entropy constant* for the gas; the state of the gas to which it refers is evidently characterized by $P = 1$, as for a monatomic gas, but the temperature to which it refers depends on the gas and is not $T = 1$.

Similar expressions can be given for polyatomic gases; the general form, of which equations 16 and 22 are special cases, is evidently

$$S_{G(T)}^0 = S_G^* + (C_P - C_i)\ln T + \int_0^T C_i\,d\ln T. \qquad (23)$$

For diatomic and polyatomic gases, as for monatomic, statistical mechanics gives values for the entropy constant S_G^* in equations 22 and 23, relative to $S_{S(0)}$. It also enables us to calculate C_i from the spectroscopically-determined energy-levels (p. 70). Hence we can find $S_{G(T)}^0 - S_{S(0)}$, the standard entropy of the gas relative to the solid at $0°$ K.† We may write for

---

† Cf., for example, Wenner, *Thermochemical Calculations* (McGraw-Hill, 1941), chap. 7.

short:
$$S^0_{G(T)} = S_{S(0)} + [\text{statistical terms for } S]. \qquad (24)$$

The actual procedure in evaluating these statistical terms is to calculate the contributions to the entropy due to translation, rotation, and vibration. This is equivalent to evaluating S^*_G and C_i, but in practice the partition function f (p. 69) is evaluated from the energy-levels, and the entropy found by means of the relation (p. 162):

$$S^0_{G(T)} - S_{S(0)} = R \ln f + RT(\partial \ln f / \partial T)_V - R \ln N + R. \qquad (25)$$

In accurate work the individual energy-levels must be used. Useful approximate values may, however, be obtained by assuming that rotation and vibration are independent, that the moment of inertia of the molecule is constant, and that the vibration is a simple harmonic motion with constant frequency. The rotational contribution to the entropy is then

$$R + R \ln(8\pi^2 I k T / \sigma h^2)$$

for linear diatomic molecules, or

$$\tfrac{3}{2} R + R \ln[8\pi^2 (8\pi^3 ABC)^{\frac{1}{2}} / \sigma h^3 (kT)^{\frac{3}{2}}]$$

for non-linear molecules; here I is the moment of inertia of the linear molecule about its mid-point, σ is a symmetry factor equal to the number of indistinguishable positions into which the molecule can be turned by simple rotation as a whole, and A, B, and C are the moments of inertia of the non-linear molecule about its three axes of rotation. The vibrational contribution to the entropy is, for each vibrational degree of freedom, $-R \ln(1 - e^x) + Rx/(e^x - 1)$, where $x = h\nu/kT$. The translational contribution is the same as for monatomic gases, as given by equation 18.

Some of the values so obtained for the standard entropies, with the corresponding values obtained by the calorimetric method (section 5.21), are given in Table 21.† Since they refer to the same reference state, and since the entropy is independent of the history of the gas, the values should agree if

† These and other values, mostly obtained by Giauque and his co-workers, are summarized with references in H. S. Taylor and S. Glasstone, *Treatise on Physical Chemistry*, vol. i, *Atomistics and Thermodynamics*, copyright 1942, van Nostrand Company Inc., p. 588.

the assumptions of the statistical-spectroscopic method are correct.

TABLE 21

Standard entropies of diatomic and polyatomic gases at 298·1° K and 1 atm by calorimetric and statistical-spectroscopic methods

Gas	$S^0_{G(298)} - S_{8(0)}$, cal deg^{-1} mole^{-1}		
	Spectroscopic	Calorimetric	Difference
HCl	44·64	44·5	..
HBr	47·48	47·6	..
HI	49·4	49·5	..
N_2	45·78	45·9	..
O_2	49·03	49·1	..
Cl_2	53·31	53·32	..
H_2	31·23	29·74	+1·5
CO	47·31	46·2	+1·1
H_2S	49·10	49·15	..
H_2O	45·10	44·28	+0·8
CO_2	51·07	51·11	..
COS	55·37	55·27	..
N_2O	52·58	51·44	+1·1
HCN	48·23	47·92	..
NH_3	45·94	45·91	..
PH_3	50·5	50·35	..
CH_4	44·35	44·30	..
C_2H_4	52·47	52·48	..
$(CN)_2$	57·88	57·64	..
SO_2	59·18	59·24	..
CH_3Br	58·74	58·61	..
CH_3Cl	55·98	55·94	..
C_2H_5Cl	67·77	65·91	+1·86
CH_3OH	58·38	56·63	+1·75

Comparison of 'calorimetric' and 'spectroscopic' values of the entropy of gases. From Table 21 it is clear that for most of these gases, as for monatomic gases (p. 207) the calorimetric and statistical-spectroscopic values of the standard entropy agree within the experimental error, which is about 0·2 cal deg^{-1} mole^{-1}. This justifies the assumptions used. When there are discrepancies, such as those noted in the last column of Table 21, they can be removed by correcting the assumptions of the statistical treatment. The corrections needed are of several kinds.

(i) It has been assumed that the solid at $0°$ K is in a state of perfect order, apart from the disorder due to random distribution of different isotopes (p. 207); that is, that all the atoms are arranged in a complete and regular lattice, and there are no holes or other flaws of molecular dimensions. Such a solid is called a 'perfect crystal'. Real crystals may, however, be imperfect. The discrepancy in the entropy values for carbon monoxide can be interpreted by supposing that in the solid the CO molecules can fit into the lattice in two different orientations, CO and OC. This assumption doubles the estimated number of possible configurations and leads to an additional entropy of $R \ln 2$ or about $1 \cdot 4$ cal $\deg^{-1}$ mole^{-1}, which accounts for the observed discrepancy. The same interpretation applies to N_2O, which can apparently take up indifferently the orientations NNO and ONN. The discrepancy for water, again, is in accord with the view that in ice the hydrogen bonding allows the molecules to take up alternative positions.†

(ii) It has been assumed that the molecules of a gas can all occupy the same set of energy-levels. The discrepancy for hydrogen is removed if it is assumed that the gas consists of a mixture of ortho- and para-hydrogen, whose molecules differ in nuclear spin and so in energy-levels, and are not interconvertible in the pure gas at ordinary temperatures. This fact by itself would not lead to a discrepancy, but it so happens that in solid hydrogen the ortho-form rotates, even at the lowest temperatures, whereas the para-form does not. This leads to an imperfect crystal of a different kind from that considered in (i). When the details are worked out, it emerges that in the solid there will be an extra entropy of $1 \cdot 63$ cal $\deg^{-1}$ mole^{-1}, which removes the discrepancy.‡

(iii) The discrepancies for methyl alcohol and ethyl chloride, at the bottom of Table 21, reflect the assumption that there is free rotation about all single bonds. They suggest that rotation about the C–O bond in methyl alcohol, for example, is

† Pauling, *Nature of the Chemical Bond* (Cornell, 2nd edn. 1940), p. 283.

‡ Rushbrooke, *Introduction to Statistical Mechanics* (1949), chap. 7; Taylor and Glasstone, *Treatise on Physical Chemistry* (1942), vol. i, pp. 582–6; A. R. Ubbelohde, *Modern Thermodynamics* (Oxford, 1952), chap. 10.

hindered, so that certain positions are preferred. The energy barrier between these positions can be calculated from the entropy discrepancy, and is found to be about 6 kcal mole^{-1} for methyl alcohol.†

In general, however, the deviations are small and exceptional, and the agreement between the calorimetric and the statistical-spectroscopic values for the standard entropy $S_{G(T)}-S_{S(0)}$ is striking. This gives us confidence that the assumptions of the statistical treatment are true. In particular it constitutes evidence that many solids pass into perfect crystals at very low temperatures. This conclusion will be important in connexion with the Third Law of thermodynamics (section 8.3). Indeed the values of the entropy given in Table 21 are often called 'Third Law entropies'; though they do not depend on the Third Law, they are used in conjunction with it.

The Gibbs free energy and chemical potential of a gas as functions of temperature. Just as calorimetric measurements at one atmosphere allow us to find the Gibbs free energy of a gas as a function of temperature (p. 203), so do the statistical-spectroscopic values of the heat capacities. For these values give us both H and S for a mole of the gas, whence we find G by the general relation $G = H-TS$. We will again consider only the pressure-independent term, which is the standard Gibbs free energy, G^0 (p. 187).

For H^0 we can use the general equation given in section 3.12 (p. 73):

$$H^0_{G(T)}-H^0_{G(0)} = \int_0^T C_i \, dT + (C_P - C_i)T, \qquad (26)$$

and for the standard entropy S^0 we can take the general equation 23 above (p. 208):

$$S^0_{G(T)}-S^*_G = \int_0^T C_i \, d\ln T + (C_P - C_i)\ln T. \qquad (27)$$

† Cf. Taylor and Glasstone, *Treatise on Physical Chemistry* (1942), vol. i, pp. 597 seq.; Pitzer, *Disc. Faraday Soc.*, 1951, no. 10, p. 69.

We then find for the standard Gibbs free energy of the gas at temperature T:

$$G^0_{G(T)} = H^0_{G(0)} - TS^*_G + \int_0^T C_i \, dT - T \int_0^T C_i \, d\ln T +$$

$$+ T(C_P - C_i)(1 - \ln T). \quad (28)$$

Since $H^0 = E^0$ at the absolute zero of temperature, we can write equation 28 as

$$G^0_{G(T)} - E^0_{G(0)} = -TS^*_G + \int_0^T C_i \, dT - T \int_0^T C_i \, d\ln T +$$

$$+ T(C_P - C_i)(1 - \ln T). \quad (29)$$

TABLE 22

Standard Gibbs free energy of gases at various temperatures

Standard state: 1 atm pressure; corrected for deviations from the perfect-gas laws.

Values of $(G^0_{G(T)} - E^0_{G(0)})/T$ in cal mole^{-1} deg^{-1}.

Gas	$-(G^0_{G(T)} - E^0_{G(0)})/T$				
	298° K	500° K	1,000° K	1,500° K	2,000 °K
H_2	24·436	27·965	32·752	35·605	37·685
N_2	38·834	42·431	47·322	50·301	52·497
O_2	42·081	45·691	50·715	53·826	56·122
F_2	41·488	45·230	50·561	53·856	56·243
Cl_2	45·951	49·865	55·453	58·876	61·363
Br_2	50·828	54·966	60·783	64·294	66·83
I_2	54·193	58·474	64·425	67·988	70·5
NH_3	37·989	42·249	48·364	53·033	56·559
H_2O	37·200	41·325	47·049	50·656	53·41
H_2S	41·184	45·36	51·27	55·11	58·08
HF	34·634	38·207	43·023	45·89	47·97
HCl	37·734	41·321	46·171	49·096	51·248
HBr	40·550	44·139	49·010	51·969	54·15
HI	42·418	46·012	50·916	53·016	56·20
CO	40·364	43·963	48·876	51·880	54·095
CO_2	43·575	47·681	54·137	58·513	61·88
SO_2	50·79	55·34	62·23	66·75	70·18

The standard free energy $G^0_{G(T)}$ is thus related to spectroscopic data, from which one can compute $(G^0_{G(T)} - E^0_{G(0)} + TS^*_G)$. Since S^*_G is known in terms of $S^0_{S(0)}$, one can thence find

$$(G^0_{G(T)} - E^0_{G(0)} + TS_{S(0)}).$$

This quantity is important in the calculation of equilibrium constants in gas reactions. It has been computed, from the spectroscopic data, for most of the simpler gases. It can be found directly from the partition functions (p. 69) without evaluating C_i as an intermediate step. Some values for various gases (divided by T for convenience) are given in Table 22.† As we have mentioned (p. 207) the Third Law suggests that as a legitimate convention for certain purposes $S_{S(0)}$ may be put equal to zero, and these values are commonly referred to as values of $(G^0 - E^0_0)$.

5.3. Mixtures of gases, without reaction

Before we can deal with chemical reactions in gas mixtures, we must consider mixtures of gases in which no reaction occurs. The properties of such mixtures cannot be predicted thermodynamically from those of the separate gases, and some new features must be introduced.

We first define *partial pressure* and *partial molar volume* and relate them to measurable properties. Suppose that a mixture of gases contains n_1 moles of species 1, n_2 moles of species 2, and in general n_i moles of species i. Then the *mole fraction* of species i is by definition

$$x_i = n_i/(n_1 + n_2 + \dots) = n_i / \sum n_i$$

and the sum of the mole fractions of all the species is necessarily unity. We define the *partial pressure* p_i of any species i in the gas mixture, as the total pressure P multiplied by the mole fraction of the species i:

$$p_i = x_i P. \tag{1}$$

The sum of the partial pressures of all the species in the mixtures

† See note ‡ on p. 200.

is thus necessarily equal to the total pressure, since

$$(p_1+p_2+...+p_i+...) = P(x_1+x_2+...+x_i+...) = P.$$

For a single gas, the mole fraction is 1 and so the 'partial pressure' is simply the total pressure P.

We define also the *partial molar volume* V_i of a species i in the gas mixture at given temperature and pressure, as

$$V_i = (\partial V/\partial n_i)_{T,P,n_j}, \tag{2}$$

where the subscript n_j indicates that apart from the variation of n_i the composition is held constant, as well as T and P. In the pure gas, V_i is simply the molar volume, written V_i^0. We can relate the total volume V of the gas mixture to the partial molar volumes of its constituents by imagining that the mixture is built up at constant temperature and pressure by bringing together successive infinitesimal volumes of the various constituents, keeping the proportions always the same as in the final mixture so that for each species V_i is constant. Under these conditions, equation 2 tells us that the volume increment contributed by each infinitesimal amount of species i is $dV = V_i\,dn_i$, so that the total contributed to the final volume by species i is $V_i n_i$, and taking all the species into account the final volume will be

$$V = (n_1 V_1 + n_2 V_2 + ... + n_i V_i + ...) = \sum n_i V_i. \tag{3}$$

All these definitions are quite general and apply to any gas mixture.

The properties of a mixture of non-reacting gases cannot be predicted by formal thermodynamics from the properties of the separate gases. This is to be expected from a molecular point of view, since the properties of the mixture will be affected by the interactions between unlike molecules, as well as the interactions between like molecules which occur in the separate gases. Even if the constituent gases are supposed to behave as perfect gases, we cannot conclude by thermodynamic reasoning that the mixture will do so. Fortunately, however, experimental work shows that the behaviour of real gases at moderate pressures approximates to simple laws, which may be usefully

studied as ideal limiting laws at low pressures. We shall therefore investigate these laws, noting deviations from them where
necessary. We shall call them the laws of perfect gas mixtures.†

5.31. *Perfect gas mixtures*

In general terms, a perfect gas mixture may be defined as
one in which each constituent species behaves as though it alone
occupied the whole volume—as if the other species were not
also present in the same region of space. The chemical potential
of each species in such a mixture will be that which the species
would have if it alone occupied the same volume at the same
temperature. Statistically, the simplest supposition that will
account for this behaviour is that at any moment the intermolecular forces contribute negligibly to the energy and other
properties.

In thermodynamic terms, then, we define a perfect gas mixture as a mixture whose constituents are perfect gases and in
which the chemical potential of each species is equal to that of
the pure species at the same partial pressure; or, equivalently,
in which the chemical potential of each species is the same
function of temperature and partial pressure as it is for the
single perfect gas. Now the chemical potential of the pure
species i, as a separate gas, is given, according to equation 15
of section 5.15 (p. 188), in terms of its pressure P (which is also
its partial pressure) by

$$(\mu_i)_{\text{separate}} - \mu_i^0 = RT \ln P,$$

where $\mu_i^0 = G_i^0$ which is given as a function of temperature by
equation 11 or 28 of section 5.2. So by our definition a perfect
gas mixture is one in which the chemical potential of the species
i is given by

$$(\mu_i)_{\text{mixture}} - \mu_i^0 = RT \ln p_i \tag{4}$$

$$= RT \ln P + RT \ln x_i. \tag{5}$$

This is the most general definition of a perfect gas mixture;
from it we can proceed to deduce Dalton's law of partial

---

† The treatment is based on that of Guggenheim, *Modern Thermodynamics*
(Methuen, 1933), chap. 4.

pressures, and other relations, whereas the converse deduction is not possible from Dalton's law alone.

5.32. *Dalton's law of partial pressures*

Differentiating equation 5 with respect to pressure at constant temperature and composition, we obtain for the relation between chemical potential and pressure

$$\left(\frac{\partial \mu_i}{\partial P}\right)_{T,n_i} = \frac{RT}{P}. \tag{6}$$

This may be compared with a general relation obtained as follows. Since $\mu_i = (\partial G/\partial n_i)_{T,P}$, it follows that

$$\left(\frac{\partial \mu_i}{\partial P}\right)_{T,n_i} = \left(\frac{\partial}{\partial P}\left(\frac{\partial G}{\partial n_i}\right)_{T,P}\right)_{T,n_i}. \tag{7}$$

The order of differentiation on the right-hand side does not matter, because dG is an exact differential. Also we know that, as a consequence of the Second fundamental equations law, $(\partial G/\partial P)_{T,n_i} = V$ (p. 156). Hence equation 7 becomes

$$\left(\frac{\partial \mu_i}{\partial P}\right)_{T,n_i} = \left(\frac{\partial}{\partial n_i}\left(\frac{\partial G}{\partial P}\right)_{T,n_i}\right)_{T,P} = \left(\frac{\partial V}{\partial n_i}\right)_{T,P}$$

$$= V_i, \quad \text{the partial molar volume of species } i.$$

Comparing this general relation with that stated in equation 6 for a perfect gas mixture, we obtain

$$V_i = RT/P. \tag{8}$$

Using our expression for the total volume (equation 3) we obtain

$$V = \sum n_i V_i = \sum n_i (RT/P)$$

or

$$PV = RT \sum n_i. \tag{9}$$

This is the equation of state for a perfect gas mixture. This result implies that the behaviour of the mixture as a whole in P-V-T experiments would be that of a perfect gas. It means that we could simply apply the perfect-gas law $PV = nRT$ taking the number of moles n to be $\sum n_i$, irrespective of the differences between the constituent gases.

From this equation of state (9) we may obtain the partial pressures p_i, by using the definition given in equation 1, $p_i = x_i P = Pn_i / \sum n_i$. This gives us

$$p_i = n_i RT/V. \tag{10}$$

This value for the partial pressure agrees with the assumption that it is equal to the pressure calculated by the perfect gas law for the same number of moles of the gas i present *alone* in the same total volume V.

Equations 9 and 10 may be taken as exact expressions of Dalton's law of partial pressures, originally expressed in the form 'one gas acts as vacuum towards another'. Dalton's original work was concerned with the vapour pressures of liquids, which he found to be nearly unchanged in the presence of an atmosphere of a non-reacting gas.† In later work it has been usual to determine experimentally the deviations of the pressures or volumes of gas mixtures from those calculated by the additive expressions 9 and 10. (In principle, the fugacities of the constituents in the mixture could be calculated from experimental work of this type, but this has seldom been done.) It is found experimentally that the deviations are small at moderate pressures; and they are smaller the more closely the separate gases approach perfect gas behaviour. In general, equation 9 holds for gas mixtures about as accurately as the perfect gas equation holds for the separate constituents.‡ For instance, up to 100 atmospheres the deviation for a nitrogen-oxygen mixture (3:1) is less than 0·1 per cent. at ordinary temperatures; for an ethylene-oxygen mixture (1:1) at 100 atmospheres, it is 18 per cent. Thus mixtures of gases have equations of state approximating to equation 9, and their chemical potentials therefore vary with pressure approximately according to equation 4 or 5. These, then, will be taken to be the limiting laws representing the behaviour of perfect gas mixtures.

† For the connexion of this work with the origin of Dalton's atomic theory, see Roscoe and Harden, *A New View of the Origin of Dalton's Atomic Theory* (Macmillan, 1896), chap. 1.

‡ Edwards and Roseveare, *J. Amer. Chem. Soc.*, 1942, **64**, 2816; Gorski and Miller, *J. Amer. Chem. Soc.*, 1953, **75**, 550.

Pressure of a perfect gas separated from a perfect gas mixture by a semi-permeable membrane. Palladium, or heated platinum, is easily permeable to hydrogen but not to other gases; this gives a more direct method for studying mixtures containing hydrogen, though it has seldom been used.† Suppose we have two vessels, A and B, separated by a membrane permeable only to hydrogen; and that we have in A pure hydrogen at pressure P_1, while in B we have a gas mixture containing hydrogen at partial pressure p_1. The temperature and the pressures in A and B are kept constant. If the pressures are low enough for hydrogen to behave as a perfect gas, and the mixture as a perfect gas mixture, the chemical potential of hydrogen in A and B respectively is given by the equations

$$\mu_1^A = \mu_1^0 + RT \ln P_1, \tag{11}$$

$$\mu_1^B = \mu_1^0 + RT \ln p_1. \tag{12}$$

Hydrogen will migrate from one side to the other until there is equilibrium. The condition for this is $\mu_1^A = \mu_1^B$. It follows at once from equations 11 and 12 that $p_1 = P_1$ at equilibrium; the partial pressure of hydrogen in the mixture is equal to the pressure of the pure hydrogen on the other side of the semi-permeable membrane and may therefore be directly determined. This will be true only for perfect-gas and perfect-gas-mixture behaviour.

5.33. *Thermodynamic functions for mixing of gases at constant pressure*

When two non-reacting gases are put in contact, they mix spontaneously. We shall therefore expect to find that this process leads to a decrease of free energy, if carried out at constant temperature and pressure. We can find the changes in free energy, heat content, and entropy that occur when perfect gases are mixed at constant pressure to form a perfect gas mixture, by the following method, which is also useful in other connexions. We first find the free energy change, with the help of equation 5 (p. 216). We then obtain the corre-

† Löwenstein, *Zeit. physik. Chem.*, 1906, **54**, 715.

sponding change in heat content, by using the Gibbs–Helmholtz relation. The entropy change is then given by the difference, since $\Delta G - \Delta H = T \Delta S$. The process we imagine may be represented as in fig. 42.

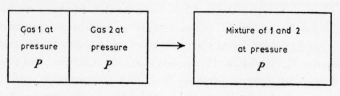

Fig. 42. Mixing of gases at constant pressure.

Suppose we have n_1 moles of gas 1 and n_2 moles of gas 2, each at pressure P. The total free energy of the separate gases is $n_1 \mu_1 + n_2 \mu_2$. If each gas is a perfect gas, this is equal to

$$(n_1 \mu_1^0 + n_2 \mu_2^0) + (n_1 + n_2) RT \ln P.$$

The free energy of the separate gases *per mole of gas*, G_{sep}, is obtained by dividing this by $(n_1 + n_2)$, giving

$$G_{\text{sep}} = x_1 \mu_1^0 + x_2 \mu_2^0 + RT \ln P. \tag{13}$$

The free energy of the mixture is obtained by the method already used in section 4.62 (p. 165). The final volume is easily shown by equation 9 to be simply the sum of the separate initial volumes. If we mix infinitesimal amounts of the gases, at constant temperature and pressure, the system will have a free energy given by

$$dG_{\text{mixt}} = \left(\frac{\partial G}{\partial n_1}\right)_{T,P,n_2} dn_1 + \left(\frac{\partial G}{\partial n_2}\right)_{T,P,n_1} dn_2 = \mu_1\, dn_1 + \mu_2\, dn_2. \tag{14}$$

If then we build up the system by adding successive small amounts of each of the two gases, keeping constant the temperature and pressure (and therefore μ_1 and μ_2), the free energy of a mixture of n_1 moles of gas 1 and n_2 moles of gas 2 will be given by

$$G_{\text{mixt}} = \mu_1 n_1 + \mu_2 n_2. \tag{15}$$

So the free energy of the mixture *per mole of gas* will be

$$G_{\text{mixt}} = x_1 \mu_1 + x_2 \mu_2. \tag{16}$$

If the mixture is a perfect gas mixture, we can substitute for μ_1 and μ_2 using equation 5 (p. 216) and obtain

$$G_{\mathrm{mixt}} = x_1\mu_1^0 + x_2\mu_2^0 + RT\ln P + RT(x_1\ln x_1 + x_2\ln x_2). \quad (17)$$

The difference between the free energy of the mixed and un-mixed gases, when the total amount is one mole, is thus

$$G_{\mathrm{mixt}} - G_{\mathrm{sep}} = RT(x_1\ln x_1 + x_2\ln x_2). \quad (18)$$

Since x_1 and x_2 are less than unity, this is a negative quantity, as it should be for spontaneous mixing. It is often written ΔG_m, and called the *free energy of mixing at constant pressure*. However, the decrease of free energy is due not to the mixing as such but to the increased volume available to each gas, leading to decreased partial pressures. If the several gases are initially in vessels of equal volume, and are mixed and compressed into one vessel, there is no change in the total free energy, because the partial pressures are unchanged.

For a perfect gas mixture resulting from the mixing of a number of non-reacting perfect gases, a calculation similar to the above gives the generalized form of equation 18:

$$\Delta G_m = G_{\mathrm{mixt}} - G_{\mathrm{sep}} = RT\sum x_i\ln x_i. \quad (19)$$

The corresponding *change of heat content* may be obtained by applying the Gibbs–Helmholtz relation (p. 156); it turns out to be zero:

$$\Delta H_m = -T^2\left(\frac{\partial}{\partial T}\left(\frac{\Delta G_m}{T}\right)\right)_{P,n_i} = -T^2\left(\frac{\partial}{\partial T}\left(R\sum x_i\ln x_i\right)\right)$$

$$= 0 \text{ since the } x_i\text{'s are independent of temperature.} \quad (20)$$

The *entropy change* when perfect gases mix at constant temperature and pressure to form a perfect gas mixture is now obtained by applying the general relation by which G is defined, $\Delta G = \Delta H - T\Delta S$. This gives for a binary mixture

$$\Delta S_m = -R(x_1\ln x_1 + x_2\ln x_2),$$

or in general

$$\Delta S_m = -R\sum x_i\ln x_i. \quad (21)$$

This is an important relation. It indicates that there is an entropy increase on mixing, since the x_i's are less than unity and the logarithms are therefore negative. The increase is related to the mole fractions x_i of the gases in a very simple way. It is due to the decrease in partial pressure of each gas (by the factor x_i) when the volume available to it becomes larger on mixing. This we can show as follows. The partial pressure of the gas i is reduced in the ratio x_i on mixing. In a perfect gas mixture, we can show (p. 223) that the partial molar entropy of each constituent varies with its partial pressure logarithmically, in the same way as the entropy of a pure gas with its pressure (equation 9 of section 5.14, p. 185). Thus, on mixing, the partial molar entropy of the constituent i is increased by $R \ln x_i$. This is the entropy increase of the mixture per mole of the species i; so the contribution due to i per mole of mixture is $R x_i \ln x_i$. The sum of these contributions is $R \sum x_i \ln x_i$. Thus we have reached the same value for ΔS_m as that given in equation 21, by considering the increase of entropy with decrease of partial pressure, due to the increase of total volume. We have already seen that in a pure gas such an entropy increase may be interpreted statistically as due to the larger volume available to each molecule, regarded as an independent non-localized particle. The same interpretation applies to the entropy of mixing at constant pressure; it is due to the larger volume available to each molecule. We shall later find a similar relation for ideal solutions, with an analogous interpretation (section 10.2, p. 368).

The variations of the three functions ΔG_m, ΔH_m, and ΔS_m with the proportions of gases in a binary perfect gas mixture are shown in fig. 43. For a 1:1 mixture, ΔS_m is $R \ln 2$ or $1 \cdot 38$ cal deg^{-1} per mole of mixture, and ΔG_m ($= T \Delta S_m$) is about $0 \cdot 4$ kcal per mole at 25° C.

Experiments on ΔH_m are in principle straightforward, since ΔH_m is simply the heat absorbed on mixing at constant pressure. There is no such direct method of measuring ΔS_m; it cannot be measured as q_{rev}/T because the mixing of gases cannot be carried out reversibly (p. 124). It may be calculated from expressions such as those derived above. Fugacities may be used in place of pressures if necessary.

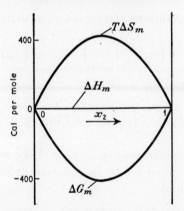

Fig. 43. Free energy, heat, and entropy of mixing for a binary perfect gas mixture, at 25° C, as functions of composition.

5.34. *Partial molar thermodynamic functions of the constituents in a perfect gas mixture*

We already have an expression for the *partial molar free energy* G_i of any constituent i of a perfect gas mixture; since $G_i = (\partial G/\partial n_i)_{T,P,n_j} = \mu_i$, it is simply given by equation 4 (p. 216) for the chemical potential μ_i:

$$G_i = \mu_i = \mu_i^0 + RT \ln p_i. \tag{22}$$

From this we can find the *partial molar entropy* as follows. We have seen that for the gas mixture, the free energy is (equation 15, p. 220)

$$G_{\text{mixt}} = n_1 \mu_1 + n_2 \mu_2 + \ldots + n_i \mu_i + \ldots.$$

By differentiation, therefore, with respect to n_i, keeping the other variables constant,

$$(\partial G_{\text{mixt}}/\partial n_i)_{T,P,n_j} = \mu_i.$$

The partial molar entropy of the species i in the mixture is by definition

$$S_i = (\partial S_{\text{mixt}}/\partial n_i)_{T,P,n_j}.$$

Using equation 9 of section 4.51 (p. 156), this becomes

$$S_i = -\left(\frac{\partial}{\partial n_i}\left(\frac{\partial G}{\partial T}\right)_{P,n_i}\right)_{T,P,n_j}.$$

Since the order of differentiation does not matter,

$$S_i = -\left(\frac{\partial}{\partial T}\left(\frac{\partial G}{\partial n_i}\right)_{T,P,n_j}\right)_{P,n_i} = -\left(\frac{\partial \mu_i}{\partial T}\right)_{P,n_i}.$$

Hence for a perfect gas mixture,

$$S_i = -\left(\frac{\partial}{\partial T}[\mu_i^0 + RT\ln p_i]\right)_{P,n_i}.$$

Since for any pure substance $\mu = G$ (p. 164), we can substitute for μ_i^0 the value given for G^0 in equation 28 of section 5.2 (p. 213). We then find

$$S_i = -\left(\frac{\partial}{\partial T}\left[H_{G(0)}^0 - TS_G^* + \int_0^T C_i\,dT - \right.\right.$$

$$\left.\left. -T\int_0^T C_i\,d\ln T + T(C_p - C_i)(1 - \ln T) + RT\ln p_i\right]\right)_{P,n_i}.$$

On differentiating and rearranging, we obtain

$$S_i = S_G^* + \int_0^T C_i\,d\ln T + (C_p - C_i)\ln T + R\ln p_i. \tag{23}$$

Comparing this with equation 23 of section 5.2 (p. 208), which expresses the standard entropy of the gas $S_{G(T)}^G$ as a function of temperature, we find

$$S_i = S_{G(T)}^0 + R\ln p_i. \tag{24}$$

The partial molar entropy of a constituent in a perfect gas mixture thus varies with its partial pressure in the same way as the entropy of the pure gas with pressure, and the constant $S_{G(T)}^0$ is the same for both if their temperatures are the same.

The *partial molar heat content* H_i may be obtained from G_i and S_i. Since $H = G + TS$, differentiation with respect to n_i of the values for the mixture gives $H_i = G_i + TS_i$. Summing the above values for G_i and S_i, and using equation 4 of section 3.12 (p. 73), we find $H_i = H_{G(T)}$. Thus the partial molar heat content of a perfect gas is the same in a perfect gas mixture as in the pure gas.

5.35. *Imperfect gas mixtures*

When deviations from the laws of perfect gas mixtures have to be taken into account, as in high-pressure work for instance, it is convenient to use fugacities in place of partial pressures, and to write, in place of equation 4 (p. 216),

$$(\mu_i)_{\text{mixt}} - \mu_i^0 = RT \ln P_i^*. \qquad (25)$$

The fugacity of a constituent in a mixture could in principle be determined from P-V-T data, but there are few experimental investigations accurate enough for the purpose. As a useful approximation, Lewis and Randall suggested[†] that the fugacity of a gas in a mixture could be calculated by multiplying its mole fraction in the mixture by the fugacity which it would have in the pure state at a pressure equal to that of the mixture. The fugacity can then be found from the equation of state of the pure gas, as in section 5.15 (p. 189). This gives good results up to 100 atm provided that none of the constituents is too close to its critical temperature.[‡]

5.4. Reactions in gas mixtures

The thermodynamic functions for gas reactions are of great chemical interest. The standard free energy change, ΔG^0, in a reaction is, as we shall see, a quantitative measure of the tendency of the reaction to occur at a given temperature and pressure; it is a measure of chemical affinity. Often the decisive factor in determining ΔG^0 is the change of heat content in the reaction, but sometimes the standard entropy change may be the more important ($\Delta G^0 = \Delta H^0 - T \Delta S^0$). The experimental determination of these quantities has received a great deal of attention. The thermodynamic relations are simplified if the reaction occurs in a perfect gas mixture, and since many reactions follow closely the resulting relations we shall devote most of our attention to them.

The standard free energy change ΔG^0 in a reaction may first

[†] Lewis and Randall, *Thermodynamics* (1923), pp. 226–7.
[‡] J. A. Beattie, *Chem. Rev.*, 1949, **44**, 191. This paper also discusses a general exact method, the 'general limit method'. For theoretical methods see Guggenheim, *Mixtures* (Oxford, 1952), chap. 8.

be defined in terms of the free energies of the separate gases, rather than of the initial and final mixtures.† It is the sum of the standard free energies (commonly at one atmosphere) of the products, minus the sum of those of the reactants. The free energy of mixing of the products or reactants is thus not involved. The standard entropy change ΔS^0 and heat content ΔH^0 are similarly defined. Since the heat content of a perfect gas does not vary with pressure, ΔH for a reaction between perfect gases will be independent of pressure, and it is then unnecessary to stipulate that standard heat contents must be used.

5.41. *The relation of ΔH^0, ΔG^0, and ΔS^0 to properties of the individual gases*

For many gases, as we have seen (section 3.12), values of the heat content have been determined at various temperatures (relative to the value of the substance at $0°$ K) either calorimetrically or by statistical-spectroscopic methods; some of the results have been given in Table 9 (p. 74). If we take these values of $(H^0_{G(T)} - H_{G(0)})$, the difference of the sum for the products and the sum for the reactants is evidently $\Delta H^0_{G(T)} - \Delta H_{G(0)}$. $\Delta H_{G(0)}$ can be determined either by making one calorimetric determination of $\Delta H_{G(T)}$ at some convenient temperature, and combining with heat capacities by means of Kirchhoff's relations (p. 58); or, for simple dissociations such as $H_2 \rightleftharpoons 2H$, by spectroscopy (p. 46). Once $\Delta H_{G(0)}$ is known, $\Delta H^0_{G(T)}$ can be found at any temperature from the properties of the individual gases.

For the standard entropy and free energy, however, matters are less simple. We have seen in sections 5.21 and 5.22 that calorimetric or statistical-spectroscopic methods allow us to compute values of $S^0_{G(T)} - S_{S(0)}$. The difference of the sums for the products and reactants is thus $\Delta S^0_{G(T)} - \Delta S_{S(0)}$, so we cannot find $\Delta S^0_{G(T)}$, the standard entropy change in the reaction at a given temperature, unless we have some independent knowledge of $\Delta S_{S(0)}$, the entropy difference for the solids at $0°$ K. The

† See, however, p. 235.

same difficulty arises in finding the standard free energy change. From the same calorimetric or spectroscopic data we can find values of $(G^0_{G(T)} - H_{G(0)} + TS_{S(0)})$, as shown in section 5.22. The difference of the sums for the products and reactants is thus $(\Delta G^0_{G(T)} - \Delta H_{G(0)} + T\Delta S_{S(0)})$. We can find $\Delta H_{G(0)}$ as before, but as yet we have no independent knowledge of $\Delta S_{S(0)}$. We shall later see that for many reactions, though not all, there is good reason to think that $\Delta S_{S(0)}$ is zero. This generalization is called the Third Law of thermodynamics (section 8.3). Where it applies, we can find $\Delta G^0_{G(T)}$ from a sufficient knowledge of the properties of the individual gases, plus a knowledge of $\Delta H^0_{G(T)}$ (section 8.4).

However, we have as yet no evidence on the value of $\Delta S_{S(0)}$, so we must consider methods of determining ΔS^0 and ΔG^0 that do not make use of the assumption that $\Delta S_{S(0)} = 0$. The classical method is the determination of equilibrium constants, to which we now turn.

5.42. *Free energy change and chemical equilibrium, for reactions in perfect gas mixtures at constant T and P*

Many reactions in gases are virtually complete in a short time—for example, the combustion of methane in oxygen. Others, conversely, are immeasurably slow, at least in the absence of a catalyst. But there are many reactions which attain an *equilibrium* in which the 'reactant' and 'product' species coexist. The proportions of the various species present are then found experimentally to have not arbitrary but definite values, independent of whether we start with 'reactants' or 'products', but depending on the reaction and the conditions. The exact form of the equilibrium relation may be derived as follows.

Suppose first that we have a perfect gas mixture, at a given constant temperature T and pressure P, containing species A, B, C, and D, at partial pressures p_A, p_B, p_C, and p_D. Suppose that the following reaction can occur and that an equilibrium is set up:

$$A + B \rightleftharpoons C + D. \tag{1}$$

The species might, for instance, be H_2O, CO, H_2, and CO_2, which when mixed react to give an equilibrium mixture according to the equation $H_2O + CO \rightleftharpoons H_2 + CO_2$. Since the system is at constant temperature and pressure, we shall use the condition of equilibrium $dG = 0$ (p. 153). Here dG means the change of free energy accompanying an infinitesimal conversion of (A+B) to (C+D). This change in free energy will be a function of the independent variables of the system, which may be taken as temperature, pressure, and composition. We are taking T and P as constant, so that only the variations in composition need be considered. Let the amounts of C and D that appear be dn_C and dn_D, and the amounts of A and B that disappear be dn_A and dn_B. Then for the effect on G we can write the general differential expression

$$dG = \left(\frac{\partial G}{\partial n_C}\right)_{T,P,n_j} dn_C + \left(\frac{\partial G}{\partial n_D}\right)_{T,P,n_j} dn_D -$$

$$- \left(\frac{\partial G}{\partial n_A}\right)_{T,P,n_j} dn_A - \left(\frac{\partial G}{\partial n_B}\right)_{T,P,n_j} dn_B. \quad (2)$$

The terms on the right-hand side can be simplified by substituting $(\partial G/\partial n_A)_{T,P,n_j} = \mu_A$, etc. We then obtain

$$dG = \mu_C dn_C + \mu_D dn_D - \mu_A dn_A - \mu_B dn_B.$$

For this type of reaction, it is evident that

$$dn_A = dn_B = dn_C = dn_D = dn$$

say, so that $$dG = dn(\mu_C + \mu_D - \mu_A - \mu_B). \quad (3)$$

Now in a perfect gas mixture, μ_A and the other chemical potentials are related to the partial pressures of the constituents by equations such as $\mu_A = \mu_A^0 + RT \ln p_A$. Substituting for the μ's, equation 3 gives

$$dG = dn[(\mu_C^0 + \mu_D^0 - \mu_A^0 - \mu_B^0) + RT \ln(p_C p_D / p_A p_B)].$$

Since $\mu_A^0 = G_A^0$, etc., the term $(\mu_C^0 + \mu_D^0 - \mu_A^0 - \mu_B^0) = \Delta\mu^0 = \Delta G^0$, the standard free energy change in the reaction. Thus

$$dG = dn[\Delta G^0 + RT \ln(p_C p_D / p_A p_B)]. \quad (4)$$

This important equation has two applications: firstly, to find the relation between the partial pressures when chemical equilibrium is set up, and secondly, to find the free energy change when the reaction proceeds.

Chemical equilibrium in perfect gas mixtures at constant temperature and pressure. The condition for equilibrium is

$$(dG)_{T,P} = 0.$$

Let the partial pressures at equilibrium take up the values p_A^e, etc. Then equation 4 gives for the equilibrium mixture

$$0 = \Delta G^0 + RT \ln(p_C^e p_D^e / p_A^e p_B^e), \qquad (5)$$

which may also be written

$$p_C^e p_D^e / p_A^e p_B^e = e^{-\Delta G^0/RT}. \qquad (6)$$

The expression $(p_C^e p_D^e / p_A^e p_B^e)$ is thus directly related to ΔG^0. At a given temperature it is fixed, since ΔG^0 is fixed (by the standard free energies of the individual gases, which depend only on T). It is therefore independent not only of the individual values of p_A^e, etc., and of the proportions of the gases initially present, but of the total pressure. It is called the *equilibrium constant*, and when thus expressed in terms of pressures, it is usually written K_p:

$$K_p = p_C^e p_D^e / p_A^e p_B^e. \qquad (7)$$

At equilibrium, the partial pressures must adjust themselves until $(p_C^e p_D^e / p_A^e p_B^e)$ becomes equal to K_p, whatever the initial proportions of A, B, C, and D. The value of K_p at a given temperature is expressed in terms of ΔG^0 by combining equations 5 and 7:

$$RT \ln K_p = -\Delta G^0. \qquad (8)$$

We could have obtained equations 7 and 8 alternatively by using the law of mass action already deduced in section 4.63, namely,

$$\mu_A + \mu_B - \mu_C - \mu_D = 0,$$

and inserting $\mu_A = \mu_A^0 + RT \ln p_A^e$, etc., when we obtain at once equation 5:

$$RT \ln(p_C^e p_D^e / p_A^e p_B^e) = \mu_A^0 + \mu_B^0 - \mu_C^0 - \mu_D^0 = -\Delta \mu^0 = -\Delta G^0.$$

We can extend this treatment to *any* type of reaction, written as

$$aA + bB + \ldots \rightleftharpoons mM + nN + \ldots,$$

either by generalizing the treatment leading to equation 4, or more quickly by using the general law of mass action (section 4.63), namely,

$$a\mu_A + b\mu_B + \ldots = m\mu_M + n\mu_N + \ldots. \tag{9}$$

This gives as the general form of the equilibrium constant in terms of pressures, for reactions in perfect gas mixtures,

$$K_p = (p_M^e)^m (p_N^e)^n \ldots / (p_A^e)^a (p_B^e)^b \ldots \tag{10}$$

and the general expression for ΔG^0 is evidently

$$\boxed{\Delta G^0 = -RT \ln K_p.} \tag{11}$$

The relation 10 between the partial pressures at equilibrium is extremely important. It was originally obtained by Guldberg and Waage (1864–7) as a consequence of the assumption that the rates of the forward and reverse reactions, which must be equal at equilibrium, are proportional to $p_A^a p_B^b \ldots$ and $p_M^m p_N^n \ldots$ respectively. This assumption has not been tested for many reactions, and is not true as a general rule. The thermodynamic treatment does not depend on any particular kinetic hypothesis.

The form of the equilibrium constant (equation 10) determines the behaviour of the mixture when the partial pressures or the total pressure is changed. Consider, for example, the effect of an increase of total pressure on the reaction

$$N_2O_4 \rightleftharpoons 2NO_2$$

for which
$$K_p = (p_{NO_2}^e)^2 / (p_{N_2O_4}^e). \tag{12}$$

Suppose the total pressure is suddenly increased from P to zP ($z > 1$), by compressing the gas mixture into a smaller volume, the temperature being kept constant. Momentarily, both the partial pressures will increase in the same porportion, to $p'_{NO_2} = zp_{NO_2}$ and $p'_{N_2O_4} = zp_{N_2O_4}$. Thus

$$(p'_{NO_2})^2 / (p'_{N_2O_4}) = (zp_{NO_2}^e)^2 / (zp_{N_2O_4}^e) = zK_p,$$

which is greater than K_p. To make it equal to K_p, the partial pressure of NO_2 must decrease relative to that of N_2O_4; in other words, the increase of pressure will cause the equilibrium composition to shift to the left—the direction which leads to a decrease in volume. This is true quite generally, as may be seen using equation 10 in place of 12. Conversely, a decrease of pressure leads to a shift of the equilibrium composition in the direction that leads to an increase in volume. Generally, then, the shift of composition is such as to reduce the effect of the change imposed upon the system; this rule was given by Le Chatelier (see also p. 242). If there is no change in volume, as in the reaction $H_2O + CO \rightleftharpoons H_2 + CO_2$, change of pressure will not alter the equilibrium composition.

The effect of change of pressure on a dissociation equilibrium such as that of N_2O_4 can also be shown by expressing K_p in terms of the fraction of gas dissociated. If this fraction is α, and we start with n moles of gas, the number of moles of N_2O_4 at equilibrium will be $n(1-\alpha)$, and that of NO_2 will be $2n\alpha$, so that the total number of moles will be $n(1+\alpha)$. The mole fraction of N_2O_4 is then $(1-\alpha)/(1+\alpha)$, and that of NO_2 is $2\alpha(1+\alpha)$; the partial pressures are therefore $P(1-\alpha)/(1+\alpha)$ and $2\alpha P/(1+\alpha)$. Hence $K_p = p_{NO_2}^2/p_{N_2O_4} = 4P\alpha^2(1-\alpha^2)$. If P increases, therefore, α must decrease, to keep the value of K_p constant.

The equation 11 for ΔG^0 is also a very important relation. It enables us to determine ΔG^0 if the equilibrium composition can be experimentally determined; or conversely to predict the position of equilibrium if ΔG^0 is already known. This method has been much used. It is not necessary to measure the equilibrium constant of every reaction directly; many reactions can be regarded as the result of several successive reactions, and the equilibrium constant for the overall reaction is the product of the changes for the several reactions. This is easily seen if we consider a series of reactions:

$$A+B \overset{K_1}{\rightleftharpoons} C+D \overset{K_2}{\rightleftharpoons} P+Q \overset{K_3}{\rightleftharpoons} X+Y.$$

The equilibrium constants K_p are

$$K_1 = p_C p_D/p_A p_B, \qquad K_2 = p_P p_Q/p_C p_D,$$

and

$$K_3 = p_X p_Y/p_P p_Q.$$

For the overall reaction

$$A + B \overset{K}{\rightleftharpoons} X + Y,$$

the equilibrium constant $K = p_X p_Y / p_A p_B = K_1 K_2 K_3$, so that K is known if K_1, K_2, and K_3 have been determined. Application of equation 11 gives for the free energy ΔG of the overall reaction

$$\Delta G = \Delta G_1 + \Delta G_2 + \Delta G_3. \tag{13}$$

Thus the free energy changes in successive reactions are additive, like the changes of heat content. This agrees with the principle that in any change ΔG depends on the initial and final states and not the intermediate path. The practical conclusion is that from a knowledge of ΔG^0 for some simple reactions, ΔG^0 for other reactions can often be deduced. For example, supposing that we could not measure the equilibrium constant for the reaction

$$2H_2 + O_2 \rightleftharpoons 2H_2O$$

we could obtain it by combining those for the reactions

$$2H_2 + 2Cl_2 \rightleftharpoons 4HCl$$

and $$4HCl + O_2 \rightleftharpoons 2H_2O + 2Cl_2.$$

A great deal of such work is surveyed in Lewis and Randall's classic *Thermodynamics* (1923).

K_p, K_c, *and* K_x. An equilibrium constant can also be defined in terms of *concentrations* in place of partial pressures. The molar concentration c_i of a species i is defined by $c_i = n_i/V$, and combining this definition with the expression obtained in section 5.32 (p. 218) for the partial pressure in a perfect gas mixture, $p_i = n_i RT/V$, we find $p_i = c_i RT$. Substituting for p_A, etc., in equation 10, we obtain

$$K_p = \frac{(c_M^e)^m (c_N^e)^n \cdots}{(c_A^e)^a (c_B^e)^b \cdots} \times RT^{m+n\cdots-a-b\cdots}, \tag{14}$$

which may be written in terms of a new constant K_c:

$$K_p = K_c (RT)^{m+n\cdots-a-b\cdots}. \tag{15}$$

K_c will, like K_p, be independent of pressure at a given temperature. It will be equal to K_p only when the numbers of molecules on the left and right sides of a stoichiometric equation are equal, as in equation 1; an example is the water-gas equilibrium, or the reaction between hydrogen and iodine. The different units in which the equilibrium constant can be expressed must be borne in mind when numerical values of ΔG^0 or ΔS^0 are concerned, since they may be calculated either for unit pressure or for unit concentration.

If we wish to use *mole fractions* in place of partial pressures or concentrations, we must substitute $p_A = x_A P$, etc., in equation 10. The result is

$$K_p = \frac{(x_M^e)^m (x_N^e)^n \cdots}{(x_A^e)^a (x_B^e)^b \cdots} \times P^{m+n\cdots-a-b\cdots}. \qquad (16)$$

If we write this in the form

$$K_p = K_x P^{m+n\cdots-a-b\cdots} \qquad (17)$$

we must remember that in general K_x is not always, like K_p, independent of the total pressure, as is evident since P appears in equation 17.

The free energy change in reactions in perfect gas mixtures at constant temperature and pressure. So far we have seen how we can use equation 4 (p. 228) to relate the partial pressures at equilibrium to ΔG^0, the difference between the free energies of the reactants and products, each in the pure state at one atmosphere. It is of interest to consider also the free energy change for other conditions when the reaction does not proceed to equilibrium—for instance, if the products are continually removed so that their partial pressures are always well below the equilibrium values and the reaction proceeds continuously. We consider for simplicity the reaction $A+B \rightleftharpoons C+D$, and refer again to equation 4. In deriving this equation we have not used the condition for chemical equilibrium, so that it refers to the free energy change when the partial pressures have *any* values, not only their equilibrium values. It expresses the change in free energy dG for a chemical change involving dn moles of each participant. The free energy change for *one* mole of each is dG/dn, and is therefore given, according to equation 4, by

$$\Delta G = dG/dn = \Delta G^0 + RT \ln(p_C p_D / p_A p_B) \qquad (18)$$

$$= -RT \ln K_p + RT \ln(p_C p_D / p_A p_B) \qquad (18\,a)$$

$$= RT[\ln(p_C p_D / p_A p_B) - \ln(p_C^e p_D^e / p_A^e p_B^e)]. \qquad (18\,b)$$

Equations 18 can be generalized to cover any type of reaction, represented by the equation at the top of p. 230. The generalized forms of equations 18 are as follows. Equation 19 is often called *van't Hoff's isotherm.*

$$\Delta G = \Delta G^0 + RT \ln(p_M^m p_N^n \ldots / p_A^a p_B^b \ldots) \qquad (19)$$

$$= -RT \ln K_p + RT \ln(p_M^m p_N^n \ldots / p_A^a p_B^b \ldots). \qquad (19\,a)$$

The free energy change ΔG in the reaction at a given temperature can thus be calculated, once K_p is known, from the partial pressures of reactants and products. If these are so related as to make ΔG negative—if $p_M^m p_N^n$ is small enough compared with $p_A^a p_B^b$—the reaction will proceed in the direction left to right, this being the direction of spontaneous change; if ΔG is positive, the reaction will go from right to left. By adjusting the partial pressures, we can make the reaction go in one direction or the other. If, for example, we remove the products M, N, etc., as fast as they are formed, or if we increase the pressure of A and B sufficiently, we make ΔG negative and favour production of M and N. The extent to which we must decrease p_M, etc., or increase p_A, etc., depends upon ΔG^0, as is evident from equation 19. The more negative is ΔG^0, the more is a reaction favoured. Thus ΔG^0 is a *quantitative measure of chemical affinity*. For this reason the measurement of equilibrium constants, which give values of ΔG^0, has been of great importance. The value of ΔG^0 tells us nothing of the *rate* at which a reaction will occur, but from it we can conclude what the conditions should be, if the rates are adequate or can be made so by use of a catalyst, to make a particular reaction proceed.†

† For discussions of the interesting concepts of 'affinity' and 'degree of reaction' developed by the Netherlands and Brussels schools see de Donder and van Rysselberghe, *Affinity* (Stanford, 1936); Prigogine and Defay, *Chemical Thermodynamics*, trans. Everett, vol. i (Longmans, 1954).

Incidentally, equations 18 and 19 show that ΔG^0 is the change in free energy in the reaction if it proceeds in the gas mixture with each reactant and product at unit partial pressure, since the last term in each equation is then zero. This enlarges our original definition of ΔG^0 as the difference in free energy between products and reactants each in the pure state at unit pressure (p. 225).

5.43. *Chemical equilibrium in perfect gas mixtures at constant V and T*

It often happens that a gaseous equilibrium can be more easily observed at constant volume than at constant pressure. For instance, to investigate the equilibrium $I_2 \rightleftharpoons 2I$ it is more convenient to enclose the iodine in an all-glass vessel of fixed volume and measure the pressure, than to measure the volume at a fixed pressure. We must therefore consider reactions at constant volume and temperature. We can proceed as in section 5.42 (p. 228), but, since our condition of equilibrium at constant temperature and volume is not $dG = 0$ but $dA = 0$ (p. 152), we must consider the change in A, the Helmholtz free energy, when an infinitesimal amount of reaction occurs. The general expression for the effect on A corresponding to equation 2, is:

$$dA = \left(\frac{\partial A}{\partial n_M}\right)_{T,V,n_j} dn_M + \left(\frac{\partial A}{\partial n_N}\right)_{T,V,n_j} dn_N + \dots -$$

$$- \left(\frac{\partial A}{\partial n_A}\right)_{T,V,n_j} dn_A - \left(\frac{\partial A}{\partial n_B}\right)_{T,V,n_j} dn_B - \dots . \quad (20)$$

The factors $(\partial A/\partial n_A)_{T,V,n_j}$, etc., are equal to the corresponding chemical potentials, μ_A, etc. (p. 164). The factors dn_A are related by the stoichiometry of the reaction

$$dn_A/a = dn_B/b = \dots = dn.$$

Equation 20 thus becomes

$$dA = dn(m\mu_M + n\mu_N + \dots - a\mu_A - b\mu_B - \dots). \quad (21)$$

At equilibrium, $dA = 0$, and so

$$m\mu_M + n\mu_N + \dots - a\mu_A - b\mu_B - \dots = 0. \quad (22)$$

This equation might alternatively have been reached by quoting the general mass-action law (p. 168). Substituting

$$\mu_A = \mu_A^0 + RT \ln p_A, \quad \text{etc.,}$$

we obtain for equilibrium at constant temperature and volume the same equilibrium constant K_p as when we considered reactions at constant temperature and pressure (equation 10):

$$K_p = (p_M^e)^m (p_N^e)^n \cdots / (p_A^e)^a (p_B^e)^b \cdots = e^{-\Delta\mu^0/RT}. \qquad (23)$$

The partial pressures are thus related in the same way at equilibrium, whether the reaction is conducted at constant volume or at constant pressure. This is not surprising, since K_p defines a *state* of equilibrium and should be independent of the type of process by which equilibrium is reached.

5.44. *Reactions in imperfect gas mixtures*

If the deviations from the perfect-gas-mixture laws are large enough compared with experimental errors to be taken into account, we must use fugacities in place of partial pressures (p. 225). In the derivation of the expression for the equilibrium constant, given in section 5.42, we shall therefore use

$$\mu_i - \mu_i^0 = RT \ln P_i^*$$

(instead of $RT \ln p_i$). We then obtain $\Delta G^0 = -RT \ln K$, where K contains fugacities in place of pressures. This relation is formally exact. But since our knowledge of fugacities in mixtures is not extensive, it is not often worth while to use this exact expression for K rather than the one in terms of partial pressures.

5.45. *Some experimental investigations on equilibrium constants*

There are two general methods for determining the composition of the equilibrium mixture without disturbing it. One is to observe some physical property of the mixture, under the equilibrium conditions. A property often chosen is the density, which can be accurately measured and can be used to determine K_p for any reaction in which the number of molecules changes. For instance, in the dissociation of N_2O_4, if a fraction α of the

N_2O_4 is dissociated, the total number of molecules present increases in the ratio $(1+\alpha)$ and the observed density d is less by this factor than the value d' calculated from the undissociated molecular weight. For a perfect gas $d' = MP/RT$, where M is the molecular weight calculated for the undissociated gas. Thus we can find α, using the relation $d'/d = 1+\alpha$; and from α we can calculate K_p by the equation given on p. 231. The procedure is easily generalized. Some reactions to which it has been applied are the dissociation of iodine, $I_2 \rightleftharpoons 2I$ (see below); the dimerization of acetic acid, $2CH_3CO_2H \rightleftharpoons (CH_3CO_2H)_2$,[†] and the association of boron trifluoride with amines,[‡]

$$BF_3 + R_3N \rightleftharpoons R_3N:BF_3.$$

Other physical properties are occasionally chosen; for instance, the equilibrium $H_2 + D_2 \rightleftharpoons 2HD$ has been followed by the thermal conductivity of the gas, and the equilibrium

$$2H_2O + O_2 \rightleftharpoons 4OH$$

by the absorption spectrum.[§]

The other general method is to 'freeze' the equilibrium so that the mixture can be analysed chemically without the composition changing meanwhile. This method can be used when the reaction occurs only at a high temperature or with a catalyst, for the gas can then be removed rapidly from the high-temperature vessel or the catalyst—by using a rapid stream of gas, for example—and analysed at leisure. The catalyst method has been applied to the equilibria $N_2 + 3H_2 \rightleftharpoons 2NH_3$ (see below), $2SO_2 + O_2 \rightleftharpoons 2SO_3$, and $4HCl + O_2 \rightleftharpoons 2H_2O + 2Cl_2$,[‖] all of which are of technical as well as scientific importance. The method of bringing gases to equilibrium on a hot wire from which they are then removed has been applied by Langmuir[††] to the dissociation of water, $2H_2O \rightleftharpoons 2H_2 + O_2$, and of carbon dioxide, $2CO_2 \rightleftharpoons 2CO + O_2$. For each of these reactions, the equilibrium

† Johnson and Nash, *J. Amer. Chem. Soc.*, 1950, **72**, 547; 1952, **74**, 4654; Taylor, ibid., 1951, **73**, 315.

‡ Brown, ibid., 1944, **66**, 431, 436.

§ Dwyer and Oldenberg, *J. Chem. Physics*, 1944, **12**, 351.

‖ Lewis, *J. Amer. Chem. Soc.*, 1906, **28**, 1380.

†† Langmuir, ibid., p. 1357.

has been approached from both sides, and the results found to agree satisfactorily.

Constancy of K_p. For such reactions at ordinary pressures, it has been found that at a given temperature the observed value of K_p is in fact independent both of the total pressure and of the proportions of the reactants, and is the same from whichever side the equilibrium is approached; the variations are random and may be attributed to experimental errors. (Even in very careful work these variations in K_p may amount to 1–2 per cent.) At high pressures, or in very accurate work, it may be worth while to use fugacities rather than partial pressures. There are not many investigations in which K_p has been measured over a wide range of pressures; the following are examples of unusually exact and extensive work.

The equilibrium $H_2 + I_2 \rightleftharpoons 2HI$, on which some classical work was done by Bodenstein,† was very carefully reinvestigated by Taylor and Crist.‡ Sealed glass tubes containing either hydrogen iodide gas or hydrogen (at a measured pressure) and iodine were heated in an electric furnace whose temperature was controlled to $\pm 0.1°$ C. The tubes were cooled rapidly to freeze the equilibrium, and then broken under potassium iodide solution. The solutions were titrated to determine the iodine and acid concentrations. Correction was made for hydrogen lost by diffusion through the glass. The equilibrium constant was calculated assuming the laws of perfect gas mixtures. The following table shows that the value obtained was (i) independent of time; (ii) the same whether the tube initially contained hydrogen iodide or hydrogen and iodine; (iii) independent of the total pressure; and (iv) independent of the ratio of hydrogen to iodine when this was varied by a factor of about two. (In Bodenstein's work this ratio was varied by a factor of about 10 and the value of K_p was constant to within a few per cent.)

The equilibrium $I_2 \rightleftharpoons 2I$ has been investigated very carefully, over a wide temperature range and with a tenfold variation of

---

† Bodenstein, *Z. phys. Chem.*, 1899, **29**, 295, and earlier papers.
‡ Taylor and Crist, *J. Amer. Chem. Soc.*, 1941, **63**, 1377. These authors studied both rates and equilibria for $H_2 + I_2 \rightleftharpoons 2HI$ and also for $D_2 + I_2 \rightleftharpoons 2DI$.

TABLE 23

Equilibrium in the reaction $H_2 + I_2 \rightleftharpoons 2HI$

Concentrations in mole/cm³

$$K = p_{H_2}\, p_{I_2}/p_{HI}^2$$

Temp. °K	Time min	$10^5[H_2]$ initially	$10^5[I_2]$ at equilm.	$10^5[H_2]$ at equilm.	$10^5[HI]$ at equilm.	$10^2 K$ uncorr.	$10^2 K$ corr.	Average $10^2 K$ and mean deviation
763·8				Combination				
	140	1·0851	0·28396	0·22754	1·7151	2·195	2·185	
	360	1·0833	0·36341	0·19350	1·7804	2·220	2·203	
	140	1·0613	0·40569	0·17207	1·7788	2·221	2·193	
	360	1·0645	0·28702	0·21930	1·6900	2·202	2·188	2·192
	120	1·0970	0·25139	0·24939	1·6952	2·181	2·172	±0·007
	120	1·0966	0·23054	0·26456	1·6641	2·202	2·194	
	1,380	1·1731	0·11851	0·42635	1·4936	2·244	2·196	
	1,380	1·1713	0·14776	0·38050	1·5763	2·255	2·202	
				Decomposition				
	120	..	0·25972	0·25972	1·7632	2·170	2·167	
	120	..	0·18961	0·18961	1·2835	2·182	2·180	2·172
	360	..	0·19806	0·19806	1·3417	2·179	2·168	±0·004
	360	..	0·24237	0·24237	1·6406	2·182	2·172	
730·8				Combination				2·018 ±0·006
				Decomposition				2·007 ±0·002
698·6				Combination				1·812 ±0·007
				Decomposition				1·811 ±0·002
666·8				Combination				1·639 ±0·010
				Decomposition				1·645 ±0·009

pressure at each temperature, by Perlman and Rollefson.†
A weighed amount of iodine contained in a silica bulb was
heated in a thermostatic electric furnace and the pressure
observed. The precision of the measurements was such that,
although the pressure was not high, it was worth while to
calculate the equilibrium constant in terms of fugacities, computed on the assumption of the Lewis–Randall rule (p. 225).
The table shows that at each temperature K is independent of

† Perlman and Rollefson, *J. Chem. Phys.*, 1941, **9**, 362.

the total pressure, the variations being random; the mean deviations are of the order of 1–2 per cent.

TABLE 24

Equilibrium in the reaction $I_2 \rightleftharpoons 2I$

$$K = (P_I^*)^2/(P_{I_2}^*)$$

Pressure (P) and K in atmospheres

T °K	P	K	Mean K and mean deviation
1,274	0·11216	0·1692	
	0·47416	0·1657	0·1678
	0·75308	0·1671	±0·0014
	0·93082	0·1692	
		$10^2 K$	$10^2 K$
1,173	0·09181	4·847	
	0·40087	4·769	4·803
	0·64446	4·798	±0·029
	0·80042	4·836	
	1·04680	4·773	
1,073	0·07500	1·110	
	0·34287	1·065	1·088
	0·55807	1·082	±0·015
	0·69640	1·108	
	0·91672	1·084	
		$10^3 K$	$10^3 K$
973	0·06244	1·805	
	0·29815	1·785	1·801
	0·48982	1·855	±0·042
	0·61283	1·852	
	0·80970	1·709	
		$10^4 K$	$10^4 K$
872	0·05346	2·11	
	0·26138	1·62	1·81
	0·43143	1·81	±0·14
	0·54123	1·86	
	0·71671	1·66	

At high pressures, the variations in the apparent value of K if fugacities are not used may be considerable. Table 25 shows some results on the ammonia equilibrium $N_2 + 3H_2 \rightleftharpoons 2NH_3$, from which it is evident that there is a variation with pressure of 'K_p' calculated from the observed partial pressures[†]

$$\text{'}K_p\text{'} = p_{NH_3}/p_{N_2}^{\frac{1}{2}} p_{H_2}^{\frac{3}{2}}.$$

[†] Larson and Dodge, *J. Amer. Chem. Soc.*, 1923, **45**, 2918; Larson, ibid., 1924, **46**, 367.

If the fugacities of the several gases are computed according to the Lewis–Randall rule, the values calculated for 'K_p' agree well with those observed, as the table shows, up to 100 atmospheres.[†]

TABLE 25

Equilibrium in the reaction $N_2 + 3H_2 \rightleftharpoons 2NH_3$

Values of 'K_p' $= p_{NH_3}/p_{N_2}^{\frac{1}{2}} p_{H_2}^{\frac{3}{2}}$, in atm^{-1}

Temp. °C		$p_{NH_3}/p_{N_2}^{\frac{1}{2}} p_{H_2}^{\frac{3}{2}}$				
		10 atm	30 atm	50 atm	100 atm	300 atm
375	Obs.	0·0181	0·0184	0·0186	0·0202	..
	Calc.	0·0180	0·0184	0·0188	0·0197	..
450	Obs.	0·00659	0·00676	0·00690	0·00725	..
	Calc.	0·00669	0·00678	0·00688	0·00711	..
500	Obs.	0·00381	0·00386	0·00388	0·00402	0·00498
	Calc.	0·00384	0·00389	0·00393	0·00403	0·00452

From these examples, and numerous others for which the reader is referred elsewhere,[‡] we conclude that the thermodynamic expression for the equilibrium constant is in accord with experimental facts, and that partial pressures rather than fugacities are adequate for many purposes at ordinary pressures, the reaction mixtures approximating to perfect gas mixtures.

5.46. *The variation of equilibrium constants with temperature.*
Heat and entropy of reaction

The equilibrium constant of a gas reaction varies with temperature; it may increase or decrease with rise of temperature, as Tables 23, 24, and 25 indicate. The general relation is easily obtained by using the Gibbs–Helmholtz relation (p. 156). Applied to the changes of G and H in a reaction between gases at unit partial pressure and constant temperature, this gives

$$\frac{d}{dT}\left(\frac{\Delta G^0}{T}\right) = -\frac{\Delta H^0}{T^2}. \qquad (24)$$

[†] Gillespie, *J. Amer. Chem. Soc.*, 1926, **48**, 28.
[‡] Haber, *Thermodynamics of Technical Gas Reactions*, trans. Lamb (Longmans, 2nd edn. 1908); Lewis and Randall, *Thermodynamics* (1923).

In section 5.42 we have found the general relation

$$\Delta G^0 = -RT \ln K_p,$$

where K_p is to be expressed in terms of partial pressures for a perfect gas mixture, or for an imperfect gas mixture in terms of fugacities, and is independent of the total pressure. Substituting in the foregoing equation, we obtain

$$\frac{d \ln K_p}{dT} = \frac{\Delta H^0}{RT^2}. \tag{25}$$

This important relation, due to van 't Hoff, is often called the *reaction isochore*. It may also be written

$$\frac{d \ln K_p}{d(1/T)} = -\frac{\Delta H^0}{R}. \tag{26}$$

The change of K_p with temperature depends therefore on the heat of reaction. Qualitatively, K_p increases with rise of temperature if the forward reaction is endothermic (ΔH positive), and decreases if it is exothermic. Thus if the temperature of the gas mixture is altered, by adding or withdrawing heat, the shift in the equilibrium is in such a direction that the change is partly neutralized. This rule, like the corresponding rule for pressure (p. 231), was given by Le Chatelier.

Equation 25 can also be obtained by using the general relation (p. 156) between the entropy and the temperature-variation of the Gibbs free energy, $(\partial G/\partial T)_P = -S$. Differentiating both sides of the expression $\ln K_p = -\Delta G^0/RT$ with respect to temperature, at constant pressure, we find

$$\frac{d \ln K_p}{dT} = \frac{\Delta G^0}{RT^2} - \frac{1}{RT}\left(\frac{\partial(\Delta G^0)}{\partial T}\right)_P = \frac{\Delta G^0 - T\,\Delta S^0}{RT^2} = \frac{\Delta H^0}{RT^2}.$$

If we express the equilibrium constant in terms of concentrations, the corresponding equation for K_c is easily found, by using equation 15 (p. 232), to be

$$\frac{d \ln K_c}{d(1/T)} = -\frac{\Delta E^0}{R}. \tag{27}$$

Determination of ΔH^0 and ΔS^0 for gas reactions. We must now look more closely at the relation between K and T. We

shall consider reactions at constant pressure; the treatment for
reactions at constant volume is similar. The fundamental relation is (p. 242)

$$\frac{d \ln K_p}{d(1/T)} = -\frac{\Delta H^0}{R}. \tag{28}$$

This implies that if we determine K_p experimentally at various
temperatures, and plot $\ln K_p$ against $1/T$, the slope of the plot
will be $-\Delta H^0/R$. If ΔH^0 is effectively constant, the plot will be

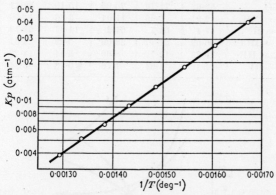

FIG. 44. Plot of $\log_{10} K_p$ against $1/T$ for the ammonia equilibrium.

a straight line. An example is provided by Larson and Dodge's
results on the ammonia equilibrium (p. 241); a plot of the
results at 10 atmospheres is shown in fig. 44.† If the temperature-range is long enough, the variation in ΔH^0 with temperature
will lead to a slight curvature, but the slope of the curve at a
given temperature can still be determined. The general form
of a plot of $\log K$ against T will be roughly hyperbolic, as
shown for various reactions in fig. 45.‡ Plots of K against T
will of course be considerably more curved than those of $\log K$.

The standard entropy change ΔS^0 in a reaction can be found
by combining the value of ΔH^0, obtained as just described,
with that of ΔG^0 (found as $-RT \ln K_p$) at the same tempera-

† From *Principles of Chemical Thermodynamics*, by Paul. Copyright, 1951,
McGraw-Hill Book Company, Inc.

‡ Wagman, Kilpatrick, Taylor, Pitzer, and Rossini, *J. Res. Nat. Bur. St.*,
1945, **34**, 160. (These values have been calculated from the tabulated free
energies for the separate gases using the Third Law.)

ture, using the relation $\Delta S^0 = (\Delta H^0 - \Delta G^0)/T$. Thus ΔG^0, ΔH^0, and ΔS^0 are all accessible from measurements of K_p. So far, we have shown how they can be found at temperatures for

TABLE 26

Reaction	298° K			1,000° K		
	$\log_{10} K_p$	$-\Delta G^0$	$-\Delta H^0$	$\log_{10} K_p$	$-\Delta G^0$	$-\Delta H^0$
$H_2 + \frac{1}{2}O_2 = H_2O$	40·04	54·64	57·80	10·06	46·04	59·24
$S + O_2 = SO_2$	52·62	71·79	70·96	15·10	69·11	86·69
$\frac{1}{2}N_2 + \frac{3}{2}H_2 = NH_3$	2·91	3·98	11·04	−3·23	−14·79	13·30
$\frac{1}{2}H_2 + \frac{1}{2}F_2 = HF$	47·4	64·7	64·2	14·37	65·78	64·91
$\frac{1}{2}H_2 + \frac{1}{2}Cl_2 = HCl$	16·69	22·77	22·06	5·22	23·91	22·42
$\frac{1}{2}H_2 + \frac{1}{2}Br_2 = HBr$	9·33	12·72	8·66	3·11	14·23	12·61
$\frac{1}{2}H_2 + \frac{1}{2}I_2 = HI$	−1·42	−1·94	1·16	−0·73	−3·34	1·56

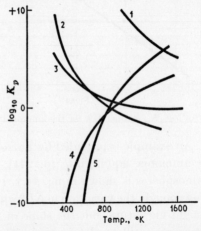

FIG. 45. Plots of $\log_{10} K_p$ against T for various equilibria:

(1) $CO + \frac{1}{2}O_2 = CO_2$.   (2) $C + 2H_2 = CH_4$.
(3) $CO + H_2O = CO_2 + H_2$.   (4) $C + H_2O = CO + H_2$.
(5) $CH_4 + CO_2 = 2CO + 2H_2$.

which K_p has been directly observed; we shall soon see how they can be found for other temperatures.

Some values of ΔG^0 and ΔH^0 for various reactions are given in Table 26; the difference gives $T \Delta S^0$ in each case.†

† Values taken from Quill (ed.), *Chemistry and Metallurgy of Miscellaneous Materials: Thermodynamics* (McGraw-Hill, 1950). (These values have been calculated from the tabulated functions H^0 and G^0 for the separate gases using the Third Law.)

5.47. *Approximate integration of the reaction isochore; relations between K_p and T and their interpretation*

Over a short enough temperature range, in which ΔH^0 may with sufficient accuracy be regarded as constant, equation 26 may be integrated at once to

$$R \ln K_p = \text{constant} - \Delta H^0 / T. \qquad (29)$$

This equation implies a linear relation between $\ln K_p$ and $1/T$, and a hyperbolic relation between $\ln K_p$ and T. This is qualitatively in obvious agreement with the results shown in fig. 44. Relations of this form have been found to cover the experimental results for the decomposition of HI from about $400°$ to $500°$ C, for example, and those for the Deacon equilibrium† from $350°$ to $420°$ C, for which Lewis found $\log_{10} K_p = -1 \cdot 811 + 1509/T$. The equilibrium constants at two different temperatures T_1 and T_2 will be related by

$$\ln\!\left(\frac{(K_p)_{T_1}}{(K_p)_{T_2}}\right) = \frac{\Delta H^0}{R}\!\left(\frac{1}{T_2} - \frac{1}{T_1}\right), \qquad (30)$$

which enables us to calculate K_p at one temperature from experimental results at another, provided that ΔH^0 is constant —that is, within a relatively short temperature range.

Since $\Delta G^0 = -RT \ln K_p$, equation 29 gives

$$\Delta G^0 = \Delta H^0 - \text{constant} \times T. \qquad (31)$$

Comparing this with the relation $\Delta G^0 = \Delta H^0 - T\,\Delta S^0$, it is obvious that the integration constant in equation 29 is simply ΔS^0, the standard entropy change in the reaction at the temperature at which K_p is measured. Like equation 29, this is true only as a first approximation, as we shall find.

For longer temperature ranges, the variation of ΔH^0 with temperature must be taken into account. We have seen (p. 71) that over the range 300 to $1,500°$ K this may be expressed approximately for gas reaction at ordinary pressures by equations of the form

$$\Delta H^0 = \Delta H' + \alpha T + \beta T^2 + \gamma T^3 + \dots.$$

Here α, β, etc., are empirical constants derived from heat-

† See note ‖ on p. 237.

capacity measurements on the separate gases. $\Delta H'$ is an empirical constant having the dimensions of H and fixed by an experimental determination of ΔH^0 at one temperature. It is not to be equated with $\Delta H_{(0)}$, the value at absolute zero, because the empirical heat-capacity equations break down below about $300°$ K; but it will not be numerically very different. If we substitute the above expression for ΔH^0 in equation 26, we obtain

$$\frac{d\ln K_p}{dT} = \frac{\Delta H'}{RT^2} + \frac{\alpha}{RT} + \frac{\beta}{R} + \frac{\gamma T}{R} + \dots.$$

Integrating, and multiplying through by R, we obtain

$$R\ln K_p = A - B/T + C\ln T + DT + ET^2 + \dots, \quad (32)$$

where A is the integration constant, $B = \Delta H'$, and C, D, etc., are related to the constants α, β, etc., which depend on the difference of heat capacities.

This approximate equation 32 will be valid in the same range as the heat-capacity equations from which it is determined. Equations of this form have been used to express the experimental results for many reactions, such as the dissociation of water and of carbon dioxide,† and that of ammonia at lower pressures.‡ For example, for the ammonia equilibrium $\frac{1}{2}N_2 + \frac{3}{2}H_2 \rightleftharpoons NH_3$, the heat-capacity data give

$$\Delta C_P^0 = -4{\cdot}96 - 0{\cdot}00115T + 0{\cdot}00051T^2.$$

Integrating, using Kirchhoff's relation,

$$\Delta H^0 = \int \Delta C_P^0 \, dT = \Delta H' - 4{\cdot}96T - 0{\cdot}0^358T^2 + 0{\cdot}0^517T^3.$$

Measurement of ΔH^0 at one temperature gave $\Delta H' = -9{,}500$ cal. Using equation 26, we find

$$\frac{R\,d\ln K_p}{dT} = \frac{\Delta H^0}{T^2} = -\frac{9500}{T^2} - \frac{4{\cdot}96}{T} - 0{\cdot}0^358 + 0{\cdot}0^517T.$$

Integrating, we obtain an expression of the form of equation 32:

$$R\ln K_p = A + \frac{9500}{T} - 4{\cdot}96\ln T - 0{\cdot}0^358T + 0{\cdot}0^685T^2. \quad (33)$$

† See note †† on p. 237.
‡ Lewis and Randall, *Thermodynamics* (1923), p. 556.

The experimental values of K_p over the range 830 to 1,370° K fit this equation well if we put $\mathring{A} = 9\cdot61$. The value of the equilibrium constant K_p can then be calculated for any temperature within the range for which the heat capacity equations are adequate. For instance, at 1,000° K equation 33 gives for K_p

$$R \ln K_p = 9\cdot61 + 9\cdot50 - 34\cdot2 - 0\cdot58 + 0\cdot85 = -14\cdot8.$$

The terms that are numerically most important in such equations are the first three, as this example shows, and it is often accurate enough to express K_p in terms of these. This is equivalent to assuming that ΔC_p is constant. Equation 32 then becomes
$$R \ln K_p = A - B/T + C \ln T, \qquad (34)$$

which may be regarded as the second approximation, if equation 29 is the first and equation 32 the third. Here $(A + C \ln T)$ represents very approximately the entropy change in the reaction, as did the constant in equation 29 above.‡ The second coefficient B represents approximately the heat of reaction, and the third C represents ΔC_P. These three are the main thermodynamic factors determining K_p.

Factors influencing the position of equilibrium. We can now begin to see which types of molecule will be favoured in gaseous equilibria, in terms of entropy and heat content.† The basic relations are $\Delta G^0 = -RT \ln K_p = \Delta H^0 - T \Delta S^0$. The value of K_p thus depends upon both the energy and the entropy factors. In a dissociation reaction such as $2NH_3 \rightleftharpoons N_2 + 3H_2$, the products will usually have a larger entropy than the reactants because of the larger number of molecules, each with its translational and rotational contribution to the entropy (for the same reason the products will usually have the larger heat capacity). Thus the sum of A and $C \ln T$ in equation 34 will be positive, and—unless the dissociation requires a considerable absorption of energy, reflected in a large negative value of $(-B/T)$

---

† Cf. Hinshelwood, *The Structure of Physical Chemistry* (Oxford, 1951), pp. 152–5.

‡ Differentiation of equation 34 and comparison with 25 will show that $\Delta H^0 = B + CT$, whence $\Delta S^0 = A + C \ln T + C$.

—the value of K_p will be considerably greater than unity, so that at equilibrium the simpler molecules will be favoured. Increase of temperature will increase K_p if the reaction is endothermic, so that simpler molecules will be more favoured the higher the temperature. For some reactions this is indeed the case; for instance, for the opening of the ring in gaseous sulphur, $S_8 \rightleftharpoons 4S_2$, the equilibrium constant is represented by†
$R \ln K = 68 \cdot 28 - 95,200/T + 6 \cdot 0 \ln T$, from which it is evident that at, say, $1,000°$ K the first and third terms will outweigh the second and lead to a large K, increasing with temperature. Similarly, in the cracking of the hydrocarbons the equilibria favour the simpler molecules, and attempts to synthesize saturated hydrocarbons would not give large yields. These are examples of gas reactions in which the heat of reaction is less important than the other factors; but such reactions are relatively rare. In most gas reactions the heat of reaction is dominant, and the term B is the major factor in determining K. For the reactions given in Table 26 (p. 244), it is evident that ΔH^0 is much more important than ΔS^0 in fixing ΔG^0 and therefore K. The Thomsen–Berthelot rule (p. 148) has thus a considerable range of practical usefulness, despite its theoretical lack of generality and precision.

5.48. *Exact integration of the reaction isochore; relations of K_p to ΔS_G^* and $\Delta S_{S(0)}$*

The exact way of integrating the reaction isochore (equation 25, p. 242) is evidently to write

$$\ln K_p = J + \int \frac{\Delta H^0}{RT^2} \, dT, \qquad (35)$$

where the integral is indefinite and J is some integration constant; and to determine the integral with the aid of heat-capacity measurements down to low temperatures. This integration can be carried through, but we obtain the same result more simply as follows. Since $\Delta G^0 = -RT \ln K_p$ and

† Gee, *Trans. Faraday Soc.*, 1952, **48**, 516.

$\Delta G^0 = \Delta H^0 - T \Delta S^0$, we can at once relate K_p at any temperature to ΔH^0 and ΔS^0 at the same temperature:

$$R \ln K_p = -\Delta H^0/T + \Delta S^0. \qquad (36)$$

The heat content change ΔH^0 at temperature T can be calculated from a determination at any one temperature and a knowledge of the heat capacities, using Kirchhoff's laws and graphical integration. The standard entropy change ΔS^0 can be expressed either (i) in terms of the entropy difference between reactants and products at $0°$ K, or (ii) in terms of the difference of entropy constants, as follows.

(i) For each individual gas, we can express the standard entropy $S^0_{G(T)}$ at $T°$ K in terms of the entropy of the solid at $0°$ K, $S_{S(0)}$, together with either calorimetric data (section 5.21) or statistical-spectroscopic data (section 5.22). The equations (pp. 200, 209) may be written: $S^0_{G(T)} - S_{S(0)} = $ [thermal terms for S] and $S^0_{G(T)} - S_{S(0)} = $ [statistical terms for S]. Now ΔS^0 is the difference between the sum of the values of $S^0_{G(T)}$ for the products and the sum of those for the reactants. Hence

$$\Delta S^0 = \Delta S_{S(0)} + \text{(difference of thermal terms}$$
$$\text{or statistical terms for } S).$$

Consequently, by equation 36,†

$$R \ln K_p = \Delta S_{S(0)} - \Delta H^0/T + \text{(difference of thermal terms}$$
$$\text{or statistical terms for } S). \qquad (37)$$

All the quantities on the right can be experimentally determined, except $\Delta S_{S(0)}$, about which we have as yet no independent knowledge (cf. pp. 226–7). Given such knowledge, we could calculate K_p from an experimental value of ΔH at one temperature, and heat capacities down to near $0°$ K.

(ii) We can also express the standard entropies of the gases in terms of their entropy constants S^*_G and heat capacities, as in equation 23 of section 5.22 (p. 208):

$$S^0_{G(T)} - S^*_G = (C_P - C_i) \ln T + \int_0^T C_i \, d \ln T.$$

† The same result is obtained using equation 10 of section 5.21 (p. 203) and the relation $\Delta G^0 = -RT \ln K_p$.

Equation 36 then gives†

$$R \ln K_p = \Delta S_G^* - \frac{\Delta H^0}{T} + (\Delta C_P - \Delta C_i)\ln T + \int_0^T \Delta C_i \, d\ln T, \quad (38)$$

where ΔS_G^* is the difference between the sum of the values of S_G^* for the products and that for the reactants. Comparing the temperature-independent terms in equations 38 and 35, we see that the integration constant J in equation 35 can be identified with $\Delta S_G^*/R$:

$$J = \Delta S_G^*/R. \quad (39)$$

All the quantities on the right of equation 38, except ΔS_G^*, can be found without difficulty. Values of S_G^* for simple gases can be calculated, as we have seen (section 5.22), by statistical-spectroscopic methods, but these values are relative to $S_{S(0)}$ and do not enable us to calculate ΔS_G^* absolutely, only $\Delta S_G^* - \Delta S_{S(0)}$. Thus the *a priori* calculation of K_p by this method, like the preceding one, requires an independent knowledge of $\Delta S_{S(0)}$. This is the problem to which the Third Law of thermodynamics gives a solution, by showing that for many reactions $\Delta S_{S(0)}$ is zero (Chapter VIII).

5.49. *The calculation of equilibrium constants from partition functions*

Using essentially the same data as in the statistical-spectroscopic method, we can express K in terms of the partition functions of the reactants and products. Each partition function is the product of contributions for translation, rotation, and vibration, and is evaluated by statistical-spectroscopic methods, using exactly the same data as are used in compiling tables of entropies and free energies (p. 209). For the reaction $A + B \rightleftharpoons C + D$, the result obtained by combining equation 33 of section 4.53 (p. 161) with the equation $\Delta G^0 = -RT \ln K_p$ is, if we write f_A, etc., for the partition functions (omitting the zero-point energies of vibration) of the reactants and products,

$$K_p = (f_C f_D / f_A f_B)\exp(-\Delta E_{G(0)}^0 / RT). \quad (40)$$

† The same result is obtained using equation 28 of section 5.22 (p. 213) and the relation $\Delta G^0 = -RT \ln K_p$.

This equation for K_p in terms of partition functions incidentally expresses again the factors that determine chemical equilibria.† The exponential term containing ΔE_0^0 (corresponding roughly to ΔH^0) is commonly dominant; but the partition-function term (contributing mainly to ΔS^0) is important when the numbers of molecules change greatly during reaction, since the translational contribution to the numerator and denominator are then very different.

Equilibrium constants have often been calculated from equation 40 or its equivalent, and the results have been found to agree with experiment. An example is the reaction

$$H_2 + D_2 \rightleftharpoons 2HD,$$

for which the statistical expresssion for the equilibrium constant $K = p_{HD}^2 / p_{H_2} p_{D_2}$ takes the simple form $K = 4 \cdot 24 \exp(-78/T)$. The calculated values are compared with the experimental results (to which root-mean-square deviations are attached) in the following table.‡

T, °K	K obs.	K calc.
273	$3 \cdot 24 \pm 0 \cdot 08$	$3 \cdot 18$
383	$3 \cdot 50 \pm 0 \cdot 06$	$3 \cdot 46$
543	$3 \cdot 85 \pm 0 \cdot 10$	$3 \cdot 67$
670	$3 \cdot 8 \pm 0 \cdot 4$	$3 \cdot 77$
741	$3 \cdot 70 \pm 0 \cdot 12$	$3 \cdot 81$

This agreement is paralleled in calculations on the dissociation of hydrogen iodide, the water-gas equilibrium, and other reactions. Equilibrium constants are now often calculated in this way using spectroscopic data. The relative values of K for reactions involving isotopic atoms are especially simple to calculate.§

† Cf. Hinshelwood, *Kinetics of Chemical Change* (Oxford, 1940), chap. 2; or the same author's *The Structure of Physical Chemistry* (1951), pp. 147–55.

‡ Fowler and Guggenheim, *Statistical Thermodynamics* (1939), pp. 167–9.

§ Theory and experiment for isotopic molecules are reviewed by Urey, *J. Chem. Soc.*, 1947, 562.

VI

REACTIONS INVOLVING CONDENSED PHASES

6.1. Equilibria in solution

VERY many chemical reactions have been found to reach equilibrium in solution. Well-known examples are the dissociation of weak acids in water,

$$HA + H_2O \rightleftharpoons A^- + H_3O^+;$$

the formation and dissociation of the tri-iodide ion in water,

$$I_2 + I^- \rightleftharpoons I_3^-;$$

and the dimerization of carboxylic acids in solvents such as benzene,

$$2RCO_2H \rightleftharpoons (RCO_2H)_2.$$

The general equation for a reaction in solution can be written as for gases:

$$aA + bB + \ldots \rightleftharpoons mM + nN + \ldots.$$

The general condition of equilibrium is, just as for gases (p. 168),

$$a\mu_A + b\mu_B + \ldots = m\mu_M + n\mu_N + \ldots. \tag{1}$$

To simplify matters we consider the reaction

$$A + B \rightleftharpoons C + D,$$

for which the condition of equilibrium is

$$\mu_A + \mu_B = \mu_C + \mu_D. \tag{2}$$

To obtain a condition in terms of concentrations, we must anticipate some of the treatment of solutions to be given later in Chapters IX and X. Just as for gases the simplest observed behaviour—that of perfect gas mixtures—is expressed by the equation (p. 216)

$$\mu_i^{gas} = \mu_i^0 + RT \ln p_i, \tag{3}$$

so for solutions the simplest observed behaviour is expressed by the equation

$$\mu_i^{soln} = \mu_i^0 + RT \ln x_i, \tag{4}$$

where x_i is the mole fraction of any solute i in solution, and μ_i^0 refers to some standard state of the solute. Such solutions are called *ideal solutions*. Now, when treating a gas reaction

$A+B \rightleftharpoons C+D$ in a perfect gas mixture (section 5.42), we combined the condition of equilibrium 2 with equations such as 3, and obtained the following expressions for the equilibrium constant K_p, the free energy change ΔG in the reaction, and the standard free energy change ΔG^0:

$$\Delta G = \Delta G^0 + RT \ln (p_C p_D / p_A p_B),$$
$$\Delta G^0 = \Delta \mu^0 = -RT \ln K_p,$$
$$K_p = p_C^e p_D^e / p_A^e p_B^e.$$

In the same way, for reactions in ideal solutions, by combining equations 2 and 4 we obtain the corresponding expressions for the free energy and standard free energy changes, and for an equilibrium constant K:

$$\Delta G = \Delta G^0 + RT \ln(x_C x_D / x_A x_B), \tag{5}$$
$$\Delta G^0 = \Delta \mu^0 = -RT \ln K, \tag{6}$$
$$K = x_C^e x_D^e / x_A^e x_B^e. \tag{7}$$

Here x_A^e, etc., are the mole fractions of the reactants at equilibrium. In dilute solutions the mole fractions are nearly proportional to the molar concentrations, and we can write

$$K' = m_C^e m_D^e / m_A^e m_B^e. \tag{8}$$

It is well known that the experimental results on the tri-iodide equilibrium, for example, obey such a relation fairly closely:[†]

$$K' = [I_3^-]/[I_2][I^-]. \tag{9}$$

Many reactions, however, especially those involving ions, deviate markedly from the simple relation 7 or 8; and, just as we can use fugacities in place of partial pressures when dealing with reactions in imperfect gas mixtures (section 5.44), so in dealing with non-ideal solutions we replace mole fractions or concentrations by *activities*, written a. Then corresponding to equations 5, 6, and 7 we have

$$\Delta G = \Delta G^0 + RT \ln(a_C a_D / a_A a_B), \tag{10}$$
$$\Delta G^0 - \Delta \mu^0 - -RT \ln K, \tag{11}$$
$$K = a_C^e a_D^e / a_A^e a_B^e, \tag{12}$$

† The reaction has been carefully reinvestigated by Davies and Gwynne, *J. Amer. Chem. Soc.*, 1952, **74**, 2748.

where a_A, etc., are the activities of the various solute species. For the general case, corresponding to equation 1, we obtain

$$\Delta G = \Delta G^0 + RT \ln[(a_M)^m (a_N)^n .../(a_A)^a (a_B)^b ...], \qquad (13)$$

$$\Delta G^0 = \Delta \mu^0 = -RT \ln K, \qquad (14)$$

$$K = (a_M^e)^m (a_N^e)^n .../(a_A^e)^a (a_B^e)^b .... \qquad (15)$$

For the dissociation of a weak acid in water, for example, represented by $HA + H_2O \rightleftharpoons H_3O^+ + A^-$, the equilibrium constant, if we omit the activity of the water since it is effectively unity in a dilute solution (section 9.23, p. 315), is

$$K = a_{H_3O^+} a_{A^-}/a_{HA}. \qquad (16)$$

We postpone the further treatment of the activities of solutes until Chapters IX to XII; here it must suffice to say that for electrolyte solutions they are usually less than for an ideal solution, and for non-electrolyte solutions they are commonly greater, while for all solutes the activity approaches that in an ideal solution as the solution is made more dilute.

The equilibrium constant for a reaction in solution is evidently independent of concentration, but depends (like K_p for gas reactions) on the temperature. It also depends (unlike K_p) on the pressure;† this is because μ^0 in a solution depends on the pressure, though μ^0 in a gas does not.

Since $\ln K = -\Delta G^0/RT$, it follows that the temperature-dependence of K is given by

$$\left(\frac{\partial \ln K}{\partial T} \right)_P = \frac{\Delta H}{RT^2} \qquad (17)$$

as for gas reactions (p. 242). The pressure-dependence of K is given, since $(\partial(\Delta G)/\partial P)_T = -\Delta V$, by

$$\left(\frac{\partial \ln K}{\partial P} \right)_T = -\frac{\Delta V}{RT}.$$

Innumerable equilibria in solution have been studied. There are relatively few measurements on series of reactions of the same type, however; the following are some examples.

(i) *Acid-base equilibria.* By far the largest and most exact

† This has been experimentally demonstrated by Buchanan and Hamann, *Trans. Faraday Soc.*, 1953, **49**, 1425. On the change of μ^0 with P, see p. 317.

series of measurements refers to acid-base reactions, especially in water ($HA + H_2O = A^- + H_3O^+$), and the results are of great theoretical and practical importance.† The equilibrium constant $K = a_{H^+} a_{A^-}/a_{HA}$ for the dissociation of an acid can be measured most accurately either by an e.m.f. method described later (section 12.24), or by conductivity methods, for which the reader is referred to books on electrochemistry. Less accurate methods employ electrometric titration or indicators.

The dissociation constants of many weak acids have been measured over the temperature range 0° to 60° C in water.‡ For each acid, the value of K reaches a maximum somewhere between 0° and 40° C, and the curve approximates to a parabola. It is, however, equally well represented by the equation§

$$\ln K = A/T + B \ln T + C, \tag{18}$$

where A, B, and C are constants. An equation of this form is obtained by integrating equation 17 with $\Delta H = A' + B'T$, i.e. assuming a constant value of ΔC_P. (The analogous case for gases is considered in section 5.47, p. 247.) By fitting an equation such as 18 to the experimental points, we can find A, B, and C, and thence ΔH, ΔC_P, and ΔS^0. The value of ΔC_P is especially interesting to interpret.‖ It is of the order of 40 cal deg^{-1} mole^{-1}. Part of this is due to the electrical energy of the ions formed in place of the neutral molecule HA; this will vary with temperature, because the dielectric constant varies, but the contribution to ΔC_P from this source is probably not more than 10 cal deg^{-1} mole^{-1}. The rest is largely accounted for by the partial 'freezing' of water molecules round an ion. If the rotations of solvent molecules are restricted more when they are near an ion than when they are near an undissociated acid molecule, there will be a change in C_P, and quantitative consideration of the motions of the solvent molecules shows that the calculated change is of the right order of magnitude.

† Bell, *Acid-base Catalysis* (Oxford, 1941); *Acids and Bases* (Methuen, 1952).

‡ Harned and Embree, *J. Amer. Chem. Soc.*, 1934, **56**, 1050.

§ Pitzer, ibid., 1937, **59**, 2365; Everett and Wynne-Jones, *Trans. Faraday Soc.*, 1939, **35**, 1380.

‖ Everett and Coulson, *Trans. Faraday Soc.*, 1940, **36**, 633.

(ii) *Formation of molecular complexes*, such as those between benzene and iodine, trinitrobenzene and aromatic hydrocarbons, or nitrocompounds and amines, has been much studied, largely by spectrophotometric methods.† It appears that many of these species are 'charge-transfer complexes'; they are not held together by a covalent bond, but owe their stability to resonance between a 'no-bond' structure (A.B) and a 'dative-bond' structure (A⁺—B⁻).

(iii) *Dimerization of carboxylic acids.* Here the two molecules are held together by hydrogen bonds, and it is possible to study the variation of the strength of these bonds when the substituents are varied.‡

(iv) *The halogenation of ketones*, studied by an e.m.f. method,§ allows the calculation of equilibrium constants for the process $RH + X \rightleftharpoons RX + H$ (X = halogen), and hence for $RI \rightleftharpoons R^- + I^+$, where R is a ketonic residue such as CH_3COCH_2.

(v) *Keto-enol equilibria* have been investigated and the results correlated with the electronic theory of organic chemistry.‖

6.2. The electromotive force of galvanic cells

6.21. *Reversible and irreversible working of cells*

Typical of galvanic cells is the one formed by placing in an aqueous solution of zinc chloride two electrodes, one of metallic zinc, the other of silver chloride deposited on silver. The cell is represented thus:††

$$Zn; ZnCl_2, AgCl; Ag.$$

† Andrews, *Chem. Rev.*, 1954, **54**, 713; Mulliken, *J. Phys. Chem.*, 1952, **56**, 801.

‡ Allen and Caldin, *Quart. Rev. Chem. Soc.*, 1953, **7**, 255.

§ Bell and Gelles, *Proc. Roy. Soc.* A, 1951, **210**, 310.

‖ Ingold, *Structure and Mechanism in Organic Chemistry* (Bell, 1953), pp. 535, 555.

†† The cells are written according to the American convention, with the positive pole on the right. The symbols used are those suggested by MacInnes, *Principles of Electrochemistry* (Reinhold, 1939), p. 167. A boundary between metal and electrolyte is represented by a semicolon, e.g. $Zn; ZnCl_2$. A liquid junction is indicated by a colon. A comma indicates that two electrolytes are present in the same solution, e.g. $ZnCl_2$, AgCl. Brackets indicate chemical inertness; thus the hydrogen electrode is shown as $(Pt)H_2$. An electrode and the ion which is reversibly discharged at it may be represented as, for example, $M; M^+$, corresponding to the electrode process $M \rightarrow M^+ + e$.

When a cell or cell reaction is written down, the state of each compound

A potential difference is found to be set up between the two electrodes, and mechanical work can be obtained from the cell; for instance, it can be made to drive an electric motor. This is because a reaction can occur spontaneously by operation of the cell. At the zinc electrode, zinc ions can be formed; at the silver–silver chloride electrode, chloride ions can be formed. If the electrodes are connected by a wire, and reaction allowed to proceed, the reactions at the two electrodes are

$$Zn = Zn^{++} + 2e, \qquad (19)$$

$$2AgCl + 2e = 2Ag + 2Cl^-. \qquad (20)$$

Here e represents an electron. Since electrical neutrality is maintained, and no free electrons appear, as many electrons are released at one electrode as are absorbed at the other, and electrons will not therefore appear in the total cell reaction. The cell reaction is obtained by summing equations 19 and 20 as

$$Zn + 2AgCl = Zn^{++} + 2Cl^- + 2Ag. \qquad (21)$$

This is the reaction observed.

If the e.m.f. of the cell is opposed by a greater e.m.f., the process at each electrode is reversed; zinc is deposited and chloride ions give silver chloride. The cell reaction is then the reverse of equation 21. If the opposing e.m.f. is nearly equal to that of the cell, the processes that go on in the cell become very slow and its working is nearly reversible in the thermodynamic sense. This is the case when the e.m.f. of the cell is measured by means of a potentiometer; the e.m.f. is balanced within perhaps 10^{-6} volts, and is very close to the e.m.f. of the cell on open circuit; within experimental error, the cell reaction then occurs reversibly. When the e.m.f. is not thus balanced, as when the cell is made to give an appreciable current, or when it is short-circuited, the reaction occurs irreversibly in the thermodynamic sense.

It is of interest to consider the work and heat changes in the

concerned must be clear. Since these states are usually obvious, they have been omitted in the interests of brevity. Thus metals, silver chloride, and mercurous chloride are solid; hydrogen and oxygen are gaseous; and soluble salts are in aqueous solution.

reversible and irreversible working of cells. The mechanical work obtained by driving an electric motor, for example, is the 'net work' as defined in section 4.46 (p. 152). It was there shown that this net work is equal to $(-\Delta G)$ under certain conditions, namely for a reversible change occurring in a closed system at constant temperature and pressure. These conditions are satisfied by a cell whose e.m.f. is being measured potentiometrically, in a thermostat at atmospheric pressure. The heat absorbed q in such a reversible process is equal to $T \Delta S$ (p. 143). At the other extreme is the short-circuited cell, from which no net work is obtained; the corresponding amount of energy appears as heat, so that the heat absorbed is $\Delta G + T \Delta S$, i.e. ΔH. In between there will be degrees of irreversibility. Thus the free energy, heat content, and entropy changes in the reaction are related as follows to the heat and work changes in reversible and irreversible working of the cell:

	−Net work	*Heat absorbed*
Reversible working	ΔG	$T \Delta S$
Irreversible working	0 to ΔG	$T \Delta S$ to ΔH

6.22. *Relations between the e.m.f. of a cell and ΔG^0, ΔH^0, and ΔS^0 for the cell reaction*

The free energy change in the reaction can be related to the e.m.f. of the cell as follows. The e.m.f. in volts is the work obtainable per coulomb of electricity. Suppose the cell reaction requires the exchange of z electrons, so that the amount of reaction represented by inserting gramme-molecular-weights into the stoichiometric equation requires zF coulombs, where F is the number of coulombs per faraday. (For instance, $z = 2$ for the reaction represented by equation 19.) Then if the e.m.f. is E, the electrical work for this amount of reaction is $zF\text{E}$. This is the net work, which for reversible working at constant temperature and pressure is equal to $-\Delta G$. Hence the free energy change for reaction is $\Delta G = -zF\text{E}$, and so

$$\text{E} = -\Delta G/zF. \qquad (22)$$

Thus to determine ΔG for the cell reaction, we have only to determine the e.m.f. on open circuit (or in practice by means of a potentiometer) and multiply by zF ($F = 96{,}493$ coulombs†). This gives ΔG in joules; to obtain the value in calories we divide by 4·18.

The value of ΔG so obtained would, however, be correct only for the concentrations obtaining in the particular cell under observation. To find the *standard free energy* ΔG^0 we use equation 13 of section 6.1 (p. 254). Equation 22 then gives

$$zF\mathbf{E} = -\Delta G^0 - RT \ln[(a_M)^m (a_N)^n \ldots /(a_A)^a (a_B)^b \ldots]. \qquad (23)$$

The activities of the various species in solution all become equal to the concentrations in the limit at infinite dilution. Hence if we measure $\mathbf{E}$ at various concentrations, and extrapolate the values of $\{zF\mathbf{E} + RT \ln[(a_M)^m \ldots /(a_A)^a \ldots]\}$ to zero concentration, we obtain ΔG^0.

The quantity $\Delta G^0/zF$ is often written $-\mathbf{E}^0$ and is called the *standard potential* of the cell in question, Equation 23 then becomes

$$\mathbf{E} - \mathbf{E}^0 = -(RT/zF)\ln[(a_M)^m \ldots /(a_A)^a \ldots]. \qquad (24)$$

For example, for the cell considered in section 6.21, whose reaction is given in equation 21, we shall have

$$\mathbf{E} - \mathbf{E}^0 = -(RT/zF)\ln(a_{Zn^{++}} a_{Cl^-}^2). \qquad (25)$$

This form is convenient for calculating the e.m.f. when $\mathbf{E}^0$ and the activities are known.

As a means of determining the free energies of chemical reactions, the e.m.f. method has the advantage of high accuracy. In the most accurate work, the e.m.f. is reproducible to $\pm 0{\cdot}01$ millivolts;‡ according to equation 22, this corresponds to an error in ΔG of only 0·2 calories per mole. Usually the electrodes cannot be prepared with such high reproducibility, but an accuracy of $\pm 0{\cdot}1$ millivolts is common. The most reliable cells are those in which two electrodes dip into a single solution, as in the cell Zn; $ZnCl_2$ aq., AgCl; Ag, considered in section 6.21. When the electrodes dip into different solutions, as in the

† Rossini *et al.*, *J. Amer. Chem. Soc.*, 1952, **74**, 2699.
‡ e.g. Hills and Ives, *J. Chem. Soc.*, 1951, 305–23.

Daniell cell Zn; $ZnSO_4$: $CuSO_4$; Cu, the results are less reliable (p. 264–5). — *hqa /hqa juctions*

If we know the variation of E^0 with temperature, we can find the standard entropy change ΔS^0 and heat content change ΔH^0 of the cell reaction. Since $(\partial G/\partial T)_P = -S$ (p. 156), it follows from equation 22 that:

$$\Delta S^0 = zF(\partial E^0/\partial T)_P \qquad (26)$$

and therefore, since $\Delta H^0 = \Delta G^0 + T \Delta S^0$,

$$\Delta H^0 = -zFE^0 + TzF(\partial E^0/\partial T)_P. \qquad (27)$$

To determine (dE^0/dT) it is not usually necessary to find E^0 at each temperature; it is enough to know E for a particular set of concentrations. For, differentiating equation 24 with respect to temperature, we obtain:

$$dE^0/dT = dE/dT + (R/zF)\ln[(a_M)^m.../(a_A)^a...] +$$
$$+ (RT/zF)d\ln[(a_M)^m.../(a_A)^a...]/dT. \qquad (28)$$

It is usually sufficiently accurate to suppose that the activities are independent of temperature and equal to the corresponding molal concentrations; then equation 28 becomes

$$dE^0/dT = dE/dT + (R/zF)\ln[(m_M)^m.../(m_A)^a...]. \qquad (29)$$

For instance, for the cell considered in section 6.21 (cf. equation 25),

$$dE^0/dT = dE/dT + (R/zF)\ln(m_{Zn^{++}} m_{Cl^-}^2). \qquad (30)$$

Thus from a knowledge of dE/dT for one set of concentrations, we can find dE^0/dT and hence ΔH^0 and ΔS^0 for the cell reaction. If only ΔH^0 is to be determined, moreover, it is not necessary that the ratio of the activities to the molalities should be unity, only that it should be independent of temperature.

We shall later come across important instances when ΔH^0 and ΔS^0 have been determined by the e.m.f. method (section 8.21, p. 295). Table 27 shows a comparison between some values of ΔH so obtained and those determined calorimetrically.[†] The electrical values are the more accurate in these particular instances, since the calorimetric values are obtained by com-

[†] The table is taken by permission from Zemansky, *Heat and Thermodynamics*. (Copyright, 1943, McGraw-Hill Book Company, Inc.)

bining thermochemical data, some of which have not been determined by modern methods and are not very accurate.

TABLE 27

Reaction	Temp. °C	z	E volts	10^4 (dE/dT) volts deg^{-1}	ΔH (electrical) kcal/mole	ΔH (calorimetric) kcal/mole
$Zn + CuSO_4 = Cu + ZnSO_4$	0	2	1·0934	−4·533	−56·09	−55·2
$Zn + 2AgCl = 2Ag + ZnCl_2$	0	2	1·0171	−2·103	−49·54	−49·1
$Cd + 2AgCl = 2Ag + CdCl_2$	25	2	0·6753	−6·5	−40·08	−39·5
$Pb + 2AgI = 2Ag + PbI_2$	25	2	0·2135	−1·73	−12·23	−12·2
$Ag + \frac{1}{2}Hg_2Cl_2 = Hg + AgCl$	25	1	0·0455	+3·38	+1·30	+0·9
$Pb + Hg_2Cl_2 = 2Hg + PbCl_2$	25	2	0·5356	+1·45	−22·90	−23·4
$Pb + 2AgCl = 2Ag + PbCl_2$	25	2	0·4900	−1·86	−25·10	−24·9

6.23. *Some reactions studied by means of cells*

A great variety of reactions can be made to occur reversibly in cells and their standard free energies can be measured by the e.m.f. method. Some examples follow.†

Reduction of metallic chlorides by hydrogen. A cell can be set up consisting of a combination of a hydrogen electrode and a silver–silver chloride electrode in hydrochloric acid. The hydrogen electrode may consist of platinized platinum over which hydrogen is bubbled; the platinum takes no part in the reaction. The cell is written

$$(Pt)H_2, \; HCl, \; AgCl; \; Ag.$$

The electrode reactions are:

Negative pole: $H_2 = 2H^+ + 2e$.

Positive pole: $2AgCl + 2e = 2Ag + 2Cl^-$.

The hydrogen ions are solvated but are written H^+ for

† For further treatment of cells, the reader is referred to the excellent books available on electrochemistry. Among the best are MacInnes, *Principles of Electrochemistry* (1939); Dole, *Experimental and Theoretical Electrochemistry* (McGraw-Hill, 1935); Harned and Owen, *The Physical Chemistry of Electrolyte Solutions* (Reinhold, 2nd edn. 1950); McKenna, *Theoretical Electrochemistry* (Macmillan, 1939); Robinson and Stokes, *Electrolyte Solutions* (Butterworth, 1955); and the relevant chapters in Butler, *Chemical Thermodynamics* (Macmillan, 1946). The values of E^0 are in general those given by MacInnes, op. cit., chaps. 10 and 14. They refer to a temperature of 25°.

brevity's sake. The cell reaction, obtained by summing the electrode reactions, is

$$H_2 + 2AgCl = 2Ag + 2H^+ + 2Cl^-.$$

The standard potential of the cell, with hydrogen at 1 atm pressure, is 0·2225 volts. The cell has been much studied; it is considered further in section 12.24.

If the silver–silver chloride electrode is replaced by a calomel electrode, consisting of calomel in contact with mercury, the cell reaction is

$$H_2 + Hg_2Cl_2 = 2Hg + 2H^+ + 2Cl^-.$$

The standard electrode potential of this cell is 0·26796 volts.†

Reduction of oxides by hydrogen. In the following cell a mercury–mercuric oxide electrode is combined with a hydrogen electrode:

$$Hg;\ HgO,\ NaOH,\ H_2(Pt).$$

The electrode reactions are

$$Hg + H_2O = HgO + 2H^+ + 2e,$$

$$2H^+ + 2e = H_2$$

and the cell reaction is therefore

$$Hg + H_2O = HgO + H_2.$$

Thus the standard free energy change for the cell reaction, with its sign changed, is the standard free energy for the reduction of mercuric oxide by hydrogen. The value of E^0 is $-0\cdot0976$ volts.

Displacement of one metal by another. An example is the cell considered in section 6.21,

$$Zn;\ ZnCl_2,\ AgCl;\ Ag$$

for which the cell reaction is

$$Zn + 2AgCl = Zn^{++} + 2Cl^- + 2Ag.$$

For this cell, $E^0 = 0\cdot9834$ volts.

† See note ‡ on p. 259.

Allotropic change. The change of white tin to grey below 18° C, or the reverse change above this temperature, can be studied by means of the cell

Sn(white); tin salt solution; Sn(grey).

The results are considered in section 8.21.

Synthesis of water from its elements. The free energy change for this reaction, which has been otherwise determined,† could be determined by the e.m.f. method if it were possible to set up a reversible oxygen electrode, as in the cell

(Pt)H$_2$, aqueous salt solution, O$_2$(Pt).

The hydrogen and oxygen streams would have to be kept apart, by using an H-tube for example. The electrode reactions would be

$$H_2 = 2H^+ + 2e,$$

$$\tfrac{1}{2}O_2 + H_2O + 2e = 2OH^-,$$

and since the hydrogen and hydroxyl ions would combine in the solution, the cell reaction would be

$$H_2 + \tfrac{1}{2}O_2 = H_2O.$$

An accurately reversible oxygen electrode does not seem to have been achieved, but it appears that the electrode reaction may be made to go at a reasonable rate by using a porous nickel plate into which the gas is pumped. This electrode combined with a similar hydrogen electrode can be used in a 'fuel cell' by means of which electrical work is extracted from hydrogen and oxygen. More work is obtained in this way than if the gases are burned and the thermal energy used in a heat-engine.

Combination of chlorine with hydrogen and metals. A reversible chlorine electrode can be set up by bubbling a mixture of chlorine and nitrogen over platinum. If this were combined with a hydrogen electrode, as in the cell

(Pt)H$_2$, HCl, Cl$_2$(Pt),

the cell reaction would be

$$H_2 + Cl_2 = 2H^+ + 2Cl^-.$$

† Lewis and Randall, *Thermodynamics* (1923), pp. 477; cf. below, p. 284.

In practice the chlorine electrode has been used with a calomel electrode or silver–silver chloride electrode. The cell reaction for the latter combination is

$$2AgCl = Cl_2 + 2Ag$$

and $E^0 = 1 \cdot 1364$ volts. Adding to this the standard electrode potential $0 \cdot 2225$ volts for the cell made up of the hydrogen and silver–silver chloride electrodes in hydrochloric acid, for which the cell reaction is

$$H_2 + 2AgCl = 2Ag + 2H^+ + 2Cl^-,$$

we obtain $E^0 = 1 \cdot 3589$ for the cell in which hydrogen and chlorine are made to combine.

Reduction of ferric ion by hydrogen. In the following cell a calomel electrode is combined with a platinum electrode dipping into a mixed solution of ferrous and ferric salts:

$$(Pt); \; Fe^{++}, \; Fe^{+++}, \; Cl^-, \; Hg_2Cl_2; \; Hg.$$

The cell reaction is easily shown to be

$$Hg_2Cl_2 + 2Fe^{++} = 2Hg + 2Fe^{+++} + 2Cl^-.$$

The value of E^0 is $0 \cdot 783$ volts. If we combine the e.m.f. of this cell with that of the cell formed by combining a calomel electrode with a hydrogen electrode,

$$(Pt)H_2, \; HCl, \; Hg_2Cl_2; \; Hg,$$

whose cell reaction is

$$Hg_2Cl_2 + H_2 = 2Hg + 2H^+ + 2Cl^-,$$

we can obtain ΔG^0 for the reaction

$$2Fe^{++} + 2H^+ = 2Fe^{+++} + H_2$$

and so for the reduction of ferric ion by hydrogen. Many oxidation-reduction reactions can be similarly treated.

Cells with liquid junction. So far we have considered cells containing only one electrolyte solution. Some reactions, however, can only be realized if the electrodes dip into different solutions. An example is the Daniell cell, consisting of a combination of zinc and copper electrodes. The cell may be written as follows, the colon indicating a liquid junction:

$$\text{Zn; ZnSO}_4 : \text{CuSO}_4 ; \text{ Cu.}$$

The chemical reaction in the cell is the displacement of copper ions in solution by zinc:

$$\text{Zn} + \text{Cu}^{++} = \text{Zn}^{++} + \text{Cu.}$$

But this is not the only change that goes on in the cell. During the working of the cell, current is carried by the different ions across the boundary between these solutions, and therefore small changes occur in their concentrations. These changes form part of the complete cell reaction and so contribute to ΔG and to the e.m.f. They are liable to be a source of uncertainty in interpreting the e.m.f.s of cells with liquid junction.† Such cells are therefore avoided when possible, except in one case discussed later (section 12.25) where no uncertainty arises; this is the case of a junction in a 'concentration cell' between two solutions of the same electrolyte at different concentrations. In the following cells it is impossible to avoid liquid junctions between solutions having only one ion in common, or even no ion in common. The results are correspondingly less certain; but it is usually possible to reduce the uncertainty to a millivolt or so by using a saturated solution of potassium chloride or nitrate as a bridge between the two solutions.‡

Neutralization of hydrogen and hydroxyl ions, or dissociation of water into ions. Two hydrogen electrodes, one in acid and the other in alkali, are connected through a liquid junction:

$$\text{(Pt)H}_2, \text{ NaOH} : \text{KCl} : \text{HCl, H}_2\text{(Pt).}$$

† MacInnes, *Principles of Electrochemistry* (1939), chap. 13; Guggenheim, *J. Amer. Chem. Soc.*, 1930, **52**, 1315.

‡ The same difficulty arises in principle in dealing with cells 'without liquid junction', though it is experimentally negligible. In the cell (Pt)H₂, HCl aq., AgCl; Ag, for example, the electrodes strictly speaking dip into different solutions, inasmuch as there is a little dissolved silver chloride near one electrode and a little dissolved hydrogen near the other. The effect of the difference, however, is not appreciable.

The main cell reaction is seen to be

$$H^+ + OH^- = H_2O.$$

The value of E^0 is 0·8279 volts.

Formation of silver chloride from its ions. This is the reaction that occurs in a cell formed by combining a silver electrode dipping into silver nitrate solution with a silver–silver chloride electrode dipping into potassium chloride solution. To prevent precipitation of silver chloride round the silver electrode, the two electrode compartments must be separated by a bridge solution of potassium nitrate:

$$Ag; \ AgCl, \ KCl : KNO_3 : AgNO_3; \ Ag.$$

The main cell reaction is

$$Ag^+ + Cl^- = AgCl.$$

Displacement of silver from silver salt solutions by hydrogen. This occurs in a cell formed by combining a silver electrode dipping into silver nitrate solution with a hydrogen electrode:

$$Ag; \ AgNO_3 : HNO_3, \ H_2(Pt).$$

The main cell reaction is

$$2Ag^+ + H_2 = 2Ag + 2H^+.$$

In practice it has been more convenient to measure the e.m.f.s of two cells, (i) a combination of the silver electrode and a calomel electrode, and (ii) a combination of the calomel and hydrogen electrodes. The value of E^0 is -0.7994 volts.

Standard electrode potentials. We have seen that it is possible to measure, directly or indirectly, the e.m.f.s of many cells formed by combining the hydrogen electrode with some other electrode. It is therefore convenient to choose as an arbitrary zero of e.m.f. the potential of the hydrogen electrode, at one atmosphere pressure, with the mean ionic activity (section 12.21) of the HCl or other solution at unity. The *standard electrode potential* of an electrode is the standard potential of a cell in which that electrode is combined with such a hydrogen electrode. Typical of the reactions in such cells are

$$\text{(i)} \quad 2Ag^+ + H_2 = 2Ag + 2H^+.$$

$$\text{(ii)} \quad Cl_2 + H_2 = 2H^+ + 2Cl^-.$$

$$\text{(iii)} \quad 2Fe^{++} + 2H^+ = 2Fe^{+++} + H_2.$$

Reactions (i) and (ii) are examples of the reduction of metallic cations to the elements, and of non-metallic elements to anions, respectively. It is therefore possible to arrange the elements according to their standard electrode potentials in the order of their electropositive character, as shown by their behaviour towards hydrogen under standard conditions. Some values are given in Table 28.† The difference between any pair of values

TABLE 28

Electrode	Standard potential, volts	Electrode	Standard potential, volts
Li; Li$^+$	$+3 \cdot 045$	Sn; Sn^{++}	$+0 \cdot 136$
K; K$^+$	$+2 \cdot 925$	Pb; Pb^{++}	$+0 \cdot 126$
Rb; Rb$^+$	$+2 \cdot 925$	(Pt)H$_2$; H$^+$	$0 \cdot 0000$
Na; Na$^+$	$+2 \cdot 714$	Cu; Cu^{++}	$-0 \cdot 337$
Zn; Zn^{++}	$+0 \cdot 763$	Pt(I$_2$); I$^-$	$-0 \cdot 5355$
Cd; Cd^{++}	$+0 \cdot 403$	Ag; Ag$^+$	$-0 \cdot 7991$
Tl; Tl$^+$	$+0 \cdot 3363$	Pt(Br$_2$); Br$^-$	$-1 \cdot 0652$
Co; Co^{++}	$+0 \cdot 277$	Pt(Cl$_2$); Cl$^-$	$-1 \cdot 3595$
Ni; Ni^{++}	$+0 \cdot 250$		

gives E^0 for a cell composed of the two electrodes in question, and hence ΔG^0 and K for the displacement reaction. In general a metal higher in the series tends to displace a lower one from solution; for instance, zinc displaces copper. It must be remembered, however, that the values given are *standard* potentials. By adjusting the relative activities of the reactants (as for instance by making the activity of one ion very small by forming a complex), it is possible to make displacements occur in the contrary direction.

Reaction (iii) is a characteristic oxidation-reduction reaction.

† Values are mostly from Latimer, *The Oxidation States of the Elements and their Potentials in Aqueous Solution* (Prentice Hall, 1952); they refer to 25°.

Such reactions also may be arranged in the order of the corresponding standard potentials. Some values are given in Table 29.† The difference between any pair of values gives E^0 for the corresponding cell, and hence ΔG^0 and K for the mutual oxidation-reduction reaction. In general the reaction at the electrode with the lower potential will occur in the oxidizing direction—for instance, ceric salts oxidize ferrous—but by adjustment of concentrations it may be possible to reverse the direction.

TABLE 29

Oxidation-reduction potentials

Electrode	Electrode reaction	Standard potential at 25°, volts
Pb; PbO, OH⁻	$Pb + 2OH^- = PbO + H_2O + 2e$	$+0.5785$
Pt(H₂); H⁺	$H_2 = 2H^+ + 2e$	0.0000
Hg; HgO, OH⁻	$Hg + 2OH^- = HgO + H_2O + 2e$	-0.0976
Sb; Sb₂O₃, H⁺	$2Sb + 3H_2O = Sb_2O_3 + 6H^+ + 6e$	-0.152
(Pt); Cu⁺, Cu⁺⁺	$Cu^+ = Cu^{++} + e$	-0.153
(Pt); Fe⁺⁺, Fe⁺⁺⁺	$Fe^{++} = Fe^{+++} + e$	-0.771
(Pt); Hg₂⁺⁺, Hg⁺⁺	$Hg_2^{++} = 2Hg^{++} + 2e$	-0.920
Pb; PbO₂, Pb⁺⁺	$Pb^{++} + 2H_2O = PbO_2 + 4H^+ + 2e$	-1.455
(Pt); Ce⁺⁺⁺, Ce⁺⁺⁺⁺	$Ce^{+++} = Ce^{++++} + e$	-1.61

From these examples, it is clear that the measurement of e.m.f.s provides a powerful method for the determination of the standard free energy of a reaction in solution. The main limitation of the method is that reversible electrodes cannot always be prepared. The application of e.m.f.s to determine activities is considered in sections 12.24 and 12.25.

† See note on p. 267.

VII

TWO-PHASE SYSTEMS

7.1. Thermal, mechanical, and chemical equilibrium in a two-phase system

Two systems in contact with one another will be in complete equilibrium only if they have equal values of the temperature, the pressure, and the chemical potential of each species present (section 4.7). This is true when the two systems are two phases, such as liquid and solid sulphur, or liquid and gaseous water. For two such phases, designated as α and β, the conditions of equilibrium are

$$T^\alpha = T^\beta, \quad P^\alpha = P^\beta, \quad \mu_i^\alpha = \mu_i^\beta,$$

where the last equality is true for each of the species present.

In some systems, equilibrium can only be partial; for instance, systems containing a semi-permeable membrane, such as the membrane used for osmosis (section 9.36). The condition $\mu_i^\alpha = \mu_i^\beta$ is then true only for the species to which the membrane is permeable.

For a pure substance, the Phase Rule (section 4.8) predicts that if there are two phases in equilibrium, the number of degrees of freedom will be one. Thus for a pure liquid or solid in contact with its vapour, if the temperature is fixed the pressure at equilibrium will be fixed. This is experimentally verified. The equilibrium pressure is called the *vapour pressure* of the solid or liquid; we shall write it P^e when it is necessary to distinguish it from pressure in general. If the temperature is varied, we expect a relation between P^e and T, as is in fact found. Similarly, there will be a relation between the pressure and the melting-point, which is the temperature of equilibrium between solid and liquid. The pressure-temperature relations found have the general form shown in fig. 46.

We have already noted that in such a phase change at constant pressure there are discontinuous changes of heat content and heat capacity (p. 75) and of entropy (p. 199).† The free energy, however, does not change discontinuously, since μ (which for a pure substance is equal to G) is equal for the two

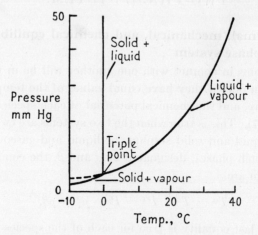

FIG. 46. Pressure-temperature relations for phase equilibria of water, ice, and water vapour.

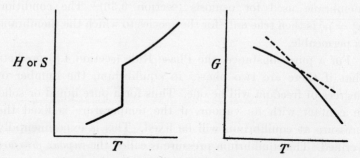

FIG. 47. Temperature-dependence of H, S, and G for a pure substance in the neighbourhood of a phase change.

phases in equilibrium; but the slope of the G–T plot will change, since $(\partial G/\partial T)_P = -S$. The temperature-variations of H, S, and G in the neighbourhood of a phase change (whether melting,

† There are certain phase changes, such as order–disorder transitions in alloys, in which the entropy change is not discontinuous; these are called second-order phase changes. Cf., for example, Zemansky, *Heat and Thermodynamics* (McGraw-Hill, 1943), chap. 15.

evaporation, or sublimation) are shown diagrammatically in fig. 47.

7.2. Vapour pressures of solids and liquids

7.21. *The Clausius–Clapeyron equation*

The pressure-temperature relation for the equilibrium between a solid or liquid and its vapour has the same general form whether the condensed phase is solid or liquid. We consider first the equilibrium between vapour and liquid. Fig. 48 *a* shows the vapour-pressure curve for water.†

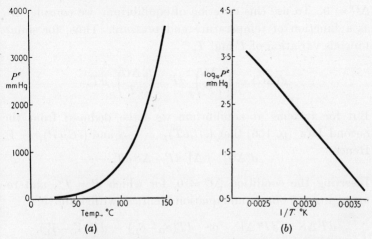

FIG. 48. (*a*) Vapour-pressure curve for water: P^e plotted against T.
(*b*) Plot of $\log_{10} P^e$ against $1/T$ for water.

We have already reached a useful stage in the derivation of the relation between temperature and vapour pressure (P^e) in section 4.82 (p. 176). The conditions for equilibrium between two systems in contact, applied to the liquid and gaseous phases, gave us the equation

$$dT(S_G - S_L) = dP^e(V_G - V_L). \qquad (1)$$

An alternative way of deriving this equation is to consider the two phases as *one* system. For mechanical and thermal

† On the experimental determination of vapour pressure, see Partington, *An Advanced Treatise on Physical Chemistry*, vol. ii, *The Properties of Liquids* (Longmans Green, 1951), section viii, *J*.

equilibrium, T and P must be uniform throughout the system. For equilibrium as regards transfer of material from one phase to another, the condition is that for the system as a whole, if T and P are kept constant, the Gibbs free energy change accompanying any transfer of material must be zero. Now transfer of a mole of material from liquid to gas is in general accompanied by a decrease G_L in the free energy of the liquid and an increase G_G in the free energy of the gaseous phase. The net change in G for the system as a whole is thus $(G_G - G_L)$ which may be written ΔG. For the particular case of equilibrium, $\Delta G = 0$. To use this criterion of equilibrium, we consider ΔG as a function of temperature and pressure. Thus, for simultaneous variation of P and T,

$$d(\Delta G) = \left(\frac{\partial \Delta G}{\partial P}\right)_T dP + \left(\frac{\partial \Delta G}{\partial T}\right)_P dT.$$

But for systems at equilibrium we have deduced from the Second Law (p. 156) that $(\partial G/\partial T)_P = -S$ and $(\partial G/\partial P)_T = V$. Hence
$$d(\Delta G) = \Delta V\, dP - \Delta S\, dT.$$

Inserting the condition $\Delta G = 0$, for which $P = P^e$, and rearranging, we obtain an equation identical with 1 above:

$$dT\, \Delta S = dP^e\, \Delta V, \quad \text{or} \quad dT(S_G - S_L) = dP^e(V_G - V_L).$$

We can now make progress by restating the entropy term in this equation. Since in general $\Delta G = \Delta H - T\, \Delta S$, and here $\Delta G = 0$, it follows that

$$S_G - S_L = \Delta S = \Delta H/T,$$

where $\Delta H = H_G - H_L$, and is thus the latent heat of evaporation L_e of the liquid, at temperature T and pressure P^e. Inserting this in equation 1, and rearranging, we obtain

$$\frac{dP^e}{dT} = \frac{L_e}{T(V_G - V_L)}. \tag{2}$$

Equation 2 is exact. If now we use the approximations (i) that V_L is negligible compared with V_G, and (ii) that the vapour behaves as a perfect gas so that $V_G = RT/P$, we obtain, remembering that $dP/P = d \ln P$,

$$\frac{d \ln P^e}{dT} = \frac{L_e}{RT^2}, \tag{3}$$

which may also be written

$$\frac{d \ln P^e}{d(1/T)} = -\frac{L_e}{R}. \tag{4}$$

This equation, which is not exact but is commonly a good approximation, is called the *Clausius–Clapeyron equation*. It relates the temperature-coefficient of the vapour pressure to the latent heat of evaporation. It applies to equilibrium or reversible change, and will represent experimental results only in so far as equilibrium is approached. It implies that L_e may be found from experimental observations by determining the slope of a plot of $\ln P^e$ against $1/T$ (fig. 48 b). More accurate results are obtained if corrections are applied to equation 4 for deviations of the vapour from the perfect-gas laws.

For evaporation of a solid, such as carbon at high temperatures, or solid carbon doxide below $-80°$ C, a similar derivation holds; in the final equation L_e must be replaced by L_s, the latent heat of sublimation:

$$\frac{d \ln P^e}{dT} = \frac{L_s}{RT^2}. \tag{5}$$

These equations 5 and 3 are similar in form to the reaction isochore (p. 242), and it is sometimes helpful to think of the vapour pressure P^e as a sort of equilibrium constant for the process: condensed phase $\rightleftharpoons$ gas.

7.22. *Approximate integration of the Clausius–Clapeyron equation*

To obtain an explicit expression for the vapour pressure in terms of temperature, we must integrate the Clausius–Clapeyron equation. The procedure is similar for the two equations 3 and 5 for solids and liquids, and we will use L to stand for either L_s or L_e. The integration is done in somewhat the same way as that of the reaction isochore (section 5.47).

Over a short enough temperature range, for which the latent heat L can be taken with sufficient accuracy as constant, we obtain at once the following relations, which correspond to equations 29 and 30 of section 5.47 (p. 245):

$$\ln P^e = \text{const.} - L/RT, \tag{6}$$

$$\ln\!\left(\frac{P^e_{T_1}}{P^e_{T_2}}\right) = \frac{L}{R}\!\left(\frac{1}{T_2} - \frac{1}{T_1}\right). \tag{7}$$

The plot of $\ln P$ against $1/T$ will be linear over this range (cf. fig. 48 b). Equation 6 can also be written

$$P^e = \text{const.} \times e^{-L/RT}.$$

This shows that, within the limits of the approximation that L is constant, we may expect the vapour pressure of a liquid or solid to vary exponentially with $(-L/RT)$, as experimental results confirm.

As a second approximation, if we express L as a linear function of temperature (corresponding to a constant difference of heat capacity between solid and vapour), we obtain the relation corresponding to equation 34 of section 5.47,

$$\ln P^e = A - B/T + C \ln T. \tag{8}$$

Experimental results for the vapour pressure of iodine, for example, may be fitted to an equation of this type over the range 0 to 100° C:†

$$\log_{10} P^e(\text{atm}) = -3512{\cdot}3/T - 2{\cdot}013 \log_{10} T + 13{\cdot}374.$$

The *exact* integration of the Clausius–Clapeyron equation presents a complication not encountered in the integration of the isochore, in that L cannot be represented exactly as a function of temperature alone by the Kirchhoff equation. This relation applies only at constant pressure (section 2.72), whereas in the liquid-vapour system at equilibrium the pressure

† Giauque, *J. Amer. Chem. Soc.*, 1931, **53**, 501. Cf. e.g. the determination of the heat of sublimation of zinc, by an effusion method, by Barrow *et al.*,*Trans. Faraday Soc.*, 1955, **51**, 1354. A much-used empirical relation is that due to Antoine (see, for example, Everett *et al.*, *Proc. Roy. Soc.* A, 1952, **212**, 158):

$$\log_{10} P^e = a + b/(c+t),$$

where t is the temperature in degrees Celsius, and a, b, and c are constants.

cannot be held constant if the temperature varies. The Kirchhoff equation, strictly speaking, can only be used as an approximation, though the error involved is small A general exact relation between vapour pressure and temperature may, however, be derived by approaching the equilibrium in quite a different way, by means of the thermodynamic functions for evaporation, as follows.

7.23. *Thermodynamic functions for evaporation of a solid or liquid*

We begin with sublimation from a solid. The changes in heat content, entropy, and Gibbs free energy for sublimation of one mole of a pure solid, at constant temperature and pressure—not necessarily, or generally, at equilibrium, i.e. at the vapour pressure—are the differences between the values for one mole of the gaseous phase and one mole of the solid. To express them as functions of temperature and pressure, we make use of general expressions already derived for the separate phases. Then in section 7.24 we apply them to the special case of equilibrium between gas and solid.

Heat of sublimation. For the solid, the heat content H_S at temperature T is given by equation 6 of section 2.72 (p. 55) as:

$$H_{S(T)} = H_{S(0)} + \int_0^T C_S \, dT.$$

For a perfect gas, $H_{G(T)}$ is given by equation 4 of section 3.12 (p. 73) as:

$$H_{G(T)} = H_{G(0)} + T(C_G - C_i) + \int_0^T C_i \, dT.$$

Thus the difference between the heat contents of the gaseous and solid phases at $T°$ K, which is the heat of sublimation, written $\Delta H_{s(T)}$ or $L_{s(T)}$, is

$$\Delta H_{s(T)} = L_{s(T)}$$

$$= H_{G(0)} - H_{S(0)} + T(C_G - C_i) + \int_0^T (C_i - C_S) \, dT. \qquad (9)$$

Writing $H_{G(0)} - H_{S(0)}$ as $L_{s(0)}$, the latent heat of sublimation at $0°$ K, this becomes

$$\Delta H_{s(T)} = L_{s(T)} = L_{s(0)} + T(C_G - C_i) + \int_0^T (C_i - C_S)\, dT. \quad (10)$$

Entropy of sublimation. For the solid, the entropy at temperature T is given by equation 4 of section 5.21 (p. 197):

$$S_{S(T)} = S_{S(0)} + \int_0^T C_S\, d\ln T.$$

For a perfect gas at pressure P, the entropy is given in terms of the entropy constant S_G^* by combining equation 9 of section 5.14 (p. 185) with equation 23 of section 5.22 (p. 208):

$$S_{G(T)} = S_G^* + \ln T(C_G - C_i) + \int_0^T C_i\, d\ln T - R\ln P.$$

Hence the entropy of sublimation $S_{G(T)} - S_{S(T)}$ is, at pressure P and $T°$ K,

$$\Delta S_{s(T)} = (S_G^* - S_{S(0)}) + \ln T(C_G - C_i) +$$

$$+ \int_0^T (C_i - C_S)\, d\ln T - R\ln P. \quad (11)$$

This may also be written

$$\Delta S_{s(T)} = \Delta S_{s(T)}^0 - R\ln P, \quad (12)$$

where $\Delta S_{s(T)}^0$ is the entropy of sublimation of the solid at unit pressure, and is independent of pressure, but depends on T and on the substance concerned.

Free energy of sublimation. Since $\Delta G = \Delta H - T\,\Delta S$, we obtain, using the preceding expressions 10 and 11 for ΔH_s and ΔS_s, an equation giving the free energy of sublimation at pressure P,

$$\Delta G_{s(T)} = \Delta G_{s(T)}^0 + RT\ln P. \quad (13)$$

Here $\Delta G_{s(T)}^0$ is the free energy change on sublimation at unit pressure, i.e. the standard free energy of sublimation. It is evidently independent of pressure, but depends on T and on the substance concerned, being given by

$$\Delta G^0_{s(T)} = L_{s(0)} + T(1-\ln T)(C_G-C_i) + \int_0^T (C_i-C_S)\, dT -$$

$$- T\int_0^T (C_i-C_S)\, d\ln T - T(S^*_G-S_{S(0)}). \quad (14)$$

7.24. *Exact relation between vapour pressure and temperature*

When the pressure P is equal to the vapour pressure P^e there will be equilibrium, and sublimation or condensation will proceed reversibly. The free energy change of the solid-vapour system as a whole will then be zero: $\Delta G_{s(T)} = 0$. Hence from equation 13,
$$R\ln P^e = -\Delta G^0_{s(T)}/T. \quad (15)$$

Thus the vapour pressure is very simply related to the standard free energy of sublimation. Moreover, by the definition of G,

$$\Delta G^0_{s(T)} = \Delta H^0_{s(T)} - T\,\Delta S^0_{s(T)} = L_{s(T)} - T\,\Delta S^0_{s(T)}, \quad (16)$$

so that from equation 15 it follows that

$$R\ln P^e = \Delta S^0_{s(T)} - L_{s(T)}/T. \quad (17)$$

This equation throws light on the factors determining the relative vapour pressures of different solids. It shows that the vapour pressure at a given temperature depends on (i) the standard entropy of sublimation, which determines the general position of the vapour-pressure curve on a P–T plot; and (ii) the latent heat of evaporation, which determines the curvature of the vapour-pressure curve. These factors are further considered in section 7.26.

An explicit exact relation between vapour pressure and temperature is obtained by substituting the expression 14 for $\Delta G^0_{s(T)}$ in equation 15. We obtain

$$R\ln P^e = -L_{s(0)}/T + \ln T(C_G-C_i) - \frac{1}{T}\int_0^T (C_i-C_S)\, dT +$$

$$+ \int_0^T (C_i-C_S)\, d\ln T + [(S^*_G-S_{S(0)}) - (C_G-C_i)]. \quad (18)$$

The last two terms, in the square bracket, are independent of temperature. The second term takes the form $\frac{5}{2}\ln T$ for monatomic gases and $\frac{7}{2}\ln T$ for diatomic gases.

Equation 18 is the general expression for the dependence of the vapour pressure of a solid on the temperature. In deriving it we have assumed that the pressure of the vapour is so low that it will exhibit perfect gas behaviour; but the equation can be corrected for deviations.† It is the full integrated form of the Clausius–Clapeyron equation 4, and must be used in accurate work over long temperature ranges. We can easily see that equations 8 and 6 are approximations to 18 by writing 18 in the equivalent form

$$\ln P^e = i - B/T + C\ln T + \frac{1}{R}\int_0^T (C_i - C_S)\, d\ln T -$$

$$- \frac{1}{RT}\int_0^T (C_i - C_S)\, dT. \quad (19)$$

Here i, B, and C are constants for a given substance. The last two terms of the equation are numerically much less important than the others (compare equation 8).

The constant of integration i which appears in the equation 19 is called the *vapour-pressure constant*. If we have once found this constant for a particular substance, we can calculate the vapour pressure at any temperature from purely thermal data on the latent heat and heat capacities. Comparison of the temperature-independent terms in equations 18 and 19 shows that the vapour-pressure constant i is equal to

$$i = [(S_G^* - S_{S(0)}) - (C_G - C_i)]/R. \quad (20)$$

Thus for a monatomic gas, for instance,

$$i = (S_G^* - S_{S(0)})/R - \frac{5}{2}. \quad (21)$$

† An equation which takes account of deviations from perfect gas behaviour has been obtained by Frost and Kalkwaif (*J. Chem. Phys.*, 1953, **21**, 264) by assuming that the gas obeys van der Waals' equation, and that ΔH varies linearly with T. They obtain

$$\log P^e = A + B/T + C\log T + DP^e/T^2,$$

where D depends on the van der Waals constant a. It is claimed that this equation reproduces experimental vapour pressures from the triple point to the critical point with an average deviation of 0·3 per cent.

Vapour-pressure constants are considered further in sections 7.25 and 8.24.

The vapour pressure of a liquid is related to the temperature in a similar way to that of a solid. The equations corresponding to 15 and 13 are

$$R \ln P^e = -\Delta G^0_{e(T)}/T = \Delta S^0_{e(T)} - L_{e(T)}/T. \qquad (22)$$

There are extra terms in the expressions for $\Delta G^0_{e(T)}$, $\Delta S^0_{e(T)}$, and $L_{e(T)}$ on account of the latent heat and change of heat capacity on melting (p. 75). The final equation has the same form as equation 19, with an integration constant i which again contains $(S^*_G - S_{S(0)})$.

7.25. *Determination of entropy constants from vapour pressures*

We have just seen that the vapour-pressure constant i of a solid or liquid depends upon $(S^*_G - S_{S(0)})$, the entropy constant of the gaseous form. If we measure the vapour pressure over a range of temperature, and also the specific and latent heats, we can use equation 19 to determine i and hence $(S^*_G - S_{S(0)})$. We have already noted in section 5.22 that values of this quantity for monatomic gases have been calculated from purely statistical considerations about the contribution to the entropy of the translational freedom of the molecules, and also for diatomic gases by taking into account the contributions of vibration and rotation. These values can now be compared with the results of some experimental vapour-pressure measurements. Table 30† shows that agreement is nearly always within experimental error. This agreement suggests that the assumptions made are justified, i.e. that the molecular properties assumed in the statistical calculations are correct, that the solid forms a perfect crystal at low temperatures, and that in the vapour-pressure experiments equilibrium was really attained.

† The values given are taken from Fowler and Guggenheim, *Statistical Thermodynamics* (Cambridge, 1939), pp. 200, 204, where references are given. They correspond to decadic logarithms and pressure in atmospheres.

TABLE 30

Vapour-pressure constants

P in atm; decadic logs.

	Monatomic gases			Diatomic gases	
Gas	i calc.	i obs.	Gas	i calc.	i obs.
He	−0·684	−0·68±0·01	N_2	−0·175	−0·16±0·03
Ne	0·370	0·39±0·04	O_2	0·53	0·55±0·02
A	0·814	0·81±0·02	CO	−0·16	−0·07±0·05
Kr	1·297	1·29±0·02	HCl	−0·42	−0·40±0·03
Xe	1·590	1·60±0·02	HBr	0·19	0·24±0·04
Na	0·757	0·63, 0·97, 0·78	HI	0·62	0·65±0·05
K	1·102	0·92, 1·13	Cl_2	1·35	1·66±0·08
Mg	0·492	0·47±0·2	Br_2	2·35	2·59±0·10
Zn	1·136	1·21±0·15	I_2	2·99	3·08±0·05
Cd	1·488	1·45, 1·57			
Hg	1·866	1·95±0·06			
Tl	2·180	2·37±0·3			

7.26. Interpretation of the vapour-pressure equation†

We can understand some of the factors that determine the
volatility of different substances by considering equation 18
(p. 277). The two main variable factors are $L_{s(0)}$ and the term
involving S_G^*. A larger entropy constant implies a higher vapour
pressure. Statistically, this means that the greater the number
W of possible states which the substance can occupy in the gas
phase relative to the number in the solid at $0°$ K, the more
volatile it will be. Since there are more translational energy-
states the larger the mass of the molecules (pp. 69, 206), an
increase of mass will increase the S_G^* term. This may be verified by consulting Table 30, where for instance the increase
from helium to xenon is very marked. This will tend to increase
the vapour pressure at a given temperature. On the other hand,
increase of mass usually goes with an increase in the latent heat
of evaporation, which has the opposite effect (equation 18).
The net result is usually that the higher the molecular weight,
the lower the vapour pressure. Thus the energy and entropy

† Cf. Hinshelwood, *The Structure of Physical Chemistry* (Oxford, 1951),
pp. 141–3.

factors, here as often, work in opposite directions, and the vapour pressure depends on the balance between them.

7.27. *Entropies of reversible evaporation*

When sublimation or evaporation is carried out as nearly as possibly reversibly, i.e. at the equilibrium vapour pressure, ΔG is zero and the entropy of evaporation ΔS_e is simply L_e/T_e. Some values for evaporation at one atmosphere pressure are given in Table 31.†

TABLE 31

Substance	Boiling-point at 1 atm °K	L_e kcal/mole	ΔS_e (P = 1 atm) cal/deg-mole
Nitrogen . . .	77·34	1·333	17·24
Oxygen . . .	90·19	1·630	18·07
Chlorine . . .	239·10	4·878	20·40
Hexane . . .	341·9	6·896	20·17
Carbon tetrachloride .	349·9	7·17	20·5
Benzene . . .	353·3	7·353	20·81
Chloroform . .	334·4	7·02	20·99
Dimethyl ether . .	248·34	5·141	20·70
Tetranitromethane .	398·9	9·2	23
Mercury . . .	629·7	13·89	22·06
Zinc	1,180	7·43	23·24
Ethyl alcohol . .	351·7	9·22	26·22
Methyl alcohol . .	337·9	8·43	24·95
Water . . .	373·16	9·7171	26·04

The entropy of evaporation is mainly to be attributed to the larger translational contribution in the vapour, due to the larger volume. For many liquids, such as hexane and chloroform, the entropy of evaporation at 1 atmosphere pressure is about 20–21 cal deg^{-1} mole^{-1}. This useful generalization is known as Trouton's rule.‡ The fact that water and other hydroxylic liquids have entropies of evaporation about 5 units higher is quite understandable because in these liquids there is an

---

† Values of the heats and entropies of evaporation of many substances are given in *Selected Values of Chemical Thermodynamic Properties* (U.S. National Bureau of Standards, Circular 500, 1952), series ii.

‡ The values for different liquids are still closer if we compare the entropies not at equal pressures but at equal volumes. Cf. Hildebrand and Scott, *Solubility of Non-electrolytes* (Reinhold, 1950), p. 89.

abnormal degree of structural order due to the linking of molecules by hydrogen bonds, and much of this order will disappear on evaporation. Interesting conclusions about the 'free volume'† and the internal order in liquids‡ have been drawn from the experimental values of entropies of evaporation.

7.3. Reactions involving both gaseous and condensed phases

Both a condensed phase (solid or liquid) and a gaseous phase are concerned in reactions such as those of sulphur with oxygen and with steam:

$$S(s) + O_2 \rightleftharpoons SO_2,$$

$$3S(l) + 2H_2O(g) \rightleftharpoons 2H_2S + SO_2.$$

By the Phase Rule (section 4.8) the number of degrees of freedom in two-phase systems such as these is equal to the number of components. For a one-component system at equilibrium, we shall therefore expect P to be fixed when T is fixed, and therefore that P and T will be related, just as for a pure liquid. For more than one component, there will be a relation between T, P, and composition. The exact forms of the relations are found as follows.

We could proceed exactly as in the derivation of the equilibrium constant for a gas reaction (section 5.42), except when substituting for the chemical potentials of the various species. For the gaseous species, assuming a perfect gas mixture, we have (p. 216) the relation $\mu_i = \mu_i^0 + RT \ln p_i$; but for the solid or liquid species the variation of μ with pressure is negligible, since it depends on the molar volume, as is clear if we make a calculation similar to the derivation of the equation for μ for a gas (p. 187). For any condensed species (excluding the special case of solid solutions) we therefore write simply $\mu_i = \mu_i^0$. We could then work through the treatment of section 5.42 with these modifications. The simplest way of deriving a general result, however, is by substituting for the μ's in the general

† Frank, *J. Chem. Phys.* 1945, **13**, 478, 493, 507.
‡ Staveley and Tupman, *J. Chem. Soc.*, 1950, 3597.

law of mass action stated in equation 63 of section 4.63 (p. 168),

$$a\mu_A + b\mu_B + \dots = m\mu_M + n\mu_N + \dots.$$

We then obtain $\qquad \Delta\mu^0 = -RT \ln K_p'.$

Here K_p' is independent of pressure, and it has the same form as K_p, the equilibrium constant for a gas reaction, but contains the partial pressures at equilibrium of the gaseous constituents only. Thus, since $\Delta\mu^0 = \Delta G^0$, the general relation $\Delta G^0 = -RT \ln K_p'$ is true for these reactions; this is analogous to the relation $\Delta G^0 = -RT \ln K_p$ for gas reactions (p. 230). Hence the general relations derived for gas reactions will have analogues for reactions involving condensed phases as well as gases, the only difference being the substitution of K_p' for K_p. The derivation of the van't Hoff isochore (section 5.46) and its integration (sections 5.47, 5.48) can be taken over. The integration constant J' in the general integrated equation for K_p' will be $\Delta S_G^*/R$, where ΔS_G^* is the difference of entropy constants for the gaseous species (cf. equation 39, p. 250). We shall need this result in considering the evidence for the Third Law (section 8.24).

Applying the result that K_p' is constant to various reactions, we can predict the following relations, which are verified by experiment:

$\mathrm{S}(s) + \mathrm{O}_2 \rightleftharpoons \mathrm{SO}_2:$ $\qquad\qquad K_p' = p_{\mathrm{SO}_2}^e / p_{\mathrm{O}_2}^e.$

$3\mathrm{S}(l) + 2\mathrm{H}_2\mathrm{O}(g) \rightleftharpoons 2\mathrm{H}_2\mathrm{S} + \mathrm{SO}_2:$ $\quad K_p' = (p_{\mathrm{H}_2\mathrm{S}}^e)^2 p_{\mathrm{SO}_2} / (p_{\mathrm{H}_2\mathrm{O}}^e)^2.$

$2\mathrm{Ag}_2\mathrm{O} \rightleftharpoons 4\mathrm{Ag} + \mathrm{O}_2:$ $\qquad\qquad K_p' = p_{\mathrm{O}_2}^e.$

$\mathrm{CaCO}_3 \rightleftharpoons \mathrm{CaO} + \mathrm{CO}_2:$ $\qquad\quad K_p' = p_{\mathrm{CO}_2}^e.$

$\mathrm{NH}_4\mathrm{HS} \rightleftharpoons \mathrm{NH}_3 + \mathrm{H}_2\mathrm{S}:$ $\qquad\quad K_p' = p_{\mathrm{H}_2\mathrm{S}}^e\, p_{\mathrm{NH}_3}^e.$

$\mathrm{Fe} + \mathrm{H}_2\mathrm{O}(g) \rightleftharpoons \mathrm{FeO} + \mathrm{H}_2:$ $\quad K_p' = p_{\mathrm{H}_2}^e / p_{\mathrm{H}_2\mathrm{O}}^e.$

Where only one gas is concerned, as in the dissociation of silver oxide or of calcium carbonate, K_p' is equal to the pressure of that gas, which will therefore be constant at a given temperature, just like a vapour pressure. It will also be related to temperature in a similar way to a vapour pressure. Measurement of the dissociation pressure P^e gives the standard free energy of such a reaction, as $\Delta G^0 = -RT \ln P^e$.

For some of these reactions the standard free energy can be obtained from the e.m.f. of a suitable cell; thus a combination of bromine and silver–silver bromide electrodes would give ΔG^0 for the reaction $Ag + \frac{1}{2}Br_2 \rightleftharpoons AgBr$.

Many such reactions have been experimentally investigated, and the above expressions for the equilibrium constants have been verified. The free energy changes of such reactions may be of technical importance, as for instance in the reduction of metal oxides by hydrogen or carbon. They are often of interest in computing the free energy changes of other reactions. For instance, the free energy of formation of water has been studied† not only by direct measurements of the equilibrium constant for the dissociation of water at high temperature,

$$H_2 + \tfrac{1}{2}O_2 \rightleftharpoons H_2O; \quad \Delta G^0_{298} = -56\cdot64 \text{ kcal mole}^{-1},$$

but also by measuring the dissociation pressure (equal to the equilibrium constant) of silver oxide and combining it with other data, as follows:

$2Ag + \frac{1}{2}O_2 \rightleftharpoons Ag_2O$: K'_p gives $\Delta G^0_{298} = -2\cdot395$ kcal mole⁻¹,

$Ag_2O + H_2O \rightleftharpoons 2Ag^+ + 2OH^-$:

solubility of Ag_2O gives $\Delta G^0_{298} = 21\cdot04$ kcal mole⁻¹,

$2Ag^+ + H_2 \rightleftharpoons 2Ag + 2H^+$:

e.m.f.s give $\Delta G^0_{298} = -36\cdot90$ kcal mole⁻¹,

$2H^+ + 2OH^- \rightleftharpoons 2H_2O(l)$:

e.m.f.s give $\Delta G^0_{298} = -38\cdot21$ kcal mole⁻¹.

Addition gives

$$H_2 + \tfrac{1}{2}O_2 \rightleftharpoons H_2O(l): \quad \Delta G^0_{298} = -56\cdot47 \text{ kcal mole}^{-1}.$$

This value agrees well with that from the dissociation of water. A similar determination using the dissociation pressure of mercuric oxide gives $\Delta G^0_{298} = -56\cdot54$ kcal mole⁻¹.

7.4. The effect of hydrostatic pressure on vapour pressure

The pressure of the vapour over a liquid is changed if the hydrostatic pressure on it is changed, though very large pressures must be imposed to cause an appreciable increase.

† Lewis and Randall, *Thermodynamics* (1923), pp. 477 seq.

Suppose we have a pure liquid in a vessel closed at one end by a piston by which pressure can be exerted, and at the other by a membrane permeable to vapour but not to liquid. (A sintered glass disk acts in this way towards mercury.) The system is thus in partial, not complete, equilibrium; the pressure of the vapour P_G need not be equal to the pressure on the liquid P_L,

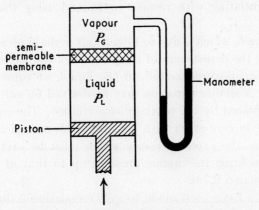

FIG. 49. Vapour pressure of a liquid under hydrostatic pressure (schematic).

but equilibrium can be set up as regards the passage of material from liquid to vapour. The condition of equilibrium, if the temperature is uniform and the pressures P_L and P_G are constant, is $\mu_L = \mu_G$. Thus for any small change at equilibrium,

$$d\mu_L = d\mu_G. \tag{1}$$

If the pressure on the liquid is slightly increased, leading to a small change in P_G, the effects on μ_L and μ_G are given by

$$d\mu_L = \left(\frac{\partial \mu_L}{\partial P_L}\right)_{T,n} dP_L = V_L \, dP_L \tag{2}$$

and

$$d\mu_G = \left(\frac{\partial \mu_G}{\partial P_G}\right)_{T,n} dP_G = V_G \, dP_G. \tag{3}$$

Hence for equilibrium, using equation 1,

$$V_L \, dP_L = V_G \, dP_G, \tag{4}$$

or

$$\frac{dP_G}{dP_L} = \frac{V_L}{V_G}. \tag{5}$$

If the vapour behaves as a perfect gas, for which $V_G = RT/P_G$, this becomes

$$\frac{d \ln P_G}{dP_L} = \frac{V_L}{RT}. \tag{6}$$

This equation can also be obtained from the relations

$$\mu_L = \mu_G = \mu_G^0 + RT \ln P$$

by differentiating with respect to P, and using the relation $(\partial \mu_L / \partial P)_T = V_L$.

Equation 5, which is due to Poynting,† is the general relation expressing the dependence of the pressure of the vapour on the hydrostatic pressure exerted on the liquid, at constant temperature. A similar equation may be derived for solutions; V_L is then replaced by the partial molar volume. The equation is of interest in connexion with osmotic pressure, which may be regarded as the excess pressure which must be exerted on a solution to bring its vapour pressure up to that of the pure solvent (section 9.36).

Attempts have been made to verify equation 5 directly by measuring the increase in the equilibrium concentration of vapour over a liquid or solid when an increasing pressure of some inert gas such as nitrogen is applied. In such experiments the vapour pressure always increases considerably more than the equation predicts. This is because the interactions of the molecules of the condensed species with those of gases at high pressure are enough to lead to an appreciable 'solubility' of the condensed phase in the gas. Such measurements are in fact used in testing theories of intermolecular forces.‡ The verification of equation 5 may be tackled indirectly, however, by observations on the following phenomenon.

The vapour pressure of small drops of liquid is greater than that of a liquid with a flat surface, on account of the hydrostatic pressure due to surface tension. Consider a spherical drop of radius r, area $A = 4\pi r^2$, and volume $V = \frac{4}{3}\pi r^3$. We can express P_L in terms of the surface tension γ by calculating the

† Poynting, *Phil. Mag.*, 1881, **12** (iv), 32.
‡ Ewald, *Trans. Faraday Soc.*, 1955, **51**, 347; *Disc. Faraday Soc.*, 1953, no. 15, p. 238, and other papers in this discussion.

virtual work when the radius changes from r to $r+dr$. In terms of P_L, this virtual work is $P_L dV$ or $4\pi r^2 P_L dr$; in terms of surface tension, it is γdA or $8\pi r\gamma dr$. Equating these, we find

$$P_L = 2\gamma/r, \quad \text{whence } dP_L = -(2\gamma/r^2)\,dr. \tag{7}$$

Substituting this relation in equation 5, we obtain

$$\frac{dP_G}{dr} = -\frac{V_L}{V_G}\frac{2\gamma}{r^2} \quad \text{or} \quad dP_G = \left(2\gamma\frac{V_L}{V_G}\right)d\left(\frac{1}{r}\right). \tag{8}$$

The pressure of the vapour will therefore increase linearly with $1/r$. For water at $20°$ C, V_G/V_L is about 5×10^4, and $\gamma = 72\cdot 3$ erg cm^{-2}; since 760 mm Hg is approximately 10^6 dynes cm^{-2}, this gives

$$dP_G\,(\text{mm Hg}) \simeq 2\times 10^{-6}\,d\left(\frac{1}{r}\right).$$

Thus a vapour-pressure increase of 10^{-3} mm Hg over that of a flat surface will be exhibited by a drop of water with a radius of about 2×10^{-3} cm.

The relation 8 between the radius of a drop and the increased pressure of the vapour over it was derived by Lord Kelvin. It has been verified† by observing a system consisting of a pure liquid with an ordinary flat surface and above it a cloud of drops of uniform size of a *solution* in the liquid. The size of the drops of a solution of known concentration, when in equilibrium with the pure liquid, was determined by light-scattering methods. The increase of vapour pressure due to the excess pressure inside the drops was then exactly balanced by the diminution of vapour pressure due to the presence of solute (section 9.31), which was known from separate experiments on bulk solutions. Good agreement with equation 8 was found.

7.5. The thermodynamics of melting

7.51. *The relation between melting-point and pressure*

Just as the system liquid+vapour exhibits at equilibrium a relation between pressure and temperature, so does the system solid+liquid, in that the melting-point is altered by change of

† LaMer and Green, *Trans. Faraday Soc.*, 1952, **48**, 410.

pressure, though the change is relatively small. The quantitative relation may be found by the methods that were used for the liquid-vapour equilibrium, and it is easily seen that equations similar to equations 1 and 2 of section 7.21 (p. 271) will hold:

$$dT(S_L - S_S) = dP(V_L - V_S), \tag{1}$$

$$dP/dT = L_f/T(V_L - V_S). \tag{2}$$

Here T and P are the temperature and pressure at equilibrium, and L_f is the latent heat of fusion. Since L_f and ΔV are practically constant over short ranges of temperature, we may write equation 2 as

$$\Delta T/\Delta P = T \Delta V/L_f. \tag{3}$$

Here ΔT is the change of melting-point due to excess pressure ΔP.† If the volume increases on melting, as with most substances, ΔT will be positive; if it decreases, as with water, ΔT will be negative. The magnitude of $\Delta T/\Delta P$ depends on L_f and ΔV; since ΔV is small compared with that for the change from liquid to vapour, while L_f is not greatly different, $\Delta T/\Delta P$ is much less for melting than for evaporation (cf. fig. 46, p. 270). For acetic acid, for example, the calculated change in freezing-point is $+0\cdot024$ degrees per atmosphere, while for water it is $-0\cdot00753$ degrees per atmosphere. Experimental results on freezing-points up to high pressures agree with these calculated values.

It follows, incidentally, that for the definition of the ice-point in thermometry (section 3.32, p. 86) it is necessary to specify the pressure. The melting-point of water under its own vapour pressure of $4\cdot6$ mm of mercury—the 'triple point', shown in fig. 46—is $+0\cdot0075°$ C.

The effect of pressure on the transition temperature of a polymorphic change such as that from rhombic to monoclinic sulphur, or of a dehydration equilibrium such as that of sodium sulphate decahydrate, is also governed by equation 3.

† Equation 3 was first obtained by James Thomson, brother of Lord Kelvin; *Trans. Roy. Soc. Edin.*, 1849, **16**, 575. Cf. Partington, *A Text-book of Thermodynamics* (Constable, 1913), pp. 195–7.

7.52. *The entropy of melting*†

X-ray and other studies indicate that there is some similarity of structure between a liquid and a solid; the arrangement of nearest neighbours round any particular molecule in a liquid just above the melting-point is very similar to that in the crystal just below the melting-point, and exhibits 'short-range order'. But in a crystal there is also 'long-range order', in that the crystal lattice usually extends for at least 1,000 molecular diameters in any direction before a major defect of regularity is encountered; whereas in a liquid this long-range order is broken down and the 'crystallinity' extends over only 2 to 10 molecular diameters before a major defect is encountered. Since the number of ways W in which the comparatively disordered liquid state can be made up is much greater than the number of ways in which the ordered solid can be made up, and $S = k \ln W$ (section 4.44, p. 145), there will be a positive entropy change on fusion, and measurements of this entropy change will throw light on the liquid state. This entropy of fusion may be obtained from measurements of the melting-point T_f and latent heat of fusion L_f; since the free energy change on freezing is zero, $\Delta S_f = L_f / T_f$.

Substances whose molecules are spherically symmetrical, such as the monatomic gases and most metals, have entropies of fusion in the region of 1·5 to 3·5 cal deg^{-1} mole^{-1}. This corresponds to the loss of long-range positional order of the crystal lattice on melting. Some of these substances are shown in the first group in Table 32.

When the molecules are not spherically symmetrical, they will not only occupy definite positions in the crystal but will also be oriented in definite directions, at least at low temperatures. This orientational order will disappear on melting. It is not therefore surprising that the entropies of fusion of polyatomic molecules are often much higher than those of monatomic, and lie in the region of 7 to 10 cal deg^{-1} mole^{-1}. Some of these substances are shown in the second group in Table 32.

---

† Ubbelohde, *Quart. Rev. Chem. Soc.*, 1950, **4**, 376, and *Modern Thermodynamics* (Oxford, 2nd edn. 1952), chap. 14; *Trans. Faraday Soc.* 1956, **52**, 882.

TABLE 32

ΔS_f = entropy of fusion, cal deg^{-1} mole^{-1}

ΔS_{tr} = entropy of transition, cal deg^{-1} mole^{-1}

Substance	ΔS_f	Number of transitions in solid	ΔS_{tr}	$\Delta S_f +$ ΔS_{tr}
(i) *Monatomic molecules*				
Ne	3·26	..	..	..
Ar	3·35	..	..	..
Kr	3·36	..	..	..
Xe	3·4	..	..	..
Li	1·53	..	..	..
Na	1·70	..	..	..
K	1·70	..	..	..
Rb	1·68	..	..	..
Cs	1·65	..	..	..
Mg	2·25	..	..	..
Zn	2·48	..	..	..
Cd	2·57	..	..	..
Hg	2·57	..	..	..
(ii) *Polyatomic without transitions in solid*				
CO_2	9·35	..	..	..
N_2O	8·58	..	..	..
CS_2	6·51	..	..	..
Cl_2	8·89	..	..	..
C_2H_4	7·70	..	..	..
SO_2	8·95	..	..	..
C_6H_6	8·44	..	..	..
HCN	7·73	..	..	..
(iii) *Polyatomic with transitions in solid*				
O_2	2·0	1	4·9	6·9
N_2	2·7	2	1·5	4·2
CO	2·9	1	2·5	5·4
HCl	3·0	1	2·9	5·9
H_2S	3·0	2	4·4	7·4
PH_3	1·97	2	5·09	7·06
CH_4	2·5	1	0·8	3·3
CCl_4	2·3	1	4·8	7·1
(iv) *Associated liquids*				
H_2O	5·25	..	..	..
CH_3OH	4·38	..	..	..
NH_3	6·91	..	..	..
N_2H_4	3·73	..	..	..

There are, however, a number of diatomic and polyatomic molecules with much smaller entropies of fusion; some of these are shown in the third group in Table 32. Here it is always found that the substance undergoes at least one transition below the melting-point, leading to an increase in entropy; we have already met the example of nitrogen (pp. 200–1). These transitions are interpreted as showing that the molecules in the crystal lattice become free (or partly free) to rotate, so that orientational order is partly lost.† When the increase in entropy of these transitions is added to the entropy of fusion, values closer to those of the second group are obtained.

Substances which melt to give associated liquids, such as water and ammonia, have lower entropies of fusion, as is shown in the fourth group in Table 32. This is easily understood, since in these liquids there is a greater degree of order than in non-associated liquids (p. 281).

† Ubbelohde, *Modern Thermodynamics* (1952), pp. 80 seq.; Staveley, *Quart. Rev. Chem. Soc.*, 1949, **3**, 65.

VIII

THE THIRD LAW OF THERMODYNAMICS

8.1. The importance of $\Delta S_{S(0)}$ for chemical reactions

THE standard free energy changes ΔG^0 in reactions are of fundamental importance in chemistry. As we have seen (section 5.42), ΔG^0 is a quantitative measure of 'chemical affinity', and in consequence is of interest both from the point of view of chemical theory, which seeks to interpret such quantities in molecular terms, and from the point of view of industrial practice.

So far we have examined two methods for the determination of the free energy change in a reaction: the measurement of the equilibrium constant and the measurement of the electromotive force of cells. Neither of these methods is applicable generally, and each involves experimental problems peculiar to each individual reaction. The direct determination of K_p is possible only when side-reactions are unimportant, when the reaction can be made to go at a reasonable rate, and when the equilibrium does not lie too far on one side. The determination of e.m.f.s requires reversible electrodes, and these are not always available; for instance, it has not been found possible to set up a reversible oxygen electrode. Clearly a general method with a standard technique would be very useful.

One method of finding ΔG^0 would be to determine ΔH^0 and ΔS^0 and use the relation $\Delta G^0 = \Delta H^0 - T\Delta S^0$. The measurement of ΔH^0 can be done calorimetrically, or in many cases spectroscopically, by techniques that are widely applicable (section 2.63). The determination of ΔS^0, however, presents the difficulty that we cannot conveniently measure it directly, as q_{rev}/T, because when reactions are carried out under conditions convenient for calorimetry they are markedly irreversible (section 4.44). Reversible conditions can be approximated in many gas reactions and cell reactions, but calorimetry is then impossible because the reactions are too slow. We can only find the value of ΔS^0 at a given temperature by taking the difference between the standard entropies of products and reactants at that temperature; these entropies may be determined by widely applicable calorimetric or statistical-spectroscopic methods (sections 5.21, 5.22), but the values are always relative to the entropy of the solid at $0°$ K, so that their difference gives not ΔS^0 absolutely but $(\Delta S^0 - \Delta S_{S(0)})$. For reactions involving solids only, for instance, each species has an entropy at temperature T given by

$$S_{S(T)} = S_{S(0)} + \int_0^T C_S \, d \ln T,$$

so that taking the difference between the sums of the entropies of the products and the reactants, and representing this operation by Δ, the entropy change in the reaction is given by

$$\Delta S_{S(T)} = \Delta S_{S(0)} + \int_0^T \Delta C_S \, d \ln T. \tag{1}$$

And in gas reactions each species has a standard entropy given by (pp. 200, 209)

$$S^0_{G(T)} = S_{S(0)} + [\text{thermal or statistical terms for } S],$$

so that the standard entropy change accompanying the reaction is

$$\Delta S^0_{G(T)} = \Delta S^0_{S(0)} + [\text{difference of thermal or statistical}$$
$$\text{terms for } S] \quad (2)$$

and consequently the resulting equations for ΔG^0 and K_p contain $\Delta S_{S(0)}$ (section 5.48). The same applies to values of ΔG^0 calculated from the values of $G^0_{G(T)}$ for the individual gaseous products and reactants (section 5.41), since these values of G^0 are obtained by combining values of $(H^0_{G(T)} - H^0_{G(0)})$ and $(S^0_{G(T)} - S_{S(0)})$ and therefore involve $\Delta S_{S(0)}$. The value of $\Delta S_{S(0)}$—the entropy difference between products and reactants at the absolute zero of temperature—is thus of great interest.

The 'third law of thermodynamics' states that, with certain important reservations which will be considered below, this quantity $\Delta S_{S(0)}$ is *zero*. For reactions for which this is true, the way is open to the determination of ΔS^0 by purely calorimetric methods, or (for gas reactions) by purely statistical-spectroscopic methods; ΔG^0 may then be found without the necessity for measuring K_p or an e.m.f. For reactions involving solids only, if $\Delta S_{S(0)}$ is zero, equation 1 becomes

$$\Delta S^0_{S(T)} = \int\limits_0^T \Delta C_S \, d \ln T. \tag{3}$$

The standard free energy change is therefore

$$\Delta G^0_{S(T)} = \Delta H^0_{S(T)} - T \int\limits_0^T \Delta C_S \, d \ln T, \tag{4}$$

in which all the terms can be measured calorimetrically. Similarly, for reactions between gases equation 2 becomes

$$\Delta S^0_{G(T)} = [\text{difference of thermal or statistical terms for } S], \tag{5}$$

so that the standard free energy change is

$$\Delta G^0_{G(T)} = -RT \ln K_p = \Delta H^0_{G(T)} - T[\text{difference of} \\ \text{thermal or statistical terms for } S]. \tag{6}$$

In these equations all the terms can be found by calorimetry or by statistical-spectroscopic methods. Thus the determination of ΔG^0 is greatly simplified by the assumption that $\Delta S_{S(0)}$ is zero. We must now consider the evidence for this assumption.

8.2. Determinations of $\Delta S_{S(0)}$

The general methods of finding $\Delta S_{S(0)}$, and so testing whether the entropy changes of reactions tend to zero at absolute zero, depend on whether the reaction involves solids only, solutions, gases only, or gases and condensed phases.

8.21. *Reactions involving solids only*

The standard entropy change in the reaction at some convenient temperature is determined experimentally as

$$\Delta S^0 = (\Delta G^0 - \Delta H^0)/T.$$

ΔH^0 is measured calorimetrically; ΔG^0 is found by means of e.m.f.s (section 6.22) or for polymorphic changes by another method described below. The resulting value of ΔS^0 is compared with $\int\limits_0^T \Delta C_S \, d \ln T$, which will be equal to ΔS^0 if $\Delta S_{S(0)} = 0$, and is often called the 'third-law entropy'; this may be determined by measuring the heat capacities of the reactants and products down to low temperatures, and integrating by finding the area under a plot of ΔC_S against $\ln T$ (p. 198). If the two values agree, $\Delta S^0 = \int_0^T \Delta C_S \, d \ln T$, and therefore by equation 1 we conclude that $\Delta S_{S(0)} = 0$.

Some reactions which have been investigated by means of e.m.f.s are the following:†

$$\text{(i)} \quad Hg + AgCl \rightleftharpoons \tfrac{1}{2}Hg_2Cl_2 + Ag.$$

$$\text{(ii)} \quad \tfrac{1}{2}Pb + AgCl \rightleftharpoons \tfrac{1}{2}PbCl_2 + Ag.$$

$$\text{(iii)} \quad \tfrac{1}{2}Pb + AgI \rightleftharpoons \tfrac{1}{2}PbI_2 + Ag.$$

Cells such as the following combination of the calomel electrode and the silver–silver chloride electrode were set up:

$$Hg; \, Hg_2Cl_2, \text{ chloride solution, } AgCl; \, Ag.$$

Addition of the electrode reactions for such a cell gives the above reactions. ΔG^0 was obtained from the e.m.f., and ΔH^0 from its temperature-coefficient (section 6.22). Hence ΔS^0 at 298° K was found. This was compared with $\int_0^{298} \Delta C_S \, d \ln T$, obtained from measurements of the heat capacities of the solids from 298° K down to low temperatures. The following table shows that the agreement is close, and that entropy changes calculated on the assumption that $\Delta S_{S(0)} = 0$ will be correct to within 0·3 cal $deg^{-1} mole^{-1}$.

TABLE 33

Test of $\Delta S_{S(0)} = 0$ for some cell reactions

Reaction	ΔS^0 at 298° K cal deg^{-1} mole^{-1}	$\int_0^{298} \Delta C_S \, d \ln T$ cal deg^{-1} mole^{-1}	Difference cal deg^{-1} mole^{-1}
(i)	7·78	7·70	0·08
(ii)	4·29	4·29	0
(iii)	3·99	3·69	0·3

† Gerke, *J. Amer. Chem. Soc.*, 1922, **44**, 1684.

There is one example of a polymorphic change that has been investigated by means of e.m.f.s, namely the transition of white to grey tin.† ΔG^0 for the reaction $Sn_{white} \to Sn_{grey}$ was found by measuring the e.m.f. of the following cell:

Sn (white); tin salt solution; Sn (grey).

ΔH was determined calorimetrically, by measuring the heats of dissolution of the two forms in acid and taking the difference. By combining the values of ΔG^0 and ΔH, ΔS^0 at 298° K was found to be $-1\cdot87$ cal deg^{-1}mole^{-1}. The heat capacities were measured down to low temperatures and gave

$$\int_0^{298} \Delta C_S \, d\ln T = -1\cdot94$$

in the same units. The agreement shows that $\Delta S_{S(0)} = 0$ within less than $0\cdot1$ cal deg^{-1}mole^{-1}.

Other polymorphic changes have been investigated by making use of the fact that they exhibit a transition temperature at which the two forms are in equilibrium so that $\Delta G^0 = 0$. At this temperature ΔH can be determined either directly, or by measuring it at some other temperature and making use of Kirchhoff's relations. The method has been applied, for example, to the transition between rhombic or α-sulphur and monoclinic or β-sulphur.‡ At the transition temperature (95·4° C) ΔH for $S_\beta \to S_\alpha$ is -95 ± 10 cal mole^{-1}, a relatively very small value which rests on a determination of ΔH at 0° by means of the ice-calorimeter (p. 48). Hence at 95·4° C

$$\Delta S = -\Delta H/T = 0\cdot26\pm0\cdot03 \text{ cal deg}^{-1}\text{mole}^{-1}.$$

By comparison, the value of $\int_0^{368\cdot6} \Delta C_S \, d\ln T$, determined from accurate heat-capacity measurements down to 15° K (fig. 50), is $0\cdot215\pm0\cdot05$. The difference, representing $\Delta S_{S(0)}$, is zero within experimental error.

A still more accurate agreement was obtained for the inter-

† Brønsted, Z. phys. Chem., 1914, 88, 479.
‡ Eastman and McGavock, J. Amer. Chem. Soc., 1937, 59, 145.

conversion of β-phosphine and γ-phosphine.† Three forms of phosphine are known; β-phosphine is stable below $49\cdot43°$ K but passes into α-phosphine at that temperature, while γ-phosphine does so at $30\cdot29°$ K. We can therefore determine the entropy of α-phosphine at $49\cdot43°$ K, starting with β-phosphine at low temperatures, and so obtaining $S_{\alpha(49\cdot43)} - S_{\beta(0)}$; and we can determine

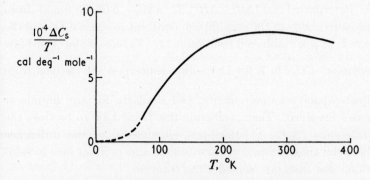

FIG. 50. Plot of $\Delta C_S/T$ against T for rhombic and monoclinic sulphur.

it at the same temperature starting with γ-phosphine at low temperatures, and so obtaining $S_{\alpha(49\cdot43)} - S_{\gamma(0)}$. The difference between the two values is $S_{\gamma(0)} - S_{\beta(0)}$, i.e. $\Delta S_{S(0)}$ for the conversion of the β to the γ form. This turns out to be zero within experimental error, as the following comparison shows.

Entropy of α-phosphine at $49\cdot43°$ K

Starting with β-phosphine	Cal deg⁻¹ mole⁻¹	Starting with γ-phosphine	Cal deg⁻¹ mole⁻¹
0–15° K (extrapolation) .	0·338	0–15° K (extrapolation) .	0·495
15–49·43° K (graphical) .	4·041	15–30·29° K (graphical) .	2·185
Transition $\beta \to \alpha$ at 49·43° K		Transition $\gamma \to \alpha$ at 30·29° K	
(185·7 cal mole⁻¹) . .	3·757	(19·6 cal mole⁻¹) .	0·647
		30·29–49·43° (graphical) .	4·800
Total	8·14	Total	8·13

† Stephenson and Giauque, *J. Chem. Phys.*, 1937, **5**, 149.

The interconversion of α- and β-cyclohexanol has been somewhat similarly investigated;† $\Delta S_{S(0)}$ is again found to be zero
within experimental error.

8.22. *Reactions in solution*

For reactions involving ions the following approach has been
used. The standard entropy change ΔS^0 of a reaction in solution
is determined as $(\Delta G^0 - \Delta H^0)/T$, where ΔG^0 is found from
measurements of the equilibrium constant (section 6.1) or of the
e.m.f. of a suitable cell (section 6.22). Values of the 'third-law
entropy' $\int_0^T C_S \, d\ln T$ for any solids concerned are derived from
heat-capacity measurements, and similarly for any liquids or
gases involved. Then, assuming the Third Law to be true, the
difference $[\Delta S^0 - \Delta$ ('third-law entropies')] is the difference
between the entropies of the reactant and product ions in solution. For instance, consider the reaction

$$Ag_2O(s) + 2H^+ \rightleftharpoons 2Ag^+ + H_2O(l).$$

The 'third-law entropies' of silver oxide and water at 25° C are
respectively 29·05 and 16·77 cal deg^{-1} mole^{-1}, so that their difference is 12·28 units. The standard entropy change ΔS^0 is 22·58
cal deg^{-1} mole^{-1}, which must be made up of a change of $-12·28$
units due to the disappearance of one mole of Ag_2O and the
appearance of one mole of H_2O, and a change of

$$(22·58 + 12·28) = 34·86 \text{ units}$$

due to the disappearance of two moles of H^+ and the appearance
of two moles of Ag^+. Thus the standard entropy difference
between one mole of silver ions and one mole of hydrogen ions
in solution at 25° is

$$(S^0_{Ag^+} - S^0_{H^+}) = \tfrac{1}{2}(34·86) = 17·43 \text{ cal deg}^{-1} \text{mole}^{-1}.$$

The standard entropies of many cations can be expressed in this
way, relative to that of the hydrogen ion. For anions, the
standard entropy so obtained is the *sum* of the standard entropy

† Kelley, *J. Amer. Chem. Soc.*, 1929, **51**, 1400.

of the anion and that of the hydrogen ion. These values are commonly called 'ionic entropies', but it must be remembered that they are not absolute entropies.

This calculation of ionic entropies depends on the assumption that $\Delta S_{S(0)}$ is zero, since this is involved in combining the 'third-law entropies' to give an entropy difference. We shall therefore obtain consistent results only if this assumption is true. The consistency may be tested by comparing values of the ionic entropies obtained from different reactions. For instance, another value of the ionic entropy of silver can be obtained as follows. Applying a treatment similar to the above to the reaction

$$HCl(g) = H^+ + Cl^-,$$

we find the standard entropy of Cl^- relative to H^+ to be

$$(S^0_{Cl^-} + S^0_{H^+}) = 13 \cdot 52 \ cal \ deg^{-1} mole^{-1}.$$

Now the reaction $AgCl(s) = Ag^+ + Cl^-$

has $\Delta S^0 = 8 \cdot 15$ units, while the 'third-law entropy' of AgCl is $23 \cdot 0$ units. Hence $(S_{Cl^-} + S_{Ag^+}) = 31 \cdot 15$ units. Combining this

TABLE 34

'Ionic entropies' at 25° C in cal deg^{-1} mole^{-1}

Cation	$S^0_{ion} - S^0_{H^+}$	Anion	$S^0_{ion} + S^0_{H^+}$
Ag^+	$\begin{cases} 17 \cdot 43 \pm 0 \cdot 2 \\ 17 \cdot 63 \pm 0 \cdot 2 \end{cases}$	Cl^-	$\begin{cases} 13 \cdot 52 \pm 0 \cdot 15 \\ 13 \cdot 49 \pm 0 \cdot 15 \end{cases}$
K^+	$\begin{cases} 24 \cdot 2 \pm 0 \cdot 2 \\ 24 \cdot 3 \pm 0 \cdot 8 \end{cases}$	Br^-	$\begin{cases} 19 \cdot 8 \pm 0 \cdot 2 \\ 19 \cdot 6 \pm 0 \cdot 3 \\ 19 \cdot 5 \pm 0 \cdot 4 \end{cases}$
Rb^+	$\begin{cases} 28 \cdot 9 \pm 0 \cdot 8 \\ 28 \cdot 5 \pm 1 \cdot 0 \end{cases}$	I^-	$\begin{cases} 25 \cdot 4 \pm 0 \cdot 5 \\ 25 \cdot 2 \pm 0 \cdot 7 \end{cases}$
Tl^+	$\begin{cases} 31 \cdot 0 \pm 0 \cdot 5 \\ 30 \cdot 1 \pm 0 \cdot 5 \end{cases}$	SO_4^{--}	$\begin{cases} 4 \cdot 4 \pm 1 \cdot 0 \\ 4 \cdot 5 \pm 2 \\ 2 \cdot 5 \pm 2 \\ 5 \cdot 2 \pm 2 \\ 3 \cdot 2 \pm 2 \end{cases}$
Na^+	$\begin{cases} 14 \cdot 1 \pm 0 \cdot 5 \\ 14 \cdot 3 \pm 0 \cdot 5 \\ 13 \cdot 7 \pm 0 \cdot 5 \end{cases}$		
Cu^{2+}	$\begin{cases} -25 \cdot 9 \pm 3 \\ -26 \cdot 6 \pm 1 \end{cases}$	NO_3^-	$\begin{cases} 35 \cdot 0 \pm 0 \cdot 3 \\ 35 \cdot 0 \pm 0 \cdot 3 \end{cases}$
		BrO_3^-	$\begin{cases} 38 \cdot 7 \pm 1 \\ 38 \cdot 1 \pm 2 \end{cases}$
		IO_3^-	$\begin{cases} 27 \cdot 9 \pm 1 \\ 28 \cdot 3 \pm 3 \end{cases}$
		F^-	$\begin{cases} -2 \cdot 4 \pm 2 \\ -0 \cdot 4 \pm 2 \\ -4 \cdot 2 \pm 2 \end{cases}$

with the value of $(S_{Cl^-} + S_{H^+})$, we find $(S_{Ag^+} - S_{H^+}) = 17{\cdot}63$ cal deg^{-1} mole^{-1}. This agrees within experimental error with the value obtained from the previous reaction. Table 34 shows that where values from two or more reactions can be compared they always agree within experimental error.†

8.23. *Reactions in the gas phase*

Various methods could be devised to use measurements on gas reactions to test whether $\Delta S_{S(0)}$ is zero. The simplest test in principle would be to calculate ΔS_G^0 at some convenient temperature from the equilibrium constant K and the heat of reaction $(\Delta S_G^0 = (\Delta H^0 - \Delta G^0)/T = \Delta H^0/T + R \ln K)$, and compare this with the value of $(\Delta S_G^0 - \Delta S_{S(0)})$ obtained as the difference of the values of the standard entropies $(S_G^0 - S_{S(0)})$ for the separate reactants and products, determined calorimetrically or spectroscopically (section 5.2). The method that has been most used in practice, which uses equivalent data, makes use of the entropy constants of gases S_G^* defined in section 5.22. From measurements of the equilibrium constant of a gas reaction over a range of temperatures, we can find ΔS_G^* for the reaction, with the help of equation 38 of section 5.48 (p. 250). We can also find $(\Delta S - \Delta S_{S(0)})$ from the values of $(S_G^* - S_{S(0)})$ for the individual gases, obtained either from vapour pressures and calorimetric data (section 7.24) or by statistical-spectroscopic calculation (sections 7.25, 5.22). If the two quantities agree, it follows that $\Delta S_{S(0)}$ is zero.‡ The vapour-pressure method was historically the earlier, but is less accurate than the statistical.

The results using the statistical method are summarized in Table 35.§ It is evident from the table that, within experimental

† Data from Latimer, Pitzer, and Smith, *J. Amer. Chem. Soc.*, 1938, **60**, 1829.

‡ The comparison of ΔS_G^* and $\Delta S_G^* - \Delta S_{S(0)}$ is equivalent to a comparison of J, the integration constant of the isochore (equation 35 of section 5.48, p. 248), with $\Delta[i + (C_G - C_i)/R]$, where i is the vapour-pressure constant (p. 278); for $RJ = \Delta S_G^*$ (equation 39 of section 5.48) and $Ri + (C_G - C_i) = S_G^* - S_{S(0)}$ (equation 20 of section 7.24). In many books the comparison is expressed in this way.

§ Values from Fowler and Guggenheim, *Statistical Thermodynamics* (Cambridge, 1939), p. 216, where references are given.

error, ΔS_G^* from K_p is always equal to $\Delta S_G^* - \Delta S_{S(0)}$ from statistical-spectroscopic calculation, so that for all these reactions $\Delta S_{S(0)} = 0$.

TABLE 35
Entropies in some gas reactions

Reaction	$\Delta S_G^*/R$ from K	$(\Delta S_G^* - \Delta S_{S(0)})/R$ from statistical calculation
$2HD \rightleftharpoons H_2 + D_2$	-0.63 ± 0.05	-0.62
$2HCl \rightleftharpoons H_2 + Cl_2$	-1.12 ± 0.2	-1.16
$2HBr \rightleftharpoons H_2 + Br_2$	-1.25 ± 0.45	-1.40
$2HI \rightleftharpoons H_2 + I_2$	-1.50 ± 0.12	-1.62
$N_2 + O_2 \rightleftharpoons 2NO$	0.95 ± 0.3	1.30
$Cl_2 \rightleftharpoons 2Cl$	1.40 ± 0.15	1.53
$Br_2 \rightleftharpoons 2Br$	1.41 ± 0.05	1.39
$I_2 \rightleftharpoons 2I$	1.35	1.35

The results using the vapour-pressure method are given in Table 36.[†] For the first reaction the figures show that $\Delta S_{S(0)}$ is zero within the rather large experimental uncertainty. For the reactions involving hydrogen and carbon monoxide there seem to be real discrepancies, leading to finite negative values of $\Delta S_{S(0)}$ of the order of 1 cal deg^{-1} mole^{-1}. These values would not lead to a large error if we calculated K_p on the assumption that $\Delta S_{S(0)}$ is zero ($\delta \log_{10} K_p = -\delta(\Delta S)/2.303R \simeq 0.2$ at $300°$ K), but they are of theoretical importance. Hydrogen and carbon monoxide are known to be unusual in forming imperfect crystals at low temperatures (p. 211), so that $S_{S(0)}$ is higher than it would be for perfect crystals. If this is the case for reactants but not for products, $\Delta S_{S(0)}$ will be lower than it would be for perfect crystals.

TABLE 36
Entropies in some gas reactions

Reaction	$\Delta S_G^*/R$ from K	$(\Delta S_G^* - \Delta S_{S(0)})/R$ from V.P. constants
$N_2 + O_2 \rightleftharpoons 2NO$	0.93 ± 0.28	0.61 ± 0.15
$2CO + O_2 \rightleftharpoons 2CO_2$	-0.8 ± 0.25	-1.38 ± 0.20
$H_2 \mid I_2 \rightleftharpoons 2HI$	-1.51 ± 0.12	-2.36 ± 0.22
$3H_2 + N_2 \rightleftharpoons 2NH_3$	-7.04 ± 0.10	-8.34 ± 0.09

[†] Results are given by Eucken and Fried, *Z. Phys.*, 1924, **29**, 36; cf. Ubbelohde, *Modern Thermodynamics* (Oxford, 2nd edn. 1952), p. 39.

Thus, supposing that the true generalization is that $\Delta S_{S(0)}$ is zero for perfect crystals, we can see a reason why negative values might be found. We return later (section 8.3) to this limitation to the generalization that $\Delta S_{S(0)} = 0$.

8.24. *Reactions involving both gaseous and condensed phases*

For these reactions, a similar method of testing whether $\Delta S_{S(0)} = 0$ can be used; $\Delta S_G^* - \Delta S_{S(0)}$ can be calculated from the vapour-pressure data, and compared with ΔS_G^* from equilibrium constants (p. 283). Alternatively, ΔS^0 can be determined by measuring ΔH^0 calorimetrically and finding ΔG^0 from the equilibrium constant or the e.m.f. of a suitable cell; this value of ΔS^0 can then be compared with $\Delta S^0 - \Delta S_{S(0)}$ obtained from the standard entropies $S^0 - S_{S(0)}$ of the reactants and products measured by the usual methods (section 5.2).

Some results obtained by the vapour-pressure method are given in Table 37,[†] and by the second method in Table 38.[‡] It is evident that for many of the reactions $\Delta S_{S(0)}$ is zero within the limits of error. For the dehydration of magnesium hydroxide, and the formation of CO from graphite and oxygen, there are discrepancies of the order of $1 \text{ cal deg}^{-1} \text{mole}^{-1}$, in the direction to be expected if the products form imperfect crystals, as water and carbon monoxide are known to do.

TABLE 37

Entropies in some heterogeneous reactions

Reaction	$\Delta S_G^*/R$ from K	$(\Delta S_G^* - \Delta S_{S(0)})/R$ from V.P. constants
$CaO + CO_2 \rightleftharpoons CaCO_3$	$0\cdot9 \pm 0\cdot15$	$0\cdot91 \pm 0\cdot15$
$H_2 + HgO \rightleftharpoons H_2O + Hg$	$-3\cdot63 \pm 0\cdot16$	$-3\cdot69 \pm 0\cdot03$
$2Hg(g) + O_2 \rightleftharpoons 2HgO$	$4\cdot32 \pm 0\cdot18$	$4\cdot44 \pm 0\cdot09$
$2CO \rightleftharpoons C(graphite) + CO_2$	$-0\cdot86 \pm 0\cdot18$	$-1\cdot01 \pm 0\cdot18$

† See note † on p. 301.

‡ Collected in H. S. Taylor and S. Glasstone, *Treatise on Physical Chemistry*, vol. i, *Atomistics and Thermodynamics* (Copyright, 1942, van Nostrand Company, Inc.), p. 518, where references are given.

TABLE 38

Entropies in some heterogeneous reactions $(cal\, deg^{-1} mole^{-1})$

Reaction	Temp. °K	ΔS^0	$\Delta S^0 - \Delta S_{S(0)}$
$Ag(s) + \frac{1}{2}Br_2(l) \rightleftharpoons AgBr(s)$.	265·9	$-3·01 \pm 0·40$	$-3·13 \pm 0·18$
			$-3·02 \pm 0·10$
$Ag(s) + \frac{1}{2}Cl_2(l) \rightleftharpoons AgCl(s)$ . .	298·2	$-13·73 \pm 0·10$	$-13·85 \pm 0·75$
$Mg(OH)_2(s) \rightleftharpoons MgO(s) + H_2O(g)$	298·2	$35·85 \pm 0·08$	$36·67 \pm 0·10$
$C(graphite) + \frac{1}{2}O_2(g) \rightleftharpoons CO(g)$.	298·2	$20·1$	$21·3$
$Zn(s) + \frac{1}{2}O_2(g) \rightleftharpoons ZnO(s)$ . .	298·2	$-24·07 \pm 0·25$	$-24·24 \pm 0·05$

8.3. The Third Law and the restrictions upon its application

We must now consider what generalization we can make about $\Delta S_{S(0)}$. We have seen that there is a considerable body of evidence that for many reactions $\Delta S_{S(0)}$ is zero. Essentially, the postulate of Nernst's 'heat theorem' (1906) was that $\Delta S_{S(0)} = 0$ for *all* reactions; but there are interesting exceptions to this rule.

(i) We have noticed that reactions in which one of the participants is believed to form imperfect crystals at low temperatures may have $\Delta S_{S(0)} \simeq 1\, cal\, deg^{-1} mole^{-1}$. This is not a large quantity in calculating an equilibrium constant, but it is large enough to be interesting from a theoretical point of view. Experiments on amorphous and glassy substances have shown that they have a larger entropy than that of the crystalline forms, so that if $\Delta S_{S(0)}$ is zero for reactions involving the crystalline forms it cannot also be zero for reactions involving the amorphous forms. For instance, the entropy difference at 0° K between crystalline glycerine and an amorphous specimen prepared by rapid chilling has been determined, by the following method.† The heat capacities of the two forms are measured, from low temperatures to the melting-point, by the Nernst method (section 2.72), and the heat of fusion of the crystalline form is also measured (the amorphous form gradually softens and is liquid at the melting-

† Gibson and Giauque, *J. Amer. Chem. Soc.*, 1923, **45**, 93. Their work has, however, been criticized on the ground that in the Nernst method the heat transfer is incomplete in the time available (Oblad and Newton, ibid., 1937, **59**, 2495). See also note † on p. 304.

point of the crystals). This gives two values for the entropy of the liquid at some fixed temperature; these values may be equated, since the entropy must be independent of the history of the substance. At the melting-point T_f, for instance,

$$\text{(i)}\quad S_{L(T)} = S^0_{cryst(0)} + \int_0^{T_f} C_{cryst}\, d\ln T + \frac{L_{cryst}}{T_f}.$$

$$\text{(ii)}\quad S_{L(T)} = S^0_{amorph(0)} + \int_0^{T_f} C_{amorph}\, d\ln T.$$

Hence the entropy difference at $0°$ K $(S^0_{cryst(0)} - S^0_{amorph(0)})$ may be determined by subtraction, all the other terms being known. It is found to be $4\cdot6$ cal deg^{-1} mole^{-1}. If reactions involving crystalline glycerine have $\Delta S_{S(0)} = 0$, this cannot be true for reactions involving amorphous glycerine. Amorphous and crystalline silica have also been investigated, with a similar result.[†] Amorphous solids must therefore be excluded from the scope of the third law.[‡]

(ii) We have seen, moreover, that even crystalline substances must be excluded if the crystals are imperfect (pp. 301, 302). A good indication of whether a substance forms perfect crystals at low temperatures is available for gases in the comparison of calorimetric and statistical-spectroscopic values for their entropy (pp. 210–12).

(iii) Care is also necessary in dealing with reactions in solution. When solutions are formed from their constituents, there is an entropy of mixing, just as for gases (sections 9.4, 5.33); and if the number of molecules changes during the reaction, there will be an entropy difference between reactants and products, even at $0°$ K, due to the different entropies of mixing. For an ionized solute, the entropy of solution may be considerable, and depends on the solute (section 8.22), so that there will again be an entropy difference between reactants and products in solution.

The third law may be stated in a form which excludes solutions,

† Simon and Lange, *Z. Phys.*, 1926, **38**, 227.

‡ Cf. Lewis *et al.*, *J. Amer. Chem. Soc.*, 1920, **42**, 1529, 1533, 1542.

amorphous substances, and imperfect crystals: 'The entropy change of a reaction between solids that form perfect crystals is zero at the absolute zero of temperature', or 'The entropy difference between reactants and products is zero at 0° K, if at this temperature they exist in the form of perfect crystals'. These statements of the third law and the restrictions upon its application are generalizations from the experimental evidence.

A common convention based on the law must be noted.† If the third law is true, the entropy of a crystalline compound at 0° K must be the sum of those of its crystalline elements. In giving numerical values of entropies, therefore (as in Table 21, p. 210), we can suppose, *as a self-consistent convention*, that the entropies of all crystalline elements are zero at 0° K, i.e. $S_{S(0)} = 0$. This is a pure convention. The entropy of an element cannot in general actually be zero at 0° K, because the presence of isotopes or of forms differing in nuclear spin will lead to an entropy of mixing. But if the element takes part in a reaction, this entropy of mixing will be the same for reactants and products, so that the entropy *difference* $\Delta S_{S(0)}$, with which the third law is concerned, is not affected. The convention can therefore be used wherever the entropies of the elements are to be combined to give the entropy of a reaction; the omission of the $S_{S(0)}$ terms makes the work less cumbersome. But it must be remembered that the convention can be applied only where the third law can be expected to hold.

Since there is evidence that most gases pass into perfect crystals at low temperatures (pp. 211–12), the convention may be applied to gases and gas reactions, with certain exceptions mentioned above. We have already noted (p. 214) the use of the convention in listing values of $(G^0 - H_0^0 + T S_{S(0)})$ as $(G^0 - H_0^0)$. Entropies of gases such as those given in Table 21 (p. 210) are commonly referred to as values of S^0, not of $S^0 - S_{S(0)}$. We have used the longer expressions because (i) absolute entropies cannot be measured, only entropy changes, (ii) the relation of calorimetric to statistical entropies may be confused if $S_{S(0)}$ is omitted; and

† Lewis and Gibson, *J. Amer. Chem. Soc.*, 1922, **44**, 1008; 1917, **39**, 2556; 1920, **42**, 1533.

(iii) the exact role of the third law is brought out, and the limits of the convention based on it are apparent.

8.4. Summary of methods for determining the standard free energies of chemical reactions

We summarize here the methods of determining the standard free energy changes in chemical reactions, noting the difference made by the third law (cf. pp. 292–4).

Reactions involving solids only

(a) For suitable reactions, e.m.f. measurements may be used (section 6.2).

(b) For polymorphic changes, $\Delta G = 0$ at the transition temperature (p. 296).

(c) Using the third law, for pure crystalline solids,

$$\Delta G^0 = \Delta H^0 - T \int_0^T \Delta C_S \, d \ln T.$$

Thus ΔG^0 can be determined by calorimetric measurements of ΔH^0 and the heat capacities C_S.

Reactions in solution

(a) For suitable reactions, e.m.f. measurements may be used (section 6.2).

(b) Where equilibrium constants can be measured, ΔG^0 may be obtained as $-RT \ln K$ (section 6.1).

(c) Using the third law, values may be assigned to ionic entropies and ΔG^0 found as $\Delta H^0 - T \Delta S^0$. Electrode potentials and equilibrium constants inaccessible to direct experiment may thus be calculated.†

Reactions in the gas phase

(a) Where equilibrium constants can be measured, ΔG^0 may be found as $-RT \ln K_p$.

(b) Combination of e.m.f. data and equilibrium constants is sometimes possible, as for the synthesis of water (p. 284).

† For instance, the electrode potential of magnesium, which is too large to be measured in aqueous solution, has been calculated by this method as −2·4 volts (Buffington and Latimer, *J. Amer. Chem. Soc.*, 1926, **48**, 2303; cf. Coates, *J. Chem. Soc.*, 1945, 478).

(c) Using the third law, several methods are available.

(i) As we have noted (p. 294),

$$\Delta G^0 = \Delta H^0 - T \, [\text{difference of thermal} \\ \text{or statistical terms for } S].$$

Thus ΔG^0 can be found by determining ΔH^0 calorimetric-ally or spectroscopically (section 2.63), and combining it with the thermal or statistical-spectroscopic values of the entropies of the gases (section 5.2).

(ii) Since the thermal or statistical-spectroscopic data have been used to compile tables of $G^0 - H^0_{(0)}$ (section 5.2), one can use these tables to find $\Delta G^0 - \Delta H^0_{(0)}$; and $\Delta H^0_{(0)}$ may be determined spectroscopically or calorimetrically. This method is widely applicable to estimate the equili-brium constants of reactions and so their thermodynamic feasibility. The equilibrium constants given in Table 26 (p. 244) were obtained in this way.

Reactions involving both gaseous and condensed phases

Methods (a) and (b) for gas reactions may be applied, *mutatis mutandis*.

(c) Using the third law,

$$\Delta G^0 = \Delta H^0 - T \int_0^T \Delta C_S \, d \ln T - T \, [\text{difference of thermal or} \\ \text{statistical terms for entropies of gases involved.}]$$

Hence ΔG^0 may be obtained calorimetrically; or statistical-spectroscopic calculation may replace the calorimetric determination of heat capacities.

The effects of the third law in thermodynamics. Since the emer-gence of the third law in the 1920's, its widespread application has had a considerable influence on research in chemical thermo-dynamics. We have noted at various points in the argument of this book that further progress required values of $\Delta S_{S(0)}$; the use of the third law has supplied them. It has provided a general method of determining free energies in reaction, using uniformly the well-known techniques of calorimetry. It has also made possible the use of the statistical-spectroscopic method of computing partition-functions and from them entropies and free energies. The effects of the use of the third law may be summarized as:

(i) A renaissance of thermochemistry; numerous determinations of heat capacities down to low temperatures have been made, by Giauque and his school and others, and many heats of reaction measured with high accuracy.

(ii) A mass of statistical calculations of partition-functions, from spectroscopic data; hence accurate values of the heat capacities, equilibrium constants, entropies and free energies of gases.†

(iii) A diminution in the relative importance of the classical type of investigation of equilibrium constants and electromotive force, upon which our knowledge of the free energies of reaction was built up until the 1920's.

8.5. Statistical interpretation of the third law

Using the relation $S = k \ln W$ (p. 145), the third law as stated in section 8.3 implies that W is the same at $0°$K for the products and reactants that take part in a chemical reaction, provided they all form perfect crystals at this temperature. It is not difficult to see from a statistical point of view why this should be so. Consider an assembly of molecules of one of the reactants. At $0°$K each of the molecules will be in its ground state, so that all the molecules occupy the same energy-level, and as far as the energy-distribution is concerned there is only one way in which the system can be made up. If, further, the molecules form a perfect crystal, and are indistinguishable one from another, then there is only one spatial arrangement possible; thus as far as position is concerned there is also only one way in which the system can be made up. Hence for such a solid, $W = 1$; and since $S = k \ln W$, $S_{S(0)} = 0$. For the difference

† For tables of such properties, see *Selected Values of Chemical Thermodynamic Properties*, series i and ii (National Bureau of Standards, Circular 500, 1952); Quill (ed.), *The Chemistry and Metallurgy of Miscellaneous Materials: Thermodynamics* (McGraw-Hill, 1950); Kelley, *Bull. U.S. Bur. Min.* 476 (1949); Din, *Thermodynamic Functions of Gases* (Butterworth, 1956).

between the reactants and products, then, $\Delta S_{S(0)} = 0$. Actually W is not normally equal to 1, because the molecules are not indistinguishable, since there are isotopic differences of mass and possibly also differences of nuclear spin; these will make $W > 1$ and give rise to an entropy of mixing. But this will be the same in the reactants and products, since the same atoms are involved; W will have some finite value, equal in reactants and products, and so again $\Delta S_{S(0)} = 0$, as the third law requires. This will not be true if some amorphous solid is involved, or if any of the crystals are imperfect, for this will increase W in either the reactant or product side. Thus we can interpret the third law and the restrictions that have been found necessary in stating it. The fact that we can understand the third law in molecular terms gives us greater confidence in using it.

Some authors prefer to regard the third law not as an empirical generalization which can be understood with the aid of statistical theory, but as deducible from statistical theory. But as the use of the theory depends on the assumption that each chemical species passes into a perfect crystal at low temperatures, an assumption that can only be checked by experiment, this point of view has not been adopted here. It is, however, justifiable for the particular case of gas reactions, where there is independent evidence that perfect crystals are formed at low temperatures, from the agreement of the statistical-spectroscopic values for entropies and entropy constants with values determined independently (section 5.22, p. 210; section 7.25, p. 279).

THE GENERAL THERMODYNAMICS OF SOLUTIONS

9.1. Introductory

A SOLUTION or mixture may be described as a homogeneous system of variable composition. In the rest of this book we shall deal with *liquid* mixtures. Solutions of gases in gases (more often called gas mixtures) have been treated in Chapter V. Solutions of solids in solids will occasionally be mentioned, but add little to the general thermodynamic theory. Solutions of solids in compressed gases are of interest because they throw light on intermolecular forces (p. 286), but they will not be considered here. We shall generally deal with *binary* solutions. It is convenient to call the constituent in excess the solvent and the other the solute. Their amounts in moles are denoted by n_1 and n_2 respectively, and their mole fractions by x_1 and x_2 (where $x_1 + x_2 = 1$). We shall usually express concentrations in terms of mole fractions, since the general relations then take the simplest forms. For electrolyte solutions, however, experimental results have often been stated in terms of the molal concentration m, i.e. moles of solute per 1,000 grammes of solvent; this is related to the mole fraction by the equation $m = 1,000 n_2 / n_1 M_1$. In dilute solution, this may be approximated to $m = 1,000 x_2 / M_1$, or $k x_2$ where k is a constant for a given solvent.

The Phase Rule tells us that, for such a two-component system, $P + F = 4$. Thus for the one-phase system consisting of the solution alone, the number of degrees of freedom F is 3, and we can vary independently the temperature, the pressure, and the composition. If we have a solution in equilibrium with its own vapour, there are two phases, so that $F = 2$. There are then three interesting special cases. (i) For solutions of fixed composition, $F = 1$, so that it is not possible to vary both P and T independently. At equilibrium there will therefore be a relation between P and T; this is the vapour-pressure curve of the solution (treated below in section 9.22). (ii) At constant temperature, there will be a relation at equilibrium between pressure and composition. This corresponds to the observed depression of the vapour pressure by solutes (section 9.31). (iii) At constant pressure, there will be a relation at equilibrium between temperature and composition. This corresponds to the observed elevation of the boiling-point by solutes (section 9.33).

For solutions in equilibrium with solid solvent, there are again two phases and $F = 2$. Thus at constant composition, there will be at equilibrium a relation between freezing-point and pressure, as for pure liquids (section 7.5). At constant pressure, there will be a relation between temperature and composition, corresponding to the observed depression of the freezing-point by solutes (section 9.34). If the solution is in equilibrium with solid solute, the conclusions from the phase rule are similar; at constant pressure, there will be at equilibrium a relation between temperature and composition, corresponding to the observed variation of the solubility with temperature (section 9.35).

If an atmosphere of some non-reacting gas is present, the number of components is increased by one, but so long as its pressure is kept constant the number of degrees of freedom is not increased and the above conclusions still hold good.

Most of our knowledge of the properties of substances in solution is derived from measurements of vapour pressures, freezing-points, and so on (section 9.3 below). All these measurements are concerned with processes occurring reversibly at constant temperature and pressure, so that the condition of equilibrium is always that the chemical potential of some species shall be the same in two phases. Chemical potentials, which are equal to the partial molar free energies, are therefore the quantities most closely concerned in the thermodynamics of solution. From them we can derive other quantities, in particular the changes in free energy, entropy, and heat content on mixing the constituents to form the solution. The study of solutions thus includes the following four parts:

(i) The general thermodynamic treatment in which vapour

pressures, freezing-points, etc., are related to chemical potentials, usually expressed in terms of activities.

(ii) The experimental determination of the depression of the vapour pressure, etc., leading to numerical values for activities in various solutions, and hence for the free energy, entropy, and heat of mixing.

(iii) The classification of solutions according to the results of (ii), as nearly ideal solutions, regular solutions, etc.

(iv) The statistical interpretation of the behaviour of solutions of these types, in terms of molecular interactions.

9.2. Chemical potentials, vapour pressures, and activities in solution

9.21. *The dependence of chemical potentials on temperature and pressure*

Since equality of chemical potentials in the two phases is the condition of equilibrium in such phenomena as the depression of the vapour pressure, the relations of the chemical potential to temperature and pressure are of fundamental importance. They may be obtained as follows, by using the rule that the order of differentiation of G with respect to two variables does not matter, together with the general relations $(\partial G/\partial T)_{P,\text{comp}} = -S$ and $(\partial G/\partial P)_{T,\text{comp}} = V$ (p. 156). Since $\mu_1 = (\partial G/\partial n_1)_{T,P,n_2}$, it follows that:

$$\left(\frac{\partial \mu_1}{\partial T}\right)_{P,x_2} = \left(\frac{\partial}{\partial T}\left(\frac{\partial G}{\partial n_1}\right)_{T,P,n_2}\right)_{P,x_2} = \left(\frac{\partial}{\partial n_1}\left(\frac{\partial G}{\partial T}\right)_{P,x_2}\right)_{T,P,n_2}$$

$$= -\left(\frac{\partial S}{\partial n_1}\right)_{T,P,n_2} = -S_1, \quad (1)$$

$$\left(\frac{\partial \mu_1}{\partial P}\right)_{T,x_2} = \left(\frac{\partial}{\partial P}\left(\frac{\partial G}{\partial n_1}\right)_{T,P,n_2}\right)_{T,x_2} = \left(\frac{\partial}{\partial n_1}\left(\frac{\partial G}{\partial P}\right)_{T,x_2}\right)_{T,P,n_2}$$

$$= \left(\frac{\partial V}{\partial n_1}\right)_{T,P,n_2} = V_1. \quad (2)$$

Thus the temperature-variation of μ_1 depends on the partial molar entropy of the solvent in the solution, S_1; and the pressure-variation depends on the partial molar volume, V_1.

We can now derive an important general relation for the variation of μ_1 when temperature, pressure, and composition are simultaneously varied. Taking T, P, and x_2 as the independent variables (x_1 may be omitted since it is fixed by x_2), we can write for the variation of μ_1:

$$d\mu_1 = \left(\frac{\partial \mu_1}{\partial T}\right)_{P,x_2} dT + \left(\frac{\partial \mu_1}{\partial P}\right)_{T,x_2} dP + \left(\frac{\partial \mu_1}{\partial x_2}\right)_{T,P} dx_2.$$

Inserting the expressions just found for the first two coefficients,

$$\boxed{d\mu_1 = -S_1\, dT + V_1\, dP + (\partial \mu_1/\partial x_2)_{T,P}\, dx_2.} \tag{3}$$

If the composition is fixed, so that $dx_2 = 0$, this becomes

$$d\mu_1 = -S_1\, dT + V_1\, dP. \tag{3a}$$

Equations 3 and 3a will be found to be extremely important in relating the properties of solutions to chemical potentials and activities. One application follows immediately.

9.22. *The vapour-pressure curve for a solution*

If we take a solution of given concentration, for instance a 0·1 molar solution of potassium chloride in water, and measure the vapour pressure at a series of temperatures, the resulting vapour-pressure curve has the same general shape as that for pure water, but lies below it (cf. fig. 51, p. 321). The thermodynamic treatment is similar to that for a pure liquid (section 7.21, p. 271). We shall suppose for simplicity that the solute is involatile. The condition of equilibrium is equality of the chemical potentials of the solvent in the solution and in the vapour, which we may write:

$$(d\mu_1)^{\text{soln}} = (d\mu_1)^{\text{vap}}.$$

Using the expression 3a for $d\mu_1$, this gives

$$dT(S_1^{\text{vap}} - S_1^{\text{soln}}) = dP(V_1^{\text{vap}} - V_1^{\text{soln}}). \tag{4}$$

This is similar to equation 1 of section 7.21. We can simplify the left-hand bracket as follows. If we differentiate the general expression $G = H - TS$ with respect to n_1, we obtain for any phase

$$\mu_1 = H_1 - TS_1.$$

Applying this to solution and vapour, and subtracting,

$$T(S_1^{\text{vap}} - S_1^{\text{soln}}) = (H_1^{\text{vap}} - H_1^{\text{soln}}) - (\mu_1^{\text{vap}} - \mu_1^{\text{soln}}).$$

At equilibrium, the last term is zero, and so

$$(S_1^{\text{vap}} - S_1^{\text{soln}}) = (H_1^{\text{vap}} - H_1^{\text{soln}})/T = L_e/T,$$

where L_e is the latent heat of evaporation of the solvent species from the *solution* into the vapour. Substitution in equation 4 gives

$$L_e \, dT/T = dP(V_1^{\text{vap}} - V_1^{\text{soln}}).$$

If we also make the approximation that V_1^{soln} may be neglected in comparison with V_1^{vap}, and that the vapour behaves as a perfect gas so that $V_1^{\text{vap}} = RT/p_1$, where p_1 is the vapour pressure of solvent over the solution, we obtain

$$\frac{d \ln p_1}{dT} = \frac{L_e}{RT^2}. \tag{5}$$

Integration gives an expression analogous to that for the pure liquid (equation 22 of section 7.24, p. 279),

$$R \ln p_1 = \Delta S_{e(T)}^0 - L_e/T, \tag{6}$$

where $\Delta S_{e(T)}^0$ is the standard entropy of evaporation of the solvent species *from the solution* at temperature T. It is this which fixes the general position of the vapour-pressure curve. L_e does not vary greatly with composition, and for the class called ideal solutions (see below) it does not vary at all, so that the curve will then have the same general shape as that for the pure liquid, as is observed. The fact that the curve lies below that for the pure liquid then means that the entropy of evaporation from the solution is less than that from the pure liquid. This can be understood as follows. When a second substance is added to a given amount of solvent, each molecule of solvent has a larger volume open to it, and so more sites that it can occupy, so that W increases and there is an increase in the configurational contribution to the entropy. We shall show later that for an ideal solution this accounts quantitatively for the observed depression of the vapour-pressure curve (p. 368).

The fact that the vapour pressure of a solution is less than that of the solvent implies that if the solution and solvent are in separate flasks but connected through the vapour phase, distillation of solvent will occur and the solution will become progressively diluted.

9.23. *The activity of the solvent species in a solution*

The solutions that show the simplest relations between vapour pressure and concentration, freezing-point and concentration, solubility and temperature, and so on, are those called *ideal solutions*, which will be dealt with in Chapter X. To anticipate for a moment, we may say that the properties of ideal solutions, such as those defined by Raoult's law, may all be deduced from the following relation between chemical potential and concentration:

$$\mu_1^{\text{soln}} - \mu_1^0 = RT \ln x_1, \tag{7}$$

where μ_1^{soln} denotes the chemical potential, at temperature T and mole fraction x_1, of the solvent species in the solution, and μ_1^0 denotes that in the pure liquid solvent.†

Solutions of all substances approach ideal behaviour when they are made sufficiently dilute. It is therefore natural to regard equation 7 as a sort of norm, and to express the behaviour of non-ideal solutions in terms of their deviations from it. We therefore define a function a_1, the *activity of the solvent*, by the equation

$$\mu_1^{\text{soln}} - \mu_1^0 = RT \ln a_1. \tag{8}$$

In the simplest case, that of ideal solutions, $a_1 = x_1$, and this is true of all solutions in the limit at low enough concentration. But for most solutions at ordinary concentrations, a_1 is greater or less than x_1; it is greater, for instance, in many regular solutions, but less in certain other solutions (p. 324). From equation 8 it is evident that the activity a_1 is unity when $\mu_1 = \mu_1^0$, that is, in the pure solvent, which may be regarded as the standard state adopted by convention in the definition of a_1 by equation 8.‡

† This equation is reminiscent of that for a perfect gas (section 5.15, p. 188), and we shall see later that the two logarithmic relations have similar molecular interpretations (section 10.2, p. 308); but μ_1^0 in 7 depends on the pressure (p. 317).

‡ The use of activities to express deviations from the simplest behaviour is analogous to the use of the fugacity in expressing the behaviour of gases (section 5.15, p. 189).

Since the partial molar free energy of the solvent is μ_1 in the solution, and μ_1^0 in the pure solvent, the change in partial molar free energy when one mole of solvent is transferred from solvent to solution is $\mu_1 - \mu_1^0$. This is the partial molar free energy of dilution and by equation 8 it is equal to $RT \ln a_1$. This is negative, since a_1 is less than 1; the negative value reflects the tendency of the solution to become diluted when in contact with the solvent through the vapour phase. It is often helpful to think of the activity as a measure of this partial free energy of dilution.

The deviations from ideal behaviour can also be expressed in terms of the *activity coefficient* of the solvent species, defined as

$$f_1 = a_1/x_1, \tag{9}$$

so that

$$\mu_1 - \mu_1^0 = RT \ln x_1 f_1. \tag{9a}$$

In ideal solutions the activity coefficient is unity; in others, it may be greater or less than unity. The behaviour of a given solution may be expressed equally accurately in terms of μ_1, a_1, or f_1; which of these is chosen in a particular problem is simply a matter of convenience.

The study of solutions is much concerned with the ways in which the activity varies with the concentration. The activity also varies slightly with temperature and pressure. The *temperature variation* may be treated as follows. The Gibbs–Helmholtz equation (p. 156) gives for the variation of G/T with temperature at constant composition (x_1) and pressure:

$$\left(\frac{\partial (G/T)}{\partial T} \right)_{P, x_1} = -\frac{H}{T^2}.$$

Differentiating both sides with respect to n_1 at constant T and P and remembering that the order of differentiation of G/T does not matter,

$$\left[\frac{\partial}{\partial n_1} \left(\frac{\partial (G/T)}{\partial T} \right)_{P, x_1} \right]_{T, P} = \left[\frac{\partial}{\partial T} \left(\frac{\partial (G/T)}{\partial n_1} \right)_{T, P} \right]_{P, x_1}$$

$$= \left(\frac{\partial (\mu_1/T)}{\partial T} \right)_{P, x_1} = -\frac{H_1}{T^2}, \tag{10}$$

where $H_1 = (\partial H/\partial n_1)_{T,P}$. Substituting for μ_1 from equation 8, we find

$$\left(\frac{\partial(\mu_1^0/T)}{\partial T}\right)_{P,x_1} + R\left(\frac{\partial \ln a_1}{\partial T}\right)_{P,x_1} = -\frac{H_1}{T^2}. \qquad (11)$$

Applying equation 11 to the pure solvent, whose heat content is written H_1^0, we find that the first term in equation 11 is $-H_1^0/T^2$. Thus

$$\left(\frac{\partial \ln a_1}{\partial T}\right)_{P,x_1} = \frac{H_1^0 - H_1}{RT^2}. \qquad (12)$$

Thus the variation of a_1 with temperature alone depends on the quantity $(H_1 - H_1^0)$, which is the partial molar heat of dilution (section 9.4). It may be quite small, even for electrolyte solutions; but for accurate work it must be known. For ideal solutions, a_1 is equal to x_1 and is therefore independent of temperature, so that the left-hand side of equation 12 is zero; consequently $(H_1 - H_1^0)$ is zero for these solutions.

The *pressure-dependence* of the activity may be expressed as follows. We know from equation 2 (p. 312) that $(\partial \mu_1/\partial P)_{T,x_1} = V_1$; also, for the pure solvent, $(\partial \mu_1^0/\partial P)_{T,x_1} = V_1^0$. And by equation 8,

$$\ln a_1 = (\mu_1 - \mu_1^0)/RT.$$

Differentiating both sides with respect to P at constant temperature and composition,

$$\left(\frac{\partial \ln a_1}{\partial P}\right)_{T,x_1} = \frac{1}{RT}\left\{\left(\frac{\partial \mu_1}{\partial P}\right)_{T,x_1} - \left(\frac{\partial \mu_1^0}{\partial P}\right)_{T,x_1}\right\} = \frac{V_1 - V_1^0}{RT}. \qquad (13)$$

The change of activity with pressure thus depends on the partial molar volume in solution compared with the molar volume in the pure solvent. The difference is usually small; in ideal solutions it is zero, as may be deduced from the fact that $a_1 = x_1$ and is therefore independent of pressure.

9.24. *The activity of the solute species in a solution*

For the solute species in a binary solution there are two definitions of activity in common use, referring to different standard states; which of them is chosen in a particular case depends on the properties of the solute in question. We distinguish them as convention I and convention II.

On *convention I*, we define the activity a_2 and activity f_2 of the solute species by equations similar to 8 and 9a of section 9.23 (p. 315):

$$\mu_2^{\text{soln}} - \mu_2^0 = RT \ln a_2 \tag{14}$$

$$= RT \ln x_2 f_2. \tag{15}$$

Here μ_2^0 is the chemical potential of the pure liquid solute, which constitutes the standard state, in which $a_2 = 1$ and $f_2 = 1$. This convention will be suitable for solutes that are liquid at ordinary temperatures, but will be inconvenient in dealing with high-melting salts, for example.

Convention II is adopted for such solutes; here the scale of activities is chosen so that the activity approaches the concentration as the solution is diluted, and becomes equal to it in a solution dilute enough to be ideal. Then

$$\mu_2^{\text{soln}} - \mu_2^{0'} = RT \ln a_2 = RT \ln x_2 f_2. \tag{16}$$

Thus $\mu_2^{0'}$ refers to a hypothetical solution of concentration unity but with the properties associated with infinite dilution. This convention is adopted by workers on electrolyte solutions. They have also commonly used molal concentrations m (or molar concentrations c) instead of mole fractions x_2, and have therefore used 'practical' activity coefficients γ defined by the equation

$$\mu_2^{\text{soln}} - \mu_2^{0'} = RT \ln a_2 = RT \ln m\gamma. \tag{17}$$

Except in dealing with electrolyte solutions, we shall use the 'rational' activity coefficients f_2 defined by equations 15 and 16.

On either convention, the partial molar free energy change when one mole of solute is transferred from the standard state to the solution is $RT \ln a_2$, and we can think of a_2 as a measure of this partial free energy of transfer, just as $RT \ln a_1$ is a measure of the partial free energy of dilution.

9.25. *The relation between the activities of solvent and solute in a solution at constant temperature and pressure*

The activities a_1 and a_2 can be related at constant temperature and pressure by applying the Gibbs–Duhem relation (p. 167):

$$x_1 \, d\mu_1 + x_2 \, d\mu_2 = 0. \tag{18}$$

If we differentiate equations 8 and 14, at constant T and P, remembering that μ_1^0 and μ_2^0 are then constant, we find

$$d\mu_1 = RT\,d\ln a_1, \qquad d\mu_2 = RT\,d\ln a_2.$$

Substituting in 18,

$$x_1\,d\ln a_1 + x_2\,d\ln a_2 = 0. \tag{19}$$

This is a most useful relation. To put it in terms of activity coefficients, we note that, since $x_1 = 1 - x_2$,

$$x_1\,d\ln x_1 + x_2\,d\ln x_2 = 0, \tag{20}$$

and subtract 20 from 19; we obtain

$$x_1\,d\ln f_1 + x_2\,d\ln f_2 = 0. \tag{21}$$

By integrating equations 19 and 21, we can express the difference of a_2 in solutions A and B in terms of the corresponding difference of a_1:

$$(\ln a_2)_\mathrm{B} - (\ln a_2)_\mathrm{A} = -\int_\mathrm{A}^\mathrm{B} (x_1/x_2)\,d\ln a_1, \tag{22}$$

$$(\ln f_2)_\mathrm{B} - (\ln f_2)_\mathrm{A} = -\int_\mathrm{A}^\mathrm{B} (x_1/x_2)\,d\ln f_1. \tag{23}$$

Thus if we know a_1 (or f_1) as a function of x_1, over a certain range of concentration, we can find the corresponding changes in a_2. If our concentration range extends low enough to allow extrapolation to zero, at which $a_1 = 1$ and $a_2 = 0$, we can find the actual values of a_2. This derivation of a_2 from a_1 is often important, since the phenomena of solutions mostly give first a_1, whereas it may be a_2 that is of more direct theoretical interest, as it is for electrolytes, for example.

For the particular case of an *ideal solution*, we may substitute $f_1 = 1$ in equation 21; hence $d\ln f_2 = 0$, which on integration gives $f_2 = $ constant. If the solution is ideal over the whole range of concentrations, this constant must be unity, both on convention I and convention II of section 9.24; then $f_2 = 1$ and $a_2 = x_2$ over the whole range. If, as is often the case, the solution becomes ideal only when dilute, the situation is different. On convention II the constant is still unity, since $f_2 = 1$ in the limit of low concentration, so that $f_2 = 1$ and $a_2 = x_2$ over the range for which the solution is ideal. On convention I we have no guide to f_2 in dilute solution, and can conclude only that it is constant over the range for which the solution is ideal, so that a_2 is proportional to x_2.

9.3. The colligative properties of solutions, in terms of activities

9.31. *The vapour pressure of the solvent species over a solution*

The problem is to investigate the equilibrium between a binary solution and the vapour phase. We may at first suppose the vapour, as well as the solution, to contain both solvent and solute; we shall later simplify the treatment by supposing the solute involatile. We wish to find the relation between the activity a_1 and the partial pressure p_1 of the solvent species, at a fixed temperature.† The problem may be pictured in terms of the vapour pressure curves of the pure solvent and of a series of solutions of increasing concentration (fig. 51 a). With increase of concentration, the curve is displaced downwards and the vapour pressure at any fixed temperature T' is evidently reduced (section 9.22); the question is by how much. We have therefore to relate the vapour pressure depressions ab, ac, etc. (fig. 51 a) to the activities.

The vapour pressure depression can also be pictured in terms of chemical potentials (fig. 51 b). Since $(\partial\mu_1/\partial P) = V_1$ (p. 312), at a fixed temperature the curves of μ_1 against pressure for the solvent and solutions will slope upwards and will be roughly linear and parallel. Since $\mu_1 = \mu_1^0 + RT \ln a_1$, and a_1 is unity in the pure solvent but less in a solution, μ_1 is reduced by addition of solute, and so the curves for solutions will lie below the curve for the pure solvent. The curve for μ_1 in the vapour will be much steeper, because the molar volume in the vapour is much larger. It will cut the curves for the solvent and solutions at a, b, c, etc. These points correspond to equilibrium. It is plain from the

---

† In this chapter we write P for total pressure, p_1, etc., for partial vapour pressures, and p_1^0, etc., for the vapour pressures of pure constituents. We omit the superscript e used in Chapter 7, since no confusion will arise.

figure that the vapour pressure is depressed by addition of solute. The depression (e.g. $p_1^0 - p_1^A$ for solution A) reflects the decrease in a_1 or μ_1 caused by adding solute.

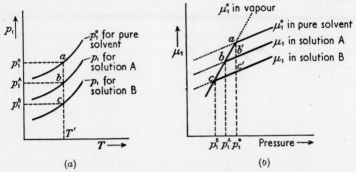

Fig. 51. (a) Vapour-pressure curves (p_1 against T) for solvent and solutions. (b) Plots of μ_1 against P for vapour, solvent, and solutions, at a fixed temperature (diagrammatic). The zero for μ_1 is arbitrary.

The condition for equilibrium as regards the transfer of solvent between solution and vapour at constant temperature and pressure is that the chemical potential of the solvent species shall be the same in the solution and in the vapour:

$$\mu_1^{\text{vap}} = \mu_1^{\text{soln}}. \tag{24}$$

The chemical potential in the vapour phase is related to the partial pressure by the following equation, if the vapour behaves as a perfect gas mixture (cf. section 5.31, p. 216):

$$\mu_1^{\text{vap}} = (\mu_1^0)^{\text{vap}} + RT \ln p_1. \tag{25}$$

For the solution, by definition of the activity (p. 315),

$$\mu_1^{\text{soln}} = (\mu_1^0)^{\text{solvent}} + RT \ln a_1. \tag{26}$$

At equilibrium, these chemical potentials are equal; hence

$$\ln a_1 = \ln p_1 + [(\mu_1^0)^{\text{vap}} - (\mu_1^0)^{\text{solvent}}]/RT. \tag{27}$$

From the fact that in the pure liquid $a_1 = 1$ and $p_1 = p_1^0$, we find that the last term on the right is equal to $-\ln p_1^0$. Substituting this in equation 27, we find

$$\boxed{a_1 = p_1/p_1^0.} \tag{28}$$

Y

This very simple result has been much used in the determination of activities and activity coefficients. It does not assume that the solute is involatile. It does, however, depend on the assumption that the vapour behaves as a perfect gas mixture. This is always an approximation, and in the most exact work it involves errors greater than the experimental uncertainties. It is then necessary to replace the pressure p_1 in equation 25 by the fugacity P_1^* (section 5.15). We then obtain as the general relation

$$a_1 = P_1^*/(P_1^*)^0. \tag{29}$$

Fugacities for use with this equation may be calculated by various methods, for instance by using the critical constants and Berthelot's equation of state (cf. p. 191).

Experimental work. (i) *Solute volatile.* In a mixture of liquids, such as benzene and toluene, where both solvent and solute are volatile, the two partial pressures p_1 and p_2 may be measured by distilling off a small quantity and analysing it; the analysis gives the composition of the vapour (i.e. x_1^{vap} and x_2^{vap}), whence the partial pressures are found from the total pressure P as $p_1 = P x_1^{\mathrm{vap}}$ and $p_2 = P x_2^{\mathrm{vap}}$ (p. 214). This method was used in the pioneer work of Zawidski and the later work of Scatchard.[†] Many binary solutions can be studied over the whole range of composition from $x_1 = 0$ to $x_1 = 1$. Some results follow.

(*a*) The simplest behaviour is shown by mixtures of non-polar or closely similar liquids, such as *n*-heptane and hexane or octane, or propylene bromide and ethylene bromide (fig. 52). Here the plot of p_1 against mole fraction is linear over the whole range within experimental error; so are those of p_2 and of the total pressure P against mole fraction. From the plot, $p_1 = x_1 p_1^0$. Together with the relation $a_1 = p_1/p_1^0$ for solutions whose vapours behave as perfect gases (equation 28), the experimental results thus give $a_1 = x_1$ over the whole range. These solutions are said to show *ideal* vapour-pressure behaviour (section 9.23).

(*b*) Many mixtures have vapour pressures higher than the ideal values over most of the range; these are said to show

---

† (*a*) Zawidski, *Z. phys. Chem.*, 1900, **35**, 129; (*b*) Scatchard *et al.*, *J. Amer. Chem. Soc.*, 1938, **60**, 1275, 1278; 1939, **61**, 3206; 1940, **62**, 712; *J. Phys. Chem.*, 1939, **43**, 119.

positive deviations from the ideal law $a_1 = x_1$. However, p_1 approaches $x_1 p_1^0$ as x_1 approaches 1; that is, ideal behaviour is approached when the solutions are dilute. Examples of mixtures that show this behaviour are those of acetone and carbon disulphide (fig. 53), and of toluene and acetic acid.

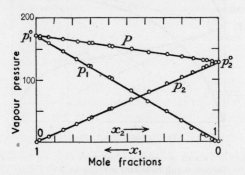

FIG. 52. Plots of vapour pressure against mole fraction for mixtures of ethylene bromide (1) and propylene bromide (2) at 85°C.

At any mole fraction x_1, the activity a_1 is given by the equation (p. 321)

$$a_1 = p_1/p_1^0. \tag{30}$$

For an ideal solution at the same mole fraction, the activity a_1 would be equal to x_1, so that the partial pressure of the solvent in such a solution, p_1^{id}, would be given by substituting x_1 for a_1 in equation 30:

$$x_1 = p_1^{\text{id}}/p_1^0. \tag{31}$$

Dividing equation 30 by 31, we find

$$f_1 = a_1/x_1 = p_1/p_1^{\text{id}}. \tag{32}$$

The activity coefficient f_1, which measures the deviation of the solution from ideal behaviour, is thus given by p_1/p_1^{id}. It can be obtained from plots such as those shown in fig. 53, as for instance from the ratio of the distance bc to ac. For the solutions illustrated, f_1 is greater than unity. A similar argument shows that $f_2 = p_2/p_2^{\text{id}}$ (p. 327) and is here greater than 1. Many regular solutions (section 11.2) belong to this type. We can picture the high values of the activities as due to a tendency of solvent and solute to separate and form two layers.

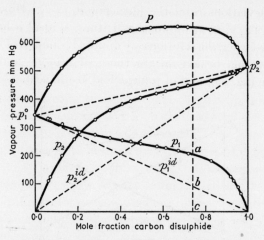

FIG. 53. Plots of vapour pressure against mole fraction for mixtures of carbon disulphide and acetone at $35 \cdot 17°$ C.

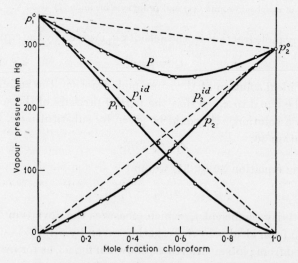

FIG. 54. Plots of vapour pressure against mole fraction for mixtures of chloroform and acetone at $35 \cdot 17°$ C.

(*c*) Other mixtures have vapour pressures lower than the ideal values, and are said to show negative deviations. The ideal law is approached when the solutions are dilute. The activity coefficient is again given by equation 32. Examples are mixtures of acetone and chloroform, and of pyridine and acetic acid (fig. 54). The activity coefficient is here less than unity. Such behaviour is shown when there is some interaction, such as hydrogen bonding, between the two constituents.

In the most accurate work, fugacities must be used instead of pressures in equation 32. The deviations from this equation due to departures from the laws of perfect gas mixtures may amount to 1 per cent., and when the whole deviation to be measured is in the region of 5 per cent. corrections must be applied for them.

(ii) *Solute involatile.* Much work has been done on aqueous solutions of involatile solutes, such as sugars or metallic salts, where the interest lies in the behaviour of dilute solutions. The problem is then to determine accurately a quite small depression of the vapour pressure; for instance, in a 0·1 molar solution of potassium chloride the depression is only about 0·06 mm of mercury. Among the *static methods* available, some workers have used the direct measurement of vapour pressure by a mercury manometer, the system being evacuated of all gases except the solvent vapour; the experimental uncertainty is of the order of 0·02 mm of mercury.† Differential methods, in which the difference of vapour pressure between solution and pure solvent is measured directly, have been used,‡ and the experimental uncertainty can be reduced to about 0·001 mm by the use of a Rayleigh manometer§ or of a metal bellows with a sensitive strain-gauge.‖ Aqueous salt solutions have been investigated by the isopiestic method,†† which is a comparative method relying on separate absolute measurements on potassium

---

† e.g. Baxendale, Enüstün, and Stern, *Phil. Trans.* A, 1951, **243**, 169, on solutions of diphenyl in benzene; cf. Everett, Allen, and Penney, *Proc. Roy. Soc.* A, 1952, **212**, 149.

‡ e.g. Hildebrand and Eastman, *J. Amer. Chem. Soc.*, 1914, **36**, 2020, on amalgams.

§ Frazer, Lovelace, *et al.*, ibid., p. 2439 (manometer); ibid., 1920, **42**, 1793 (results on aqueous solutions of mannite); ibid., 1921, **43**, 102 (results on KCl aq).

‖ Brown and Delaney, *J. Phys. Chem.*, 1954, **58**, 255. Another ingenious differential manometer is described by Puddington, *Rev. Sci. Instruments*, 1948, **19**, 577.

†† Robinson and Sinclair, *J. Amer. Chem. Soc.*, 1934, **56**, 1830, and later papers by Robinson *et al.*

chloride solutions. In an evacuated desiccator are placed dishes containing solutions of the given salt and of potassium chloride; these solutions are allowed to come to equilibrium by distillation of water from one to the other, and the concentrations are subsequently determined.

In the simplest of the *dynamic methods*, a known volume of air or other gas is saturated with solvent vapour by passing it over the solution; the solvent is then removed from the gas and estimated. Since $p_1 V = n_1 RT$ if the gas forms a perfect gas mixture with the solvent (equation 10 of section 5.3, p. 218), we can find p_1 from our knowledge of n_1, V, and T. The measurement of a large volume of gas may be avoided by using electrolytic gas and calculating its volume from the amount of electricity used.[†] In a modification of the method, air is saturated with solvent by passing it over the solution; the same air is then passed over a weighed quantity of solvent, when the mass taken up at equilibrium is $k(p_1^0-p_1)$, where k is a constant depending on the volume of air; the whole of the solvent vapour is then removed and estimated, its mass being kp_1^0. The ratio of the two masses is thus $(p_1^0-p_1)/p_1^0$, the relative lowering of the vapour pressure.[‡]

The results show that the behaviour of dilute solutions of cane-sugar and other non-electrolytes approximates closely to the ideal law, at least up to concentrations of the order of $0\cdot1$ molar, while electrolytes deviate considerably even at much lower concentrations.

9.32. *The vapour pressure of the solute species over a solution*

A volatile solute will be present in appreciable concentration in the vapour over the solution. The condition for equilibrium as regards the solute species is

$$\mu_2^{\mathrm{vap}} = \mu_2^{\mathrm{soln}}. \tag{33}$$

The same thermodynamic treatment may be applied to the vapour pressure of the solute as to that of the solvent (section 9.31). The results are similar; if the vapour behaves as a perfect

† Pearce and Snow, *J. Phys. Chem.*, 1927, **31**, 231.
‡ Berkeley and Hartley, *Proc. Roy. Soc.* A, 1906, **17**, 156.

gas mixture, a relation holds at equilibrium analogous to equation 27 of section 9.31 (p. 321):

$$\ln a_2 = \ln p_2 + [(\mu_2^0)^{\text{vap}} - (\mu_2^0)^{\text{solvent}}]/RT. \tag{34}$$

If we choose as standard state the pure solute, in accordance with convention I of section 9.24 (p. 318), then $a_2 = 1$ when $p_2 = p_2^0$, and the last term is equal to $(-\ln p_2^0)$, so that

$$a_2 = p_2/p_2^0. \tag{35 a}$$

If we define the activity as equal to the mole fraction in a solution dilute enough to be ideal, in accordance with convention II (p. 318), then $a_2 = x_2$ in the limit as p_2 tends to zero, and the constant term in equation 34 is equal to the limiting value of $\ln(a_2/p_2)$; this will not in general be equal to p_2^0, but it remains true from equation 34 that

$$a_2 = kp_2, \tag{35 b}$$

where k is constant at a given temperature. For higher accuracy, fugacities must be substituted for pressures in equations 35 a and 35 b.

These simple relations give us the means of determining the activities of volatile solutes, by methods similar to those of section 9.31 for volatile solvents (pp. 322 seq.). The activity coefficient f_2 can also be obtained; since for an ideal solution $p_2^{\text{id}} = x_2 p_2^0$, equation 35 a gives for the activity coefficient on convention I:

$$f_2 = a_2/x_2 = p_2/p_2^{\text{id}}. \tag{35 c}$$

Experimental work. For systems of two volatile constituents miscible over the whole range, we have already sketched experimental methods and results in section 9.31. Other systems that may be mentioned are aqueous solutions of hydrochloric acid in water[†] and solutions of bromine in carbon tetrachloride,[‡] for which the dynamic method of measurement has been used; the behaviour of these solutions approaches ideality at low concentrations.

[†] Bates and Kirschman, *J. Amer. Chem. Soc.*, 1919, **41**, 1991. Cf. p. 352.
[‡] Lewis and Storch, ibid., 1917, **39**, 2552.

The Duhem–Margules relation. When both constituents of a solution are volatile and the vapour behaves as a perfect gas mixture, $a_1 = p_1/p_1^0$ and a_2 is proportional to p_2, so that

$$d\ln a_1 = d\ln p_1 \quad \text{and} \quad d\ln a_2 = d\ln p_2.$$

We have already obtained a relation between a_1 and a_2 in terms of the mole fraction in solution, namely equation 19 of section 9.25:

$$x_1 d\ln a_1 + x_2 d\ln a_2 = 0.$$

Substituting for $d\ln a_1$ and $d\ln a_2$ we find

$$x_1 d\ln p_1 + x_2 d\ln p_2 = 0. \tag{36}$$

This equation relates the partial vapour pressures of the two constituents in terms of the mole fractions in the solution. It is known as the Duhem–Margules relation. The corresponding general relation in terms of fugacities, to be used when the deviations of the vapour from the perfect-gas-mixture laws are too great, is evidently

$$x_1 d\ln P_1^* + x_2 d\ln P_2^* = 0. \tag{36a}$$

These relations have been experimentally verified for various systems. Equation 36 was found to hold within the limits of experimental error in the work of Zawidski already referred to (p. 322); both for ideal and non-ideal solutions, comparison of $(d\ln p_1/d\ln p_2)$ with $(-x_2/x_1)$ gave satisfactory agreement, as the equation requires. The more precise work of Scatchard shows distinct deviations from equation 36, but these agree with the deviations of the vapour from the perfect-gas-mixture laws, so that equation 36a is obeyed.

9.33. *The boiling-point of a solution*

We have now to consider the effect of addition of solute on the boiling-point of a solution, at a fixed pressure such as that of the atmosphere. The process concerned is the same as that considered in sections 9.31 and 9.32, namely reversible evaporation, and can be pictured in terms of the same set of vapour-pressure curves (fig. 55), from which it is clear that the boiling-point T_e at a fixed pressure P' is raised by addition of solute, since T_e^A or T_e^B is greater than T_e^0. The problem is to relate the boiling-point elevations ab, ac, etc., to the activities of the solutions.

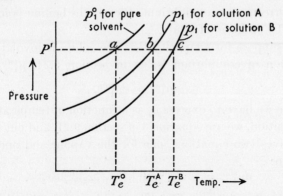

FIG. 55. Vapour-pressure curves and the elevation of the boiling-point.

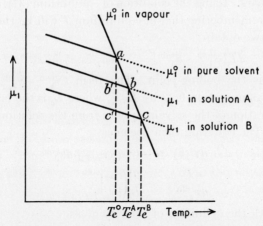

FIG. 56. Plots of μ_1 against T for vapour, solvent, and solutions, at a fixed pressure (diagrammatic). The zero for μ_1 is arbitrary.

In terms of chemical potentials, the situation is shown in fig. 56. Curves of μ_1 against temperature at a fixed pressure for the solvent and solutions will slope downwards, because

$$(\partial \mu_1 / \partial T)_P = -S_1 \quad \text{(p. 312).}$$

They will be roughly linear and parallel, being displaced downwards with increase of concentration, like the μ_1–P curves

(p. 320). The curve for μ_1 in the vapour will be steeper, because S_1 is larger than in the liquid. The points of intersection a, b, c, etc., correspond to equilibrium. Clearly the boiling-point will be raised by addition of solute.

We suppose for simplicity that the solute is involatile. The condition of equilibrium is, as in section 9.31, $\mu_1^{\text{vap}} = \mu_1^{\text{soln}}$, whence

$$d\mu_1^{\text{vap}} = d\mu_1^{\text{soln}}, \tag{37}$$

Since we have to express μ_1 as a function of temperature and composition, we use equation 3 of section 9.21, and put $dP = 0$. This gives two equations, one for the vapour and one for the solution:

$$d\mu_1^{\text{soln}} = -S_1^{\text{soln}} dT + (\partial\mu_1/\partial x_2)_{T,P}^{\text{soln}} dx_2^{\text{soln}},$$

$$d\mu_1^{\text{vap}} = -S_1^{\text{vap}} dT + (\partial\mu_1/\partial x_2)_{T,P}^{\text{vap}} dx_2^{\text{vap}}.$$

Since the solute is involatile, dx_2^{vap} is zero and the term containing it disappears. Using the condition of equilibrium (37), rearranging, and remembering that at equilibrium T will be the boiling-point T_e, we obtain

$$dT_e(S_1^{\text{vap}} - S_1^{\text{soln}}) = -(\partial\mu_1/\partial x_2)_{T,P}^{\text{soln}} dx_2^{\text{soln}}. \tag{38}$$

Here T_e is the boiling-point. The term $(S_1^{\text{vap}} - S_1^{\text{soln}})$ can be replaced as in section 9.22 by L_e/T_e, where L_e is the latent heat of evaporation of the solvent species from the solution into the vapour. The equation then becomes

$$L_e \, dT_e/T_e = -(\partial\mu_1/\partial x_2)_{T,P}^{\text{soln}} dx_2^{\text{soln}}$$

or

$$\frac{dT_e}{dx_2^{\text{soln}}} = -\frac{T_e}{L_e}\left(\frac{\partial\mu_1}{\partial x_2}\right)_{T,P}^{\text{soln}}, \tag{39}$$

which with the definition of activity gives

$$\frac{dT_e}{dx_2^{\text{soln}}} = -\frac{RT_e^2}{L_e}\left(\frac{\partial\ln a_1}{\partial x_2}\right)_{T,P}. \tag{40}$$

This is an exact relation when the solute is involatile. The left-hand side is the variation of boiling-point with solute concentration; the equation relates it to $(\partial\ln a_1/\partial x_2)_{T,P}$, the variation of a_1 with solute concentration. This means that the boiling-point elevation (for example $T_e^A - T_e^0$ in figs. 55 and 56) reflects the decrease in a_1, or μ_1, caused by adding solute at constant temperature and pressure (ab', ac' in fig. 56). Thus a_1 refers to the activity of the solvent in the solution when at the boiling-point of the pure solvent, T_e^0, not at the actual boiling-point of the solution. This being kept in mind, we can omit both the dx_2's in equation 40, and obtain as the differential relation between the activity and the boiling-point:†

$$\frac{d \ln a_1}{dT_e} = -\frac{L_e}{RT_e^2}. \tag{41}$$

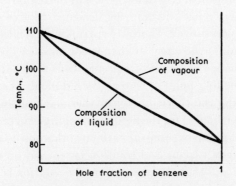

FIG. 57. Boiling-point of benzene–toluene mixtures plotted against composition of liquid and vapour.

As a first approximation, in the integration of this equation we can assume that L_e is constant, independent of both temperature and concentration. Integration then gives at once

$$\ln a_1 = \frac{L_e}{R}\left(\frac{1}{T_e} - \frac{1}{T_e^0}\right) = -\frac{L_e \Delta T}{RT_e T_e^0} \simeq -\frac{L_e \Delta T}{R(T_e^0)^2}. \tag{42}$$

Thus a knowledge of ΔT, the boiling-point elevation, with the latent heat of evaporation L_e, allows us to calculate the activity a_1.

Experimental work. (i) *Solute volatile.* Boiling-points of binary liquid mixtures, like their vapour pressures, can often be studied over the whole composition range. Some results are shown in fig. 57. It will be noticed that corresponding to each boiling-point there are two compositions, one of the liquid and one of the vapour. In general these are not the same; the separation of

† Equation 41 has the same form as equation 12 of section 9.23 (p. 317) but its meaning is quite different.

constituents by fractional distillation depends on this fact. When they are the same, as sometimes happens, the solution distils as a 'constant-boiling mixture'. For further discussion of these phenomena the reader is referred to works on phase equilibria (p. 177, note).

(ii) *Solute involatile.* Here equation 41 is applicable. As with vapour pressures, the main interest lies in the behaviour of dilute solutions. The boiling-point elevation is then small; for a 0·1 molar solution of KCl in water, it is in the region of 0·1 degrees. Ebulliometers must therefore be designed to give very steady boiling temperatures.† There are two main difficulties: (*a*) superheating; and (*b*) the effect of changes of pressure on the boiling-point—a change of 3 mm of mercury causes a change of about 0·1° in the boiling-point of water. Both difficulties are overcome by supporting the thermometer or thermocouple in the vapour phase, and arranging for the liquid to be sprayed over it, by means of a Cottrell pump or some other device; this ensures that equilibrium between vapour and solution is reached on the thermometer bulb, and that the pressure on the solution is the same as that in the vapour, which can be kept constant by means of a barostat. The effect of changes of pressure is still further reduced by using twin ebulliometers, connected to the same barostat, one containing solution and the other pure solvent; the boiling-point elevation is then measured directly by means of a thermocouple. Temperatures can be kept steady to about ±0·0005°.‡ Activities of aqueous alkali chloride solutions have been determined in this way; the accuracy was such that the approximate equation 42 was inadequate and the temperature-variation of L_e had to be taken into account. The activity coefficients are less than unity, and agree with those determined at 25° when compared with the help of equation 12 of section 9.23 (p. 317). The earlier work

† Reviews are given in Weissberger (ed.), *Physical Methods of Organic Chemistry* (Interscience Publications, 2nd edn. 1949), vol. i, chap. 4, pp. 111–22; W. Swietoslawski, *Ebulliometric Measurements* (Reinhold Publishing Co., 1945).

‡ Saxton and Smith, *J. Amer. Chem. Soc.*, 1932, **54**, 2626 (KCl in water); Smith, ibid., 1939, **61**, 497, 500, 1123 (NaCl in water); Allen and Caldin, *Trans. Faraday Soc.*, 1953, **49**, 895 (carboxylic acids in benzene).

done with Beckmann's or Landsberger's apparatus is much less precise than this, but suffices to show that many non-electrolyte solutions behave approximately ideally (section 10.13).

9.34. *The freezing-point of a solution*

The equilibrium here is between the solution and the solid solvent, at a fixed pressure such as that of the atmosphere. The vapour-pressure curves are shown in fig. 58. The curve for the solid is steeper than those for the liquid and solutions, because the latent heat of evaporation is larger (section 7.21). Equilibrium corresponds to the points a, b, c, where the curves cross and the vapour pressures of the two phases are equal. The curves of μ_1 against T at a fixed pressure are shown in fig. 59; the temperature-range shown is lower than in fig. 56 (p. 329). The curve for solid solvent is less steep than for liquid or solution, because S_1, which fixes $(\partial\mu_1/\partial T)_P$, is less for the solid. When the curves cross, μ_1 has the same value in solid and liquid, and there will be equilibrium. From both figures it is clear that the freezing-point T_f will be depressed by addition of solute. The problem is to relate the depression (for example $T_f^0 - T_f^A$) to the activity.

The condition for equilibrium is

$$\mu_1^{\text{solid}} = \mu_1^{\text{soln}}.$$

The thermodynamic argument now runs parallel to that for boiling-points (section 9.33), except that the superscript 'solid' replaces 'vapour' throughout; the result is a relation analogous to equation 40 (p. 330):†

$$\frac{dT_f}{dx_2} = \frac{RT_f^2}{L_f}\left(\frac{\partial\ln a_1}{\partial x_2}\right)_{T,P}. \tag{43}$$

Here L_f is the latent heat of fusion of the solid into the solution. The equation relates the depression of freezing-point to the decrease in a_1 or μ_1 due to addition of solute, at constant temperature and pressure (ab', ac' in fig. 59). Thus a_1 refers to the activity of the solvent in the solution at the freezing-point of the pure

---

† The sign is changed because, whereas in section 9.33 we had

$$T(S_1^{\text{vap}} - S_1^{\text{soln}}) = (H_1^{\text{vap}} - H_1^{\text{soln}}) = L_e,$$

in section 9.34 $T(S_1^{\text{solid}} - S_1^{\text{soln}}) = (H_1^{\text{solid}} - H_1^{\text{soln}}) = -L_f.$

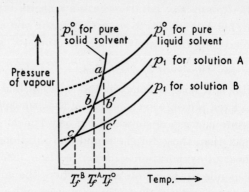

FIG. 58. Plots of vapour pressure against temperature for solutions, liquid solvent and solid solvent.

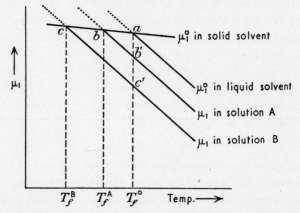

FIG. 59. Plots of μ_1 against temperature for solutions, liquid solvent and solid solvent (diagrammatic). The zero for μ_1 is arbitrary.

solvent, T_f^0, not at the actual freezing-point of the solution T_f. Omitting now the dx_2's in equation 43, we obtain as the differential relation between a_1 and freezing-point:

$$\frac{d\ln a_1}{dT_f} = \frac{L_f}{RT_f^2}. \tag{44}$$

As a first approximation, we can assume in the integration of this equation that L_f is constant, independent of both temperature and concentration. Integration then gives

$$\ln a_1 = \text{constant} - L_f/RT.$$

The integration constant can be determined if we recall that in the pure solvent $a_1 = 1$ and $T_f = T_f^0$. Hence

$$\ln a_1 = -\frac{L_f}{R}\left(\frac{1}{T_f} - \frac{1}{T_f^0}\right) = -\frac{L_f \Delta T}{R T_f T_f^0} \simeq -\frac{L_f \Delta T}{R(T_f^0)^2}. \quad (45)$$

The activity a_1 can thus be calculated from a knowledge of the freezing-point depression ΔT and the latent heat of fusion. L_f may be determined calorimetrically, or the term $(L_f/R(T_f^0)^2)$ may be found as the ratio $(\ln x_1)/\Delta T$ for an ideal solution, for which we may put $a_1 = x_1$ in equation 45.

As a second approximation, when greater accuracy is needed, the temperature-variation of L_f may be taken into account. In equation 44, L_f may be written according to Kirchhoff's relation as $A + B\Delta T$, where A is equal to L_f at T_f^0 and B is a constant fixed by the change of heat capacity on fusion. The integrated expressions are then more cumbersome and the calculations are done graphically.

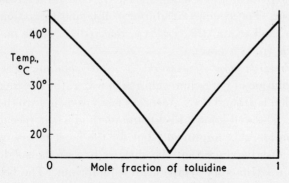

FIG. 60. Freezing-point plotted against mole fraction for mixtures of p-toluidine and o-nitrophenol.

Experimental work. (i) *Constituents miscible over the whole range.* In a system such as a mixture of p-toluidine and o-nitrophenol, the freezing-point of each of the pure constituents is depressed by addition of the other, and if we measure the freezing-points over the whole range and composition we obtain two curves of freezing-point against temperature, which cut at the 'eutectic' temperature and composition (fig. 60). If the system is nearly ideal, each curve follows fairly closely an equation derived from 45 by putting $a_1 = x_1$. For greater accuracy, the temperature-variation of L_f must be taken into account, since the depressions are considerable. For certain systems the agreement with the ideal law is then good; for example, the following table shows the observed and calculated freezing-points for mixtures of o- and m-dinitrobenzene.

Freezing-points of mixtures of dinitrobenzenes

Mole fraction	100	90	80	70	60	50	40	30	20	10	0
Ideal f.p.,°C	..	110·0	104·5	97·2	89·6	80·7	70·4	67·6	75·5	83·2	..
Observed f.p.	116·9	110·0	104·8	97·2	86·7	79·5	68·7	67·6	75·5	83·2	89·8

Other mixtures whose behaviour over the whole composition range is predicted by the ideal law are those of benzene and naphthalene, benzene and diphenyl, the mononitro-anilines, and the mononitrochlorobenzenes.† Most systems deviate from ideal behaviour. For systems exhibiting compound-formation, solid solution, and so on, the reader is referred to works on phase equilibria (p. 177, note).

(ii) *Freezing-point depressions in dilute solution.* For a 0·1 molar solution of potassium chloride in water, the freezing-point depression is around 0·4°. Accurate measurements are therefore needed. The well-known Beckmann method has in recent years been considerably improved,‡ but for the most precise work it has the disadvantage that the surface area of the solid is too small for satisfactory temperature-equilibrium. The best way of ensuring equilibrium is to use an intimate mixture of solution and crystalline solid. When the temperature has become steady, the concentration of the solution is determined by removing a sample and analysing it. This method can be used with a simple arrangement of Dewar vessel and Beckmann thermometer.§ For higher accuracy, the freezing-point depression can be

† Johnston, Andrews, and Kohman, *J. Phys. Chem.*, 1925, **29**, 882, 914, 1041, 1048, 1317; Lee and Warner, *J. Amer. Chem. Soc.*, 1935, **57**, 318.

‡ Gillespie *et al.*, *J. Chem. Soc.*, 1950, 2473, and following papers.

§ Bell *et al.*, ibid., 1934, 1969; 1935, 1432.

measured directly by using twin Dewar vessels, one containing
solid with solution and the other solid with pure solvent, the
temperature-difference ΔT being measured by a thermocouple.
Very steady readings are attained, and the uncertainty in ΔT
can be reduced to $\pm 10^{-4}$ degrees or even less.† With measurements of this accuracy, the first approximation given by equation
45 is not adequate; it is necessary to take into account the
variation of L_f with temperature.

The interest of such measurements lies in the behaviour of the
solute at low concentrations, and we usually wish to find a_2
rather than a_1. To do this, we combine equation 44 with the
general relation (equation 19, p. 319):

$$d \ln a_2 = -(x_1/x_2) \, d \ln a_1.$$

The result is
$$d \ln a_2 = -\frac{x_1}{x_2} \frac{L_f}{RT_f^2} \, dT. \tag{46}$$

In dilute solutions we can as a good approximation put $x_1 = 1$
and $T_f^2 = (T_f^0)^2 = $ constant. As before, we put $L_f = A + B\Delta T$.
Thus

$$[\ln a_2] = -\frac{1}{(RT_1^0)^2} \int_{T_1^0}^{T} \frac{(A + B\Delta T)}{x_2} \, dT. \tag{47}$$

The integration may be done graphically.‡ The error that would
arise if the temperature-variation of L_f were neglected is about
3 per cent. for a 1 molar solution of sodium chloride in water,
and about 20 per cent. for a 5 molar solution. A correction is
also applied for the variation of L_f with concentration. Values
of a_2 correct to the third decimal place can be obtained. One
application of such measurements is the successful test of the
Debye–Hückel theory of dilute solutions of strong electrolytes
(section 12.26).

9.35. *The dependence of solubility on temperature*

Thermodynamically, the variation of solubility with temperature is closely analogous to the variation of the freezing-point

---

† Adams, *J. Amer. Chem. Soc.*, 1915, **37**, 481; Hovorka and Rodebush,
ibid., 1925, **47**, 1614; Scatchard *et al.*, ibid., 1932, **54**, 2676.

‡ Cf. Lewis and Randall, *Thermodynamics* (1923), chaps. 23 and 27.

with concentration. If the pure solvent separates when a solution is cooled, we speak of the freezing-point at a given concentration; if the pure solute separates, we commonly use a different terminology and speak of the solubility at a given temperature; but thermodynamically the two equilibria are very similar, the only difference being that in the first the solid phase consists of the constituent in excess, and in the second it consists of the other constituent. The condition for saturation is

$$\mu_2^{\text{solid}} = \mu_2^{\text{soln}}.$$

The thermodynamic argument is identical with that for freezing-points (section 9.34) except that the subscript 2 replaces 1. The result is similar to equation 44 of section 9.34; if T_s is the temperature at which the solution is saturated,

$$\frac{d \ln a_2}{dT_s} = \frac{L_f}{RT_s^2}, \tag{48}$$

where a_2 is the activity of the solute in the saturated solution at a fixed temperature, and L_f is the latent heat of fusion of the solute into the solution. Since a_2 is expressed in terms of the corresponding activity coefficient f_2 as $x_2 f_2$, and x_2 is here the solubility s (in mole-fraction units), a_2 may be equated with sf_2.

The first approximation for the integration of equation 48 is obtained by supposing that L_f is constant. Then

$$\ln a_2 = \ln sf_2 = \text{constant} - L_f/RT_s. \tag{49}$$

The value of the integration constant depends on our choice of the standard state relative to which a_2 and f_2 are measured.

For mixtures of non-electrolytes, solubilities can often be measured up to high concentrations of solute, or even up to $x_2 = 1$, when T_s becomes simply T_f^0, the melting-point of the solute. It is then convenient to adopt convention I (section 9.24, p. 318); the standard state is taken as the pure solute, in which $a_2 = f_2 = 1$ and $T_s = T_f^0$. Then equation 49 gives

$$\ln a_2 = \ln sf_2 = -\frac{L_f}{R}\left(\frac{1}{T_s} - \frac{1}{T_f^0}\right). \tag{50}$$

This relation expresses the activity or activity coefficient of the solute in a solution of concentration s (mole fraction), in terms of the temperature of saturation T_s for this solution. It is similar in form to equation 45 for a_1. Indeed, we have already encountered experimental results which involve both a_1 and a_2, namely the freezing-point plots for mixtures of constituents miscible over the whole range (section 9.34; fig. 60). Such plots may be regarded as made up either of two freezing-point curves or of two solubility curves; the curve of freezing-point depression of constituent 1 by 2 is also the curve of solubility of 1 in 2.

Some systems that exhibit nearly ideal behaviour over the whole range have been noted in section 9.34. Others that behave similarly are solutions of naphthalene and similar substances in hydrocarbons and other non-polar liquids (fig. 61 a).† Many systems exhibit considerable deviations, however. For instance, metallic salts such as sodium chloride are many times more soluble in water than would be expected from their high melting-points and heats of fusion if the solutions were ideal; their high solubility is due to the strong forces leading to hydration of the ions.‡ The simplest behaviour, after ideal behaviour, is shown by such solutions as those of sulphur, phosphorus, and iodine in organic solvents. These are called *regular solutions*; their properties will be considered in section 11.2. Solubility studies are particularly convenient for these solutions, though they have the disadvantage that only one concentration can be used at each temperature in a given solvent. Some typical curves are shown in fig. 61 a, b.§

The activity coefficient of the solute is very simply obtained, as follows. For many substances, L_f is known from calorimetric experiments, and it is then possible to calculate the 'ideal' solubility s^{id} at a given temperature by putting $f_2 = 1$ in equation 50:

$$\ln s^{\mathrm{id}} = -\frac{L_f}{R}\left(\frac{1}{T_s} - \frac{1}{T_f^0}\right). \tag{51}$$

A plot of s^{id} calculated in this way against $1/T_s$ is evidently linear.

† Hildebrand and Scott, *Solubility of Non-electrolytes* (Reinhold, 1950), pp. 283–4.

‡ Cf. N. V. Sidgwick, *The Electronic Theory of Valency* (Oxford, 1927), pp. 138–49.

§ From Hildebrand and Scott, op. cit., pp. 273–5.

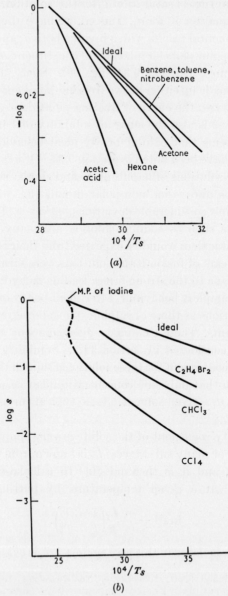

FIG. 61. (a) Plots of $\log_{10} s$ against $1/T_s$ for the solubility of naphthalene in various solvents. (b) Plots of $\log_{10} s$ against $1/T_s$ for the solubility of iodine in various solvents.

If we compare the actual solubility s of some substance with s^{id} at the same temperature, it is clear from 50 and 51 that

$$s^{id} = f_2 s, \quad \text{or} \quad f_2 = s^{id}/s. \tag{52}$$

Thus the deviations from ideality of the plot of s against $1/T_s$ give at once a measure of $\ln f_2$. This will still be true when the temperature-variation of L_f is taken into account.

For electrolyte solutions, in which solubilities can usually be measured only at relatively low values of solute concentration x_2, the activity scale adopted is that of convention II of section 9.24; in a solution dilute enough to be ideal, $f_2 = 1$ and $a_2 = x_2$. Then equation 49 gives

$$\ln s + \frac{L_f}{RT_s} = A - \ln f_2, \tag{53}$$

where A is some constant depending on the solvent and solute. The right-hand side becomes equal to A when the solution is dilute enough to be ideal, for then $f_2 = 1$ and $\ln f_2 = 0$. Thus if we determine the solubility s at a series of temperatures T_s chosen so that s decreases, and compute $(\ln s + L_f/RT_s)$ for each determination, we shall find that the values of this quantity tend to a constant, which is equal to A. Once the constant A has been found for a given solvent and solute, the activity coefficient can be calculated from the solubility using equation 53.

Changes in activity coefficient due to the addition of a second electrolyte may also be studied. So long as the solid phase consists of the pure constituent 2, the condition of equilibrium $\mu_2^{solid} = \mu_2^{soln}$ holds good, and therefore so does the whole argument leading to equation 49 or 53. Then for saturation at a fixed temperature, either of these equations gives

$$a_2 = sf_2 = \text{a constant, } k. \tag{54}$$

Hence the activity coefficient f_2 of the salt whose solubility is measured, in a solution containing a second salt such as potassium chloride, can be found from the solubility s once the constant k has been determined. This can be done by measuring s at various concentrations c of added salt and extrapolating to $c = 0$, when $f_2 = 1$ and so the intercept s' gives $k = 1/s'$. The results are of interest in testing the Debye–Hückel theory of strong electrolyte solutions (section 12.26). Some results are shown in fig. 62.†

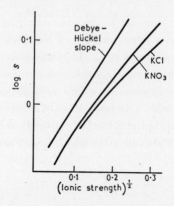

Fig. 62. Solubility of barium iodate in aqueous potassium chloride and potassium nitrate solutions; plots of $\log_{10} s$ against square root of ionic strength.

The measurement of solubilities.‡ Two main methods are used. (*a*) Mixtures of known amounts of the two constituents are made up, and the temperature adjusted until a saturated solution is formed. Mixtures of volatile substances are handled in sealed glass tubes. (*b*) The temperature is kept fixed and the solvent allowed to come to equilibrium with excess of solute; afterwards the solution is analysed. The solvent and solute may simply be shaken in a flask in a thermostat, or the solvent may be made to trickle down a tower containing the solute, equilibrium being reached when the concentration of the resulting solution is independent of the rate of flow.§

Three-dimensional representation of the P–T–x relations for solutions. At this point it is worth pointing out that we have given examples of the following relations. (i) The pressure-temperature relation at constant composition for solution-vapour

† Macdougall and Davies, *J. Chem. Soc.*, 1935, 1416.

‡ Reviews are given by Zimmerman, *Chem. Rev.*, 1952, **51**, 25, and in Weissberger (ed.), *Physical Methods of Organic Chemistry* (Interscience Publishers, 2nd edn. 1949), vol. i, chap. 7, pp. 313–21.

§ Brønsted and LaMer, *J. Amer. Chem. Soc.*, 1924, **46**, 555; Davies, *J. Chem. Soc.*, 1938, 277; Davies and Griffiths, *Trans. Faraday Soc.*, 1953, **49**, 1405; Bell and George, ibid., p. 619.

equilibrium (section 9.22). (ii) The pressure-composition relation at constant temperature, for solution-vapour equilibrium (sections 9.31, 9.32). (iii) The temperature-composition relation at constant pressure, both for solution-vapour and for solution-solid equilibrium (sections 9.33, 9.34, 9.35). These relations can be represented by a three-dimensional diagram, of which figs. 53, 57, 58, 60, etc. are sections in particular planes. The construction of this diagram is left to the reader as an exercise.

9.36. *The osmotic pressure of a solution*

Osmosis and osmotic pressure. If an aqueous sugar solution is separated from water by a membrane made of parchment or various other substances, water passes through the membrane into the solution. This process is called osmosis. The membrane allows water to pass into the solution, but does not allow cane-sugar to pass into the water; it is said to be semi-permeable. The direction of movement of the water can be reversed by applying a sufficient pressure to the solvent. The excess pressure on the solvent which is just enough to halt the movement, and so to

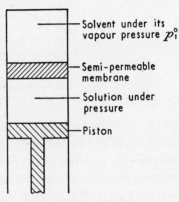

Fig. 63. Osmotic pressure (diagrammatic).

bring about equilibrium, at constant temperature, is called the *osmotic pressure*. Thus if a pressure P^{soln} must be exerted on the solution to bring it into osmotic equilibrium with the solvent under its vapour pressure p_1^0, the osmotic pressure π is defined as the excess pressure:

$$\pi = P^{\text{soln}} - p_1^0. \tag{55}$$

This excess pressure is not perceptibly different if the solvent is exposed to atmospheric pressure, and the osmotic pressure is commonly measured under these conditions.

Thermodynamically, the interpretation of osmosis is that the chemical potential and activity of the solvent species are less in the solution than in the pure solvent, and that migration occurs in the direction of lower chemical potential (section 4.7). The interpretation of osmotic pressure is that the chemical potential of the solvent species in the solution can be raised by applying pressure, according to equation 13 of section 9.23 (p. 317); when it becomes equal to the chemical potential of the pure solvent

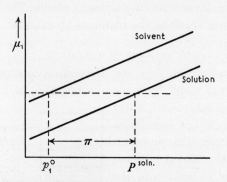

FIG. 64. Plots of μ_1 against pressure for solvent and solution at a fixed temperature (diagrammatic). The zero for μ_1 is arbitrary.

which is not under increased pressure, equilibrium is set up. The situation is illustrated in fig. 64. Alternatively, we can regard the osmotic pressure as the excess pressure required to raise the vapour pressure of the solution, according to equation 5 of section 7.4 (p. 285), until it equals that of the solvent.

In a thermodynamic treatment we are not under any obligation to discuss the *mechanism* of osmosis, which is not well understood. As a working hypothesis we may imagine that the membrane is traversed from side to side by capillary channels, which are not wetted by solution or solvent; then distillation will occur from the solvent, which has the higher vapour pressure, to the solution, unless the vapour pressure of the solution is raised by applying an external pressure.† The original theory suggested by van 't Hoff, that osmotic pressure is due to bombardment of the vessel and membrane by solute molecules, is definitely wrong. It gives incorrect results when quantitatively applied,‡ and is based on

† Cf. Callender, *Proc. Roy. Soc.* A, 1908, **80**, 476, 483.
‡ Guggenheim, *Modern Thermodynamics* (Methuen, 1933), pp. 85–88.

the notion that a solute molecule is in the same situation as in a gas, whereas the evidence suggests rather that, being closely surrounded by solvent molecules, its situation more nearly resembles that in a liquid. For instance, the entropies of solution of gases in various solvents† are not zero but are of the same order of magnitude as the entropy changes on condensation.

The mechanism of semi-permeability also is not fully understood, and may be different for different membranes. It does not appear to depend on chemical effects, since septa of unglazed porcelain have been reported to show semi-permeability.‡ In the suggested working hypothesis, the membrane is semi-permeable because the capillaries are not wetted and consequently only vapour can pass along them. A simple sieve action may explain semi-permeability towards high polymer solutions. There is evidence that electrical effects are important in copper ferrocyanide membranes.§

Thermodynamics of osmotic pressure. The condition for equilibrium as regards transfer of solvent species between the solvent under its vapour pressure and the solution under an excess pressure is, as represented in fig. 64,

$$\mu_1^{\text{soln}} = \mu_1^{\text{solvent}}.$$

But the solvent remains in the same state, at constant temperature, pressure, and composition, so that its chemical potential is constant. Hence the condition for equilibrium is

$$\mu_1^{\text{soln}} = \text{constant},$$

or for any small change:

$$d\mu_1^{\text{soln}} = 0. \tag{56}$$

At constant temperature, the factors affecting μ_1^{soln} are the concentration and the pressure on the solution. Thus in general terms, using equation 3 of section 9.21 (p. 313):

$$d\mu_1^{\text{soln}} = V_1 \, dP^{\text{soln}} + (\partial \mu_1 / \partial x_2)_{T,P}^{\text{soln}} \, dx_2^{\text{soln}}. \tag{57}$$

† Frank and Evans, *J. Chem. Phys.*, 1945, **13**, 507.
‡ Bigelow and Bartell, *J. Amer. Chem. Soc.*, 1909, **31**, 1194.
§ Willis, *Trans. Faraday Soc.*, 1942, **38**, 169; 1944, **40**, 520.

For equilibrium, this expression must be equated to zero. Inserting as usual $(\partial \mu_1/\partial x_2)^{\text{soln}}_{T,P} = RT(\partial \ln a_1/\partial x_2)$ we find

$$\frac{dP^{\text{soln}}}{dx_2} = -\frac{RT}{V_1}\left(\frac{\partial \ln a_1}{\partial x_2}\right)_{T,P}. \tag{58}$$

Here P^{soln} is the pressure required to bring a solution of concentration x_2 into osmotic equilibrium with the solvent. Equation 58 means that (dP^{soln}/dx_2) reflects the change of activity on adding solute at constant temperature and pressure, represented by $(\partial \ln a_1/\partial x_2)_{T,P}$; thus a_1 in this equation is the activity at pressure p_1^0, not at P^{soln}. This being kept in mind, we can omit the dx_2's and rewrite the relation:

$$d\ln a_1 = -(V_1/RT)\,dP^{\text{soln}}. \tag{59}$$

If we integrate this between the pressure limits p_1^0 and P^{soln}, the value of a_1 corresponding to p_1^0 will be zero since p_1^0 refers to the pure solvent in which $a_1 = 1$. Hence

$$\ln a_1 = -\frac{1}{RT}\int_{p_1^0}^{P^{\text{soln}}} V_1\,dP^{\text{soln}}. \tag{60}$$

This is an exact equation. If we assume as a first approximation that V_1 is constant, which implies that it is independent of concentration (as in ideal solutions) and also of pressure, we can integrate to

$$\ln a_1 = -\frac{V_1}{RT}(P^{\text{soln}} - p_1^0)$$

$$= -\frac{\pi V_1}{RT}. \tag{61}$$

This equation permits the determination of the activity a_1 from the osmotic pressure. For precise work at high pressures, the dependence of V_1 on pressure may be taken into account and expressed in terms of the compressibility.

Comparison of equation 61 with equation 28, $a_1 = p_1/p_1^0$, which applies to any solution whose vapour can be regarded as a perfect gas (section 9.31, p. 321), gives the relation between the osmotic pressure π and the vapour pressure p_1 of the solvent over the solution:

$$\frac{\pi V_1}{RT} = \ln\left(\frac{p_1^0}{p_1}\right). \tag{62}$$

This has been experimentally verified for aqueous sugar solutions at $0°$ C (Table 39).[†] Historically, equation 62 was derived independently of 28 and 61, by expressing the work done in transferring solvent from solvent to solution in terms of (a) vapour pressure and (b) osmotic pressure, and equating the two values.[‡]

TABLE 39

Comparison of osmotic pressure and vapour pressure for some aqueous solutions at $0°$ C

Solute	Concentration, g per 100 g water	$\frac{RT}{V_1}\ln\frac{p_1^0}{p_1}$ atm	π atm	f_1
Sucrose . . .	56·50	43·9	43·8	0·99
	81·20	67·4	67·7	0·99
	112·00	100·5	100·4	0·98
	141·00	134·9	134·7	0·97
α-Methyl glucoside .	35·00	48·3	48·1	0·99
	45·00	64·2	64·0	0·99
	55·00	80·5	81·0	0·98₅
	64·00	115·7	115·9	0·97

The simplest mode of variation of osmotic pressure with concentration is shown by dilute aqueous solutions of sugars and their derivatives; for these solutions the measured osmotic pressures give, on applying equation 61, activities a_1 nearly equal to the mole fraction, so that the solutions are approximately ideal (section 10.16):

$$\ln x_1 = -\pi V_1/RT. \tag{63}$$

Stronger solutions deviate somewhat from ideality, as is shown by the values of f_1 given in Table 39. Solutions of high polymers in solvents such as benzene also deviate systematically (section

† Data of Berkeley, Hartley, and Burton, *Phil. Trans.* A, 1919, **218**, 344.
‡ Porter, *Proc. Roy. Soc.* A, 1907, **79**, 519.

11.3). Very few measurements have been made on electrolyte solutions, since no suitable membrane has been found.

The measurement of osmotic pressure.† (*a*) *Aqueous solutions.* The osmotic pressure of a 0·1 molar solution of sucrose in water at 25° C is about 2·5 atmospheres. Accurate investigations on aqueous solutions of non-electrolytes, in which pressures up to

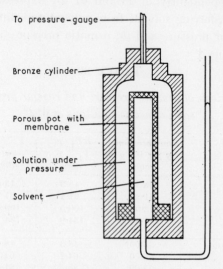

FIG. 65. Osmotic pressure apparatus of Frazer and Myrick‡ (diagrammatic).

270 atmospheres have been measured, have all made use of the membrane which is formed when dilute solutions of Cu^{++} and $Fe(CN)_6^{4-}$ ions come into contact. This copper ferrocyanide membrane can be precipitated inside the walls of a porous pot, either by diffusion or electrolytically. In some forms of apparatus the solution was contained in a confined volume, so that as solvent entered by osmosis the pressure rose, until after some hours the equilibrium pressure was set up (fig. 65).‡ In others, an opposing

† Reviews are given by Frazer in Taylor's *Treatise on Physical Chemistry* (Macmillan, 2nd edn. 1931), vol. i, chap. 7, and by McGoury and Mark in Weissberger, *Physical Methods of Organic Chemistry* (1949), vol. i, chap. 8, pp. 488–549.

‡ Morse, *Publications of the Carnegie Institute*, no. 198 (1914); Frazer and Myrick, *J. Amer. Chem. Soc.*, 1916, **38**, 1907.

pressure was applied to the solution and adjusted until there was no movement of solvent in either direction (fig. 66).†

(b) *High-polymer solutions.* The osmotic pressure of a 1 per cent. solution of a polymer of molecular weight 200,000 is in the region of 10 mm of water. Membranes of collodion and various other substances are satisfactorily semi-permeable for polymers

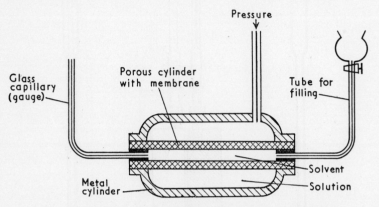

FIG. 66. Osmotic pressure apparatus of Berkeley and Hartley†
(diagrammatic).

of molecular weight 20,000 to 500,000. Large membranes can be used and equilibrium is quickly attained; the solvent itself is used as manometric liquid. One form of apparatus is shown in fig. 67.

(c) *The vapour phase as semi-permeable membrane.* Osmotic pressures have not been measured for solutions of electrolytes in water, nor for non-electrolytes of low molecular weight in organic solvents, because no semi-permeable membrane is available; the copper ferrocyanide membrane is peptized by electrolytes and cannot be prepared in the absence of water, and the membranes which behave satisfactorily towards high polymers are permeable to solutes of lower molecular weight. Attempts have been made to use the vapour phase, which would be a perfect semi-permeable membrane for any solution containing

† Berkeley and Hartley, *Phil. Trans.* A, 1906, **206**, 481; *Proc. Roy. Soc.* A, 1916, **92**, 477.

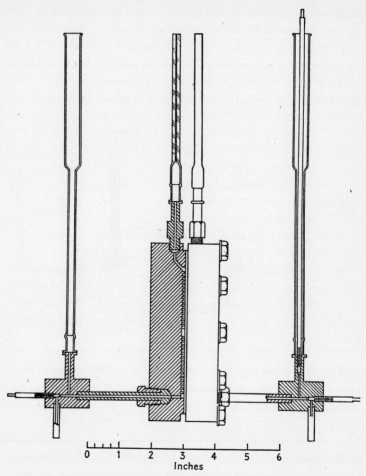

FIG. 67. Osmotic pressure apparatus of Fuoss and Mead.† The vertical
tubes at the sides are for filling. The movement of the meniscus in the
capillary is followed.

an involatile solute. The principle is illustrated in fig. 68.‡ The
solvent is confined below a porous disk of sintered glass, and a
tension is exerted on it by a mercury column below. Vapour

† Fuoss and Mead, *J. Phys. Chem.*, 1943, **47**, 59.
‡ Townend, *J. Amer. Chem. Soc.*, 1928, **50**, 2958; Ullmann, *Z. phys. Chem.*
A, 1931, **156**, 419; Martin and Schultz, *J. Phys. Chem.*, 1931, **35**, 628;
Williamson, *Proc. Roy. Soc.* A, 1948, **195**, 97.

can pass through the porous disk, to or from the solution. The length of the mercury column is adjusted until there is equilibrium. The tension on the solvent has the same effect as the pressure exerted on the solution in the more usual type of apparatus, in bringing solvent and solution into osmotic equilibrium. The great practical difficulty in the method is that a small temperature-difference between solvent and solution causes solvent to distil from one to the other, so that temperature control must be very exact; and further, that temperature-equilibrium is easily upset when distillation occurs, because of the considerable heat changes occurring at the separated liquid-vapour interfaces. The apparatus appears to have been used successfully in very few investigations.†

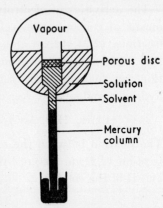

Fig. 68. Principle of porous-disk osmometer.

9.37. *Distribution of a solute between two immiscible solvents*

The condition of equilibrium for the distribution of a solute between two solvents α and β is

$$\mu_2^\alpha = \mu_2^\beta.$$

But the activities in the two solvents are defined (on convention I) by

$$\mu_2^\alpha = \mu_2^0 + RT \ln a_2^\alpha$$

and

$$\mu_2^\beta = \mu_2^0 + RT \ln a_2^\beta.$$

Consequently the activities of the solute in the two solutions, a_2^α and a_2^β, are equal. Thus if we know a_2 in one solution—if, for instance, it is dilute enough to be ideal, so that $a_2 = x_2$—then we know it in the other. Activity coefficients of picric acid in benzene have been found by determining the distribution

† Eichelberger, *J. Amer. Chem. Soc.*, 1931, **53**, 2025.

between benzene and water and treating the aqueous solution as ideal.†

9.38. *The electromotive force of concentration cells*

The activities of electrolytes in solution can be studied by means of concentration cells. These will be dealt with later (sections 12.24, 12.25) and we will only briefly mention them here. An example of a 'concentration cell without liquid junction', or 'back-to-back' cell, is the following combination of hydrogen and silver–silver chloride electrodes:

$$(Pt)H_2, HCl, AgCl; Ag–Ag; AgCl, HCl, H_2(Pt).$$

The relation between the e.m.f. E and the 'mean activity' $a_\pm$ (section 12.21, p. 388) of hydrochloric acid in the two halves A and B of the cell is

$$EF = 2RT \ln(a_\pm)_A/(a_\pm)_B. \tag{64}$$

This relation has been used to determine the activities of many electrolytes.

If the electrolyte is volatile, as in the above example, the e.m.f. may be expressed in terms of vapour pressure. If the vapour behaves as a perfect gas, $a_\pm = p_2/p_2^0$, and equation 64 gives

$$EF = 2RT \ln(p_2)_A/(p_2)_B. \tag{65}$$

This equation has been verified for solutions in water‡ and in methyl alcohol.§

9.39. *Comparison of the methods for determining activities*

The advantages and disadvantages of the various methods of determining activities may be compared under several headings. (i) Accuracy, which may be measured by the magnitude of the effect in, say, 0·1 molar solution, divided by the least effect detectable. Here the freezing-point method scores high marks, and the osmotic pressure method for high polymers. (ii) Variability of temperature; the temperature can be varied in all except

---

† Lewis and Randall, *Thermodynamics* (1923), p. 330.
‡ Bates and Kirschman, *J. Amer. Chem. Soc.*, 1919, **41**, 1991.
§ Nonhebel and Hartley, *Phil. Mag.*, 1925, **50** (vi), 729.

the freezing-point method. (iii) Need for thermal data in the calculation; this is a limitation in accurate work on boiling-points, freezing-points and solubility. (iv) Applicability; for instance, the e.m.f. method is restricted to electrolytes, the boiling-point and vapour-pressure methods are simpler if one constituent is involatile, and the osmotic pressure method is restricted to those systems for which a semi-permeable membrane can be found.

Results obtained by the various methods agree well where they can be compared. Table 40 permits a comparison of the values obtained by measurements of vapour pressure, freezing-point, boiling-point, and electromotive force for aqueous solutions of potassium chloride at 25° C. The quantity calculated is the relative molar lowering of vapour pressure $(p_1^0-p_1)/mp_1^0$, which is equal to $(1-a_1)/m$.

TABLE 40

Relative molar vapour-pressure lowering for aqueous solutions of KCl *at* 25°, *calculated from various measurements*†

Concentration m	$10^5 \times relative\ lowering$			
	V.P.	F.P.	B.P.	e.m.f.
0·1	3,332	3,347	3,321	3,323
0·2	3,279	3,290	3,305	3,270
0·5	3,212	3,230	3,223	3,209
1·0	3,128	3,190	3,182	3,169
1·5	3,173	3,176	3,198	3,167
2·0	3,180	3,188	3,221	3,190
3·0	3,210	3,107	3,253	3,132

9.4. Heats, entropies, and free energies of mixing

In section 9.3 we expressed the properties of solutions in terms of the chemical potentials (or activities), that is in terms of the *partial* free energies of the constituents in the solution. We now turn to the changes in free energy and other thermodynamic functions undergone by the system *as a whole* when the constituents are mixed at constant pressure. The change of heat content can be directly measured; the others must be found

† Robinson and Sinclair, *J. Amer. Chem. Soc.*, 1934, **56**, 1832; vapour pressures from Robinson, *Trans. Roy. Soc. N.Z.*, 1945, **75**, 203, cf. *J. Phys. Chem.*, 1956, **60**, 501.

from determinations of the activities. We shall see later (p. 373) that these functions can be used to characterize ideal solutions and various types of non-ideal solutions.

Heats of mixing. The heat that can be experimentally measured is the heat absorbed or evolved when finite amounts of the constituents are mixed. This is called the *total* or *integral heat of dilution* if solvent is added to a solution; if solute is added, it may be called a *heat of solution*. These heats of mixing can be related to the properties of the constituents as follows.

Before mixing, the heat content of n_1 moles of solvent is $n_1 H_1^0$, where H_1^0 is the molar heat content; similarly that of n_2 moles of solute is $n_2 H_2^0$. After mixing, the heat content of the whole may be obtained by supposing the solution to be built up from infinitesimal increments at constant temperature and pressure:

$$dH^{\text{soln}} = (\partial H/\partial n_1)_{T,P,n_2} dn_1 + (\partial H/\partial n_2)_{T,P,n_1} dn_2 = H_1 dn_1 + H_2 dn_2,$$
(1)

where H_1 and H_2 are the partial molar heat contents of the solvent and solute species in the solution. This equation can be integrated, at constant temperature, pressure, and composition, to give
$$H^{\text{soln}} = n_1 H_1 + n_2 H_2.$$
(2)

The change of heat content on mixing n_1 moles of solvent with n_2 moles of solute is thus

$$\Delta H_m = n_1 H_1 + n_2 H_2 - n_1 H_1^0 - n_2 H_2^0$$
$$= n_1(H_1 - H_1^0) + n_2(H_2 - H_2^0).$$
(3)

For the formation of one mole of solution, we must divide by $(n_1 + n_2)$, and so obtain

$$\Delta H_m = x_1(H_1 - H_1^0) + x_2(H_2 - H_2^0).$$
(4)

Since the mixing is done at constant temperature and pressure, ΔH_m will be equal to the heat absorbed on mixing, q_m (section 2.5, p. 35). From the variation of q_m with x_1, therefore, it is possible to determine $(H_1 - H_1^0)$ and $(H_2 - H_2^0)$. These quantities are the *partial or differential molar heats of dilution and of solution* respectively; for the heat absorbed when dn_1 moles of solvent is added to a large volume of solution is the increase in heat content of the solution $(H_1 \, dn_1)$ minus the heat content of the added solvent $(H_1^0 \, dn_1)$, that is $dn_1(H_1 - H_1^0)$, or $(H_1 - H_1^0)$ per mole; and similarly for $(H_2 - H_2^0)$. We have already met the partial molar heat of dilution, expressed in terms of the temperature-variation of a_1 (equation 12, p. 317); and the partial molar heat of solution is related to the temperature-variation of a_2 by a similar equation. Combining these relations with equation 4 gives

$$\Delta H_m = -RT^2[x_1(\partial \ln a_1/\partial T)_{P,x_1} + x_2(\partial \ln a_2/\partial T)_{P,x_1}]. \qquad (5)$$

The heat of mixing can therefore be computed from a knowledge of the activities over a range of temperature, as well as by direct calorimetric measurement. Heats of dilution are commonly small, and sensitive calorimeters are needed to measure them.† Equation 5 implies that for ideal solutions ΔH_m is zero, since the activities are then equal to the mole fractions, which do not vary with temperature. Experimentally, this is found to be approximately true for systems that have the other properties of ideal solutions (Chapter X). For non-ideal solutions, ΔH_m may be plotted against x_1; the results for mixtures of water and hydrogen peroxide are shown in fig. 70.

Free energy of mixing. The free energy of mixing may be expressed in terms of the properties of the constituents by a similar method. Corresponding to equation 1, the free energy of an infinitesimal quantity of solution is

$$dG^{\text{soln}} = (\partial G/\partial n_1)_{T,P,n_2} \, dn_1 + (\partial G/\partial n_2)_{T,P,n_1} \, dn_2$$
$$= \mu_1 \, dn_1 + \mu_2 \, dn_2. \qquad (6)$$

Hence for $(n_1 + n_2)$ moles of solution, we obtain by integration

$$G^{\text{soln}} = \mu_1 n_1 + \mu_2 n_2. \qquad (7)$$

But for n_1 moles of solvent and n_2 moles of solute, before mixing, the free energies are $\mu_1^0 n_1$ and $\mu_2^0 n_2$. The free energy change on mixing is therefore

$$\Delta G_m = n_1(\mu_1 - \mu_1^0) + n_2(\mu_2 - \mu_2^0). \qquad (8)$$

† e.g. Gucker, Pickard, and Planck, *J. Amer. Chem. Soc.*, 1939, **61**, 459; Meares, *Trans. Faraday Soc.*, 1949, **45**, 1066. See the review by Sturtevant in Weissberger, *Physical Methods of Organic Chemistry* (1949), vol. i, chap. 14.

Since $\mu_1 - \mu_1^0 = RT \ln a_1$, and $\mu_2 - \mu_2^0 = RT \ln a_2$, this may be written

$$\Delta G_m = RT(n_1 \ln a_1 + n_2 \ln a_2). \tag{9}$$

For one mole of solution the free energy of mixing is

$$\Delta G_m = RT(x_1 \ln a_1 + x_2 \ln a_2). \tag{10}$$

The free energy of mixing can therefore be computed from the activities. We notice that, since a_1 and a_2 are always less than unity in solution, ΔG_m is always negative, as it must be if mixing is to occur spontaneously. For an ideal solution it is equal to

$$\Delta G_m^{\mathrm{id}} = RT(x_1 \ln x_1 + x_2 \ln x_2). \tag{11}$$

This function is plotted against x_1 in fig. 69. For non-ideal solutions it is convenient to plot the difference between the actual ΔG_m and ΔG_m^{id}.† This quantity is called the excess free energy of mixing, ΔG_m^{E}, and from equation 10 it is evidently equal to $RT(x_1 \ln f_1 + x_2 \ln f_2)$. Some results are shown in fig. 70.

The partial molar free energy of dilution, found by differentiating equation 9 with respect to n_1 at constant n_2, is $RT \ln a_1$ (p. 316), or in ideal solutions $RT \ln x_1$.

Entropy of mixing. The relation $\Delta S_m = -(\Delta G_m - \Delta H_m)/T$, together with the above relations for ΔG_m and ΔH_m, gives for the entropy of mixing:

$$\begin{aligned}
\Delta S_m &= -R[x_1 \ln a_1 + x_2 \ln a_2 + \\
&\quad + Tx_1(\partial \ln a_1/\partial T)_{P,x_1} + Tx_2(\partial \ln a_2/\partial T)_{P,x_2}] \\
&= -R[x_1 \ln a_1 + x_2 \ln a_2] + x_1(H_1^0 - H_1)/T + x_2(H_2^0 - H_2)/T.
\end{aligned} \tag{12}$$

For an ideal solution, when the activities are equal to the mole fractions and independent of temperature, this becomes

$$\Delta S_m^{\mathrm{id}} = -R(x_1 \ln x_1 + x_2 \ln x_2). \tag{13}$$

In fig. 69, $T\Delta S_m^{\mathrm{id}}$ is plotted against x_1. The excess entropy of mixing for non-ideal solutions may be plotted, as in fig. 70. The data required for such a plot are evidently the activities

---

† Scatchard, *Chem. Rev.*, 1931, **8**, 321; Everett, *Disc. Faraday Soc.*, 1953, no. 15, 'The Equilibrium Properties of Solutions of Non-electrolytes', pp. 126–30.

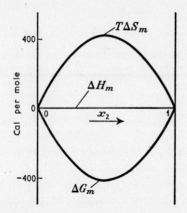

FIG. 69. Free energy, heat, and entropy of mixing of ideal solutions, at 25° C, as functions of compositions.

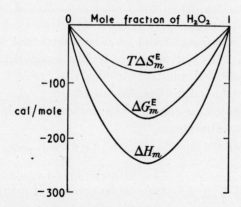

FIG. 70. Excess free energy, heat, and entropy of mixing of hydrogen peroxide and water at 75° C.†

a_1 and a_2 and either their temperature-coefficients or the partial molar heats of solution and dilution. For instance, measurements of osmotic pressure at various temperatures have been used to determine ΔS_m for polymer solutions.‡

A demonstration that there is an entropy of mixing, even at 0° K, has been given by calorimetric measurements on glycerol,

† Mitchell and Wynne-Jones, *Disc. Faraday Soc.*, 1953, no. 15, 'The Equilibrium Properties of Solutions of Non-electrolytes', p. 162. Curves for alcohol-water mixtures are also given in this paper.

‡ e.g. Eley, Saunders, and Sparks, *Trans. Faraday Soc.*, 1952, **48**, 758.

water, and a mixture of the two, down to low temperatures. Starting with two constituents A and B at $0°$ K, it is possible to pass to a mixture of the two at $273°$ K by two paths, for which the entropy changes must be equal. By the first path, A and B are mixed at $0°$ K and the mixture raised to $273°$ K; then

$$S_{\text{mixture (273)}} - S_{\text{unmixed (0)}} = \Delta S_m + \int_0^{273} C_{\text{mixture}}\, d\ln T. \quad (14)$$

By the second path, A and B are raised separately from $0°$ K to $273°$ K, and then the ice is melted into the glycerol; the entropy change $\Delta S'$ for this last step is found by determining $\Delta H'$ calorimetrically and $\Delta G'$ from vapour pressures. Then

$$S_{\text{mixture (273)}} - S_{\text{unmixed (0)}} = \Delta S' + \int_0^{273} C_A\, d\ln T + \int_0^{273} C_B\, d\ln T. \quad (15)$$

Comparing equations 14 and 15, it is evident that ΔS_m can be determined. The experimental value for the particular glycerol-water mixture used was $1\cdot30\pm0\cdot36$ cal deg^{-1} mole^{-1}, compared with $1\cdot14$ calculated from equation 13.†

Volume change on mixing. The volume of an infinitesimal amount of solution is

$$dV^{\text{soln}} = (\partial V/\partial n_1)_{T,P}\, dn_1 + (\partial V/\partial n_2)_{T,P}\, dn_2$$
$$= V_1\, dn_1 + V_2\, dn_2,$$

where V_1 and V_2 are the partial molar volumes. Integration gives for the volume of (n_1+n_2) moles of solution

$$V^{\text{soln}} = V_1 n_1 + V_2 n_2. \quad (16)$$

Before mixing, the separate volumes are $V_1^0 n_1$ and $V_2^0 n_2$. Thus the volume change on mixing is, for (n_1+n_2) moles,

$$\Delta V_m = n_1(V_1 - V_1^0) + n_2(V_2 - V_2^0). \quad (17)$$

For one mole of solution, therefore,

$$\Delta V_m = x_1(V_1 - V_1^0) + x_2(V_2 - V_2^0). \quad (18)$$

This equation relates the volume change to the changes of the

---

† Simon, *Handbuch der Physik*, vol. 10 (Springer, Berlin, 1926) p. 392; Eastman, *Chem. Rev.*, 1936, **18**, 263. For a demonstration for a solid solution of AgCl in AgBr, see Eastman and Milner, *J. Chem. Phys.*, 1933, **1**, 444.

partial molar volumes. Using equation 13 of section 9.23 (p. 317), the relation may be expressed as

$$\Delta V_m = RT[x_1(\partial \ln a_1/\partial P)_{T,x_1} + x_2(\partial \ln a_2/\partial P)_{T,x_2}]. \qquad (19)$$

For an ideal solution, a_1 and a_2 are independent of pressure, so that both terms in the bracket are zero, and consequently $\Delta V_m = 0$ and there is no volume change on mixing.

Some experimental data on mixing. We can now turn our attention to some specific classes of actual solutions. A broad picture of the relation of activity coefficients (section 9.3) to the heat and volume changes on mixing (section 9.4) is given by Table 41,† which summarizes results on mixing equal quantities of various substances. In the first column, Q is the heat evolved; in the second, ΔV is the volume change; in the third is given the ratio of the ideal total vapour pressure P^{id} (which would be observed if there were a linear relation between P and x_1) to the measured value P. The figures in each column may be compared. It will be seen that the solutions whose vapour pressures are nearly ideal tend to have relatively small values of Q and ΔV; those which have positive deviations ($P/P^{id} > 1$), corresponding to solute-solvent repulsion, tend to have negative Q and positive ΔV; and those which have negative deviation, corresponding to solute-solvent attraction, tend to have positive Q and negative ΔV.

TABLE 41

Solution	Q cal/g	$10^4 \Delta V$	$\dfrac{P}{P^{id}}$
Ethyl acetate-methyl acetate .	−0·21	−5	1·03
Methyl alcohol-propyl alcohol .	−0·55	−11	1·01
Benzene-carbon tetrachloride .	−0·25	51	1·03
Benzene-toluene . . .	−0·22	10	1·06
Benzene-ethyl ether . . .	0	−60	1·00
Ether-ethyl acetate . . .	−0·70	−61	1·00
Benzene-ethyl acetate . .	−0·36	15	1·43
Benzene-acetic acid . . .	−1·43	120	1·55
Chloroform-carbon disulphide .	−1·59	53	1·15
Acetone-carbon disulphide . .	−5·00	140	1·59
Chloroform-acetone . . .	+5·56	−20	0·79
Chloroform-ether . . .	+6·34	−190	0·88

† G. C. Schmidt, *Z. phys. Chem.* A, 1926, **121**, 247, 252.

X

IDEAL SOLUTIONS

I**T** is evident from the results mentioned in Chapter IX that the type of solution whose behaviour is thermodynamically simplest is the ideal solution, in which the activity of the solvent a_1 is equal to its mole fraction x_1, so that the activity coefficient $f_1 = a_1/x_1 = 1$.† The statement that $a_1 = x_1$, taken with the definition of the activity (section 9.23, p. 315), implies of course that

$$\mu_1 - \mu_1^0 = RT \ln x_1. \tag{1}$$

This means that (i) the chemical potential of the solvent in solution, relative to the pure solvent, is proportional to $\ln x_1$; (ii) it is also proportional to the absolute temperature; (iii) the proportionality constant is equal to the gas constant, R. To test such statements requires measurements of the activity (by the methods of section 9.3) over a range of concentrations and temperatures.

For dilute solutions, we may make the approximation

$$\ln x_1 = \ln(1 - x_2) \simeq -x_2;$$

this is true within about 1 per cent. when $x_2 = 0.01$. We may then use in place of equation 1:

$$\mu_1 - \mu_1^0 = -RT x_2. \tag{2}$$

It is found experimentally that some solutions approximate closely to ideal behaviour over the whole range of composition from mole fraction 0 to 1. Examples are mixtures of hexane and heptane, of ethanol and methanol, and of ethylene bromide and propylene bromide. Others agree within a few per cent. over a large range, for instance chlorine and carbon tetrachloride, iodine and stannic iodide, chlorobenzene and naphthalene. Others again show nearly ideal behaviour when dilute, as do sugars in water. All solutions approach ideal behaviour when they are made dilute enough. In molecular terms, we may say in general

† For the activity and activity coefficient of the solute, see p. 319.

that solutions appear to approach ideal behaviour in proportion as they fulfil the conditions that solvent and solute consist of molecules of similar types and similar sizes, and are free from specific interactions such as hydrogen-bonding.

We now collect up and extend the results obtained in sections 9.31 and 9.4 for the properties of ideal solutions.

10.1. The colligative properties of ideal solutions

10.11. *The vapour pressure of the solvent*

We found in section 9.31 (p. 320) that the activity of the solvent is given in general by $a_1 = P_1^*/(P_1^*)^0$ (equation 29); or, if the vapour behaves as a perfect gas mixture, by $a_1 = p_1/p_1^0$ (equation 28). For an ideal solution, therefore, putting $a_1 = x_1$, we find in general

$$x_1 = P_1^*/(P_1^*)^0, \tag{3}$$

and, as an approximation whose accuracy depends on the deviations of the vapour from the laws of perfect gas mixtures,

$$x_1 = p_1/p_1^0 \tag{4}$$

or

$$\frac{p_1^0 - p_1}{p_1^0} = 1 - x_1 = x_2. \tag{4a}$$

Equations 4 and 4a are statements of *Raoult's law*,† which in its original form stated a proportionality between the relative lowering of vapour pressure $(p_1^0 - p_1)/p_1^0$, and the concentration, for various organic solvents and solutes. The vapour-pressure plots for solutions that are ideal over the whole range are exemplified in fig. 52 (p. 323), which shows Zawidski's results for mixtures of propylene and ethylene bromides.‡ Similar plots are given by benzene-toluene, hexane-heptane, and various other mixtures.§ The behaviour of non-ideal solutions approaches Raoult's law at low concentrations, as may be seen from figs. 53 and 54 (p. 324), in which the plots of p_1 against x_1 become tangential to the line representing ideal behaviour when x_2 becomes small. Aqueous solutions of cane-sugar below a concentration

† Raoult, *C.R. Acad. Sci.*, 1887, **104**, 1430; *Z. phys. Chem.*, 1888, **2**, 353.

‡ Zawidski, *Z. phys. Chem.*, 1900, **35**, 129.

§ For a list see Hildebrand and Scott, *Solubility of Non-electrolytes* (1950), p. 210, and note †, p. 359.

of 0·1 M follow Raoult's law closely, but show appreciable deviations at 1 M;[†] aqueous solutions of mannite follow the law closely up to 0·8 M.[‡] Some of the liquid mixtures have been investigated over the temperature range from 0° to 60°.

10.12. *The vapour pressure of the solute*

Henry's law states that the vapour pressure of the solute in an ideal solution is proportional to its mole fraction. This relation may be derived from our definitions of ideal solutions as follows. On convention I (p. 318), f_2 is constant in the range for which the solution is ideal, and so a_2 is proportional to x_2 so that $a_2 = k'x_2$ where k' is some constant (section 9.25, p. 319). The general relation between activity and vapour pressure, from equation 35 a of section 9.32 (p. 327), is $a_2 = p_2/p_2^0$. Hence, for ideal solutions,

$$p_2 = k''x_2, \tag{5}$$

where $k'' = k'p_2^0$ and so is constant at a given temperature.

On convention II, $a_2 = x_2$ for the range in which the solution is ideal, and from equation 35 b of section 9.32 we have the general relation $a_2 = kp_2$. Hence, for ideal solutions,

$$x_2 = kp_2, \tag{6}$$

which has the same form as equation 5.

Equations 5 and 6 are statements of Henry's law. In the particular case of solutions ideal over the whole range, $x_2 = p_2/p_2^0$; so that the constant $k = 1/p_2^0$. This situation is shown in fig. 52 (p. 323). Results for solutions that are ideal only when dilute are shown in figs. 53 and 54 (p. 324); the plots of p_2 against x_2 approach linearity when x_2 is small, but the constant is no longer equal to $1/p_2^0$.[§]

Any solution that obeys Raoult's law for p_1 over a certain range of concentration must obey Henry's law for p_2 over the same range, for the two are related by the Duhem–Margules relation $x_1 d \ln p_1 + x_2 d \ln p_2 = 0$ (section 9.32, p. 328). From Raoult's law, $p_1 = p_1^0 x_1$, so that $d \ln p_1 = d \ln x_1$; substitution

---

† Berkeley and Hartley, *Phil. Trans.* A, 1919, **218**, 295.

‡ Frazer, Lovelace, and Rogers, *J. Amer. Chem. Soc.*, 1920, **42**, 1793.

§ The particular case of regular solutions is dealt with on p. 377.

in the Duhem–Margules relation gives

$$d \ln p_2 = -(x_1/x_2)d \ln x_1 = -dx_1/x_2 = dx_2/x_2 = d \ln x_2,$$

whence $p_2 = \text{constant} \times x_2$, which is Henry's law. The experimental relations between the two laws are shown in figs. 52 to 54.

10.13. *The boiling-point of an ideal solution*

The relation between the composition and the boiling-point T_e of an ideal solution of an involatile solute is obtained by putting $a_1 = x_1$ in equation 41 of section 9.33:

$$\frac{d \ln x_1}{dT_e} = -\frac{L_e}{RT_e^2}. \tag{7}$$

This is an exact relation. For *dilute* solutions, for which the temperature-elevation is small, we can put $L_e = \text{constant}$ and $T_e = T_e^0$ (the boiling-point of the pure solvent), and use the approximate equation 42 of section 9.33; also, we may put $\ln x_1 = -x_2$ (p. 360). We then obtain

$$\frac{\Delta T}{x_2} = \frac{R(T_e^0)^2}{L_e}. \tag{7 a}$$

If we use molal concentrations, $m = 1000x_2/M_1$ (p. 310), and so

$$\frac{\Delta T}{m} = \frac{RM_1(T_e^0)^2}{1000L_e} = \frac{R(T_e^0)^2}{1000L_e'}, \tag{8}$$

where L_e' is the latent heat of evaporation per *gram*.

Thus for ideal dilute solutions the boiling-point elevation ΔT will obey the following rules:

(i) For given solvent and solute, ΔT will be proportional to concentration.

(ii) For a given solvent, ΔT at a given mole fraction will be the same for all solutes.

(iii) On varying the solvent, ΔT for a given solute at a fixed mole fraction will be proportional to $(T_e^0)^2/L_e'$. The 'molecular elevation', i.e. the value of ΔT for a 1 M solution, will be $R_1(T_e^0)^2/1000L_e'$.

The linear relation between ΔT and concentration has been found to hold as a limiting law for various solutions, such as those of cane-sugar in water, or azobenzene in benzene, though deviations may be noted in the behaviour of these solutions at concentrations above about 0·1 M.† The molecular elevations have not usually been determined with any great accuracy, but Table 42 shows that various non-electrolyte solutions approximate to ideal behaviour.‡ The molecular weight of the solute can therefore be determined if ideal behaviour can be confidently expected.

TABLE 42

Elevation of the boiling-point for some non-electrolyte solutes

Solvent	Boiling-point at 1 atm, °K	L_e kcal/mole	Molecular elevation calc.	Molecular elevation obs.
Water . . .	373·2	9·72	0·513	0·51
Acetone . . .	329·3	7·28	1·72	1·72
Carbon tetrachloride .	349·9	7·17	5·22	4·9
Chloroform . . .	334·4	7·02	3·78	3·9
Ethyl alcohol . .	351·7	9·22	1·23	1·20
Methyl alcohol . .	337·9	8·43	0·86	0·84
Diethyl ether . .	307·6	6·61	2·11	2·16
Benzene . . .	353·3	7·35	2·63	2·6

10.14. *The freezing-point of an ideal solution*

The relation between the composition and the freezing-point T_f of an ideal solution is obtained by putting $a_1 = x_1$ in equation 44 of section 9.34:

$$\frac{d \ln x_1}{dT_f} = \frac{L_f}{RT_f^2}. \tag{9}$$

This is exact. For *dilute solutions*, for which the depression is small, we can put $L_f = $ constant and $T_f = T_f^0$ (the freezing-point of the pure solvent). We may also put $\ln x_1 = -x_2$. Using equation 45 of section 9.34, we then obtain

$$\frac{\Delta T}{x_2} = \frac{R(T_f^0)^2}{L_f}. \tag{10}$$

In terms of molal concentrations and the latent heat per gram, L'_f,

$$\frac{\Delta T}{m} = \frac{R(T_f^0)^2}{1000 L'_f}. \tag{11}$$

† Swietoslawski, *Ebulliometric Measurements* (Reinhold, 1945), pp. 178, 179.

‡ Observed values from Landolt–Bornstein, *Tabellen* (Springer, Berlin, 5th edn. 1923); other data from *Selected Values of Chemical Thermodynamic Properties*, 1952.

The freezing-point depression will therefore have the following characteristics in ideal dilute solutions:

(i) For a given solvent and solute, ΔT will be proportional to the concentration.

(ii) For a given solvent, ΔT at a given mole fraction will be the same for all solutes.

(iii) On varying the solvent, the 'molecular depression of the freezing-point', which is the value of ΔT for a 1 M solution, will be given by $R(T_f^0)^2/1000L_f'$.

Several solutions which show the proportionality (i) over a wide range have been noted in section 9.34 (p. 336); this relation applies to many dilute non-electrolyte solutions, and is the limiting law for electrolyte solutions also. Consequently, it has often been used in determining molecular weights, as for instance in the study of molecular association. (Freezing-point depressions are easier to measure accurately with simple apparatus than boiling-point elevations.) As regards (iii), the agreement of the observed and calculated molecular depressions for some non-electrolyte systems is shown in Table 43.†

TABLE 43

Depression of the freezing-point for some non-electrolyte solutes

	Freezing-point °K	L_f kcal/mole	Molecular depression	
Solvent			calc.	obs.
Water . . .	273·2	1·436	1·86	1·86
Benzene . .	278·7	2·378	5·07	5·12
Naphthalene . .	353·4	4·565	6·97	6·9
Carbon tetrachloride .	250·3	0·60	32	30
Chloroform . . .	209·7	2·2	4·7	4·9
Ethylene dibromide .	283·1	2·62	11·4	12·5
Acetic acid . . .	289·8	2·80	3·6	3·9
Phenol . . .	314·2	2·70	6·8	7·3

10.15. *The dependence of solubility on temperature*

The relation between the temperature and the solubility s (in mole-fraction units) for an ideal solution may be obtained

† See note ‡ on p. 364.

by using equation 48 of section 9.35 (p. 338) and putting a_2 proportional to x_2, i.e. to s; the assumption will be true for ideal solutions on either of the two conventions for a_2 (section 9.24, p. 318). The result is, since $d \ln a_2 = d \ln s$,

$$\frac{d \ln s}{dT_s} = \frac{L_f}{RT_s^2}. \tag{12}$$

When L_f can be taken as constant, we can use equation 50 of section 9.35 and obtain

$$\ln s = -\frac{L_f}{R}\left(\frac{1}{T_s} - \frac{1}{T_f^0}\right). \tag{13}$$

Here L_f is the latent heat of fusion of the solute and T_f^0 is the freezing-point of the solute. We have already seen that the eutectic plots for various binary mixtures fit this relation, or the more accurate relation which takes into account the temperature-variation of L_f (sections 9.34, 9.35). Equation 13 implies that, for solutions which behave ideally, (i) the plots of $\ln s$ against $1/T_s$ will be linear; (ii) the slopes for a given solute will be the same for all solvents, and (iii) will be given by $-L_f/R$. The data for naphthalene in various solvents plotted in fig. 61 a (p. 340) show that several of these solutions approximate closely to ideal behaviour.†

10.16. *The osmotic pressure of an ideal solution*

The relation between the concentration and the osmotic pressure of an ideal solution is obtained by putting $a_1 = x_1$ in equation 60 of section 9.36 (p. 346):

$$\ln x_1 = -\frac{1}{RT} \int_{p_1^0}^{P^{\text{soln}}} V_1 \, dP^{\text{soln}}. \tag{14}$$

The less exact equation 61 (p. 346), which neglects the compressibility of the solution, gives

$$\ln x_1 = -\pi V_1/RT. \tag{15}$$

For a *dilute solution*, using the approximation $\ln x_1 \simeq -x_2$, we obtain

$$\pi = x_2 RT/V_1. \tag{16}$$

† For discussions of solubility in this and other systems see Hildebrand and Scott, *Solubility of Non-electrolytes* (1950), chap. 17.

Here V_1 is approximately the volume containing x_2 moles of solute. If V^* is the volume containing one mole of solute, therefore, $V^* \simeq V_1/x_2$; substituting this in equation 16, we find

$$\pi V^* = RT. \qquad (17)$$

Historically, this is the law stated originally by van 't Hoff.[†] Its form is similar to the perfect-gas equation; but it is to be noted that it is only the limiting equation in dilute solution, equation 15 being more exact; and that the explanation suggested by van 't Hoff, that osmotic pressure is a bombardment pressure analogous to that of a gas, cannot be sustained (cf. pp. 344, 371).

Equations 16 and 15 imply that, for ideal solutions, (i) the osmotic pressure will be proportional to $\ln x_1$, or in dilute solution to x_2, for a given solvent and solute; (ii) if the concentration is fixed, the osmotic pressure will be proportional to T/V_1; and (iii) the proportionality constant is R. The most extensive series of measurements are those on aqueous solutions of sugars, whose behaviour approximates to ideality, as Table 44 shows.[‡] These are some of the few experiments showing ideal behaviour in which the temperature has been systematically varied.

TABLE 44

Osmotic pressures of aqueous sucrose solutions

Concentrations are weight normal; temperatures are in °C

	Ratio of observed to calculated osmotic pressure at					
Conc.	0°	15°	25°	40°	60°	80°
0·1	1·106	1·082	1·084	1·003	1·000	..
0·2	1·061	1·061	1·059	1·011	1·001	..
0·3	1·061	1·061	1·060	1·024	0·999	..
0·4	1·060	1·059	1·059	1·038	1·000	..
0·5	1·069	1·068	1·065	1·046	1·006	..
0·6	1·077	1·073	1·071	1·054	1·015	..
0·7	1·083	1·083	1·083	1·059	1·020	..
0·8	1·093	1·093	1·093	1·067	1·027	1·001
0·9	1·104	1·102	1·102	1·076	1·033	1·000
1·0	1·115	1·115	1·113	1·085	1·044	1·000

[†] van 't Hoff, *Phil. Mag.*, 1888, **26**, 81.
[‡] Morse *et al.*, *Amer. Chem. J.*, 1912, **48**, 29.

10.2. Heats, entropies, and free energies of mixing in ideal solutions

Relations between these thermodynamic functions and the activities were obtained in section 9.4 (p. 353), and by putting $a_1 = x_1$ and $a_2 = x_2$ we obtained for one mole of an ideal solution the following relations (illustrated in fig. 69, p. 357):

$$\Delta H_m^{id} = 0, \tag{18}$$

$$\Delta G_m^{id} = RT(x_1 \ln x_1 + x_2 \ln x_2), \tag{19}$$

$$\Delta S_m^{id} = -R(x_1 \ln x_1 + x_2 \ln x_2), \tag{20}$$

$$\Delta V_m^{id} = 0. \tag{21}$$

We have seen that experimental results approximating to these relations are obtained for various solutions whose vapour pressures approximate to Raoult's law (Table 41, p. 359).

It is also possible, conversely, to show that the equation $a_1 = x_1$, and hence Raoult's law and the other properties of ideal solutions, will be true for a solution that has the ideal values for both ΔH_m and ΔS_m. For an ideal mixture of n_1 moles of solvent and n_2 of solute, the entropy of mixing is

$$-\Delta S_m = R(n_1 \ln x_1 + n_2 \ln x_2).$$

Differentiating with respect to n_1, the partial molar entropy of dilution is (where S_1^0 refers to the pure solvent)

$$\Delta S_1 = S_1 - S_1^0 = \{\partial(\Delta S_m)/\partial n_1\}_{T,P,n_2} = -R \ln x_1.$$

The corresponding value of ΔH_1 is zero. Hence the partial molar free energy of dilution is

$$G_1 - G_1^0 = -T(S_1 - S_1^0) = RT \ln x_1. \tag{22}$$

Since

$$G_1 - G_1^0 = \mu_1 - \mu_1^0 = RT \ln a_1,$$

it follows, using equation 22, that for such a solution $a_1 = x_1$. Since $a_1 = p_1/p_1^0$, we obtain $x_1 = p_1/p_1^0$, which is Raoult's law.

We can reach the same result by considering the vapour-pressure curve for a solution of an involatile solute, at a fixed concentration. The vapour pressure of the solution is given by equation 6 of section 9.22 (p. 314):

$$R \ln p_1 = \Delta S_{e(T)}^0 - L_e/T. \tag{23}$$

Here $\Delta S^0_{e(T)}$ is the standard entropy change on evaporation of one mole of solvent from the solution. This will differ from the entropy change for evaporation from the pure solvent; when solute is added to solvent, the entropy of the solvent species is increased (because more room is available to it), whereas the entropy of the vapour is unchanged, so that ΔS^0_e decreases. We can find the amount of the decrease as follows. The total entropy increase when the solution is formed, if it is ideal, is given by $\Delta S_m = -R(n_1 \ln x_1 + n_2 \ln x_2)$. The increase of entropy of the solvent species alone, per mole, is obtained by differentiating this with respect to n_1; the result is $-R \ln x_1$ (a positive quantity, since $x_1 < 1$). The entropy increase on evaporation will be reduced by this amount. The latent heat of evaporation will not be changed, since $H_1 = H^0_1$ for an ideal solute. Hence, by equation 23, $R \ln p_1$ will be lower by $(-R \ln x_1)$ than in the pure solvent:

$$R \ln p^0_1 - R \ln p_1 = -R \ln x_1. \tag{24}$$

It follows from this equation that

$$p_1/p^0_1 = x_1, \tag{25}$$

which is Raoult's law. We thus reach the interesting result that the depression of the vapour-pressure curve (fig. 51, p. 321) for an ideal solution is due entirely to the entropy of mixing.

Statistical interpretation of ideal behaviour. The molecules of a liquid, unlike those of a gas, must interact considerably, otherwise the liquid will evaporate. The molecules of the two constituents 1 and 2 of a solution will likewise interact. The simplest interpretation of the zero heat of mixing in ideal solutions is that the interchange of molecules 1 and 2 always leaves the energy of the solution unchanged, so that the 'interchange energy' of 1 and 2 is zero. Similarly, the simplest interpretation of the ideal entropy of mixing,

$$\Delta S_m = -R \sum x_1 \ln x_1,$$

proves to be that there is random distribution of the molecules in solution, leading to an increased number of possible sites for each molecule and so to an increased configurational entropy.

This is easy to show if we suppose the molecules to be arranged as in a crystal lattice. This assumption cannot be strictly true, since the long-range structure characteristic of a solid must break down on melting (p. 289), but it is a useful approximation.[†] Suppose then that the N_1 molecules of constituent 1 and N_2 molecules of constituent 2 can each occupy any site in a crystal lattice indifferently, so that there is random mixing.[‡] If all the molecules were alike, the number of ways in which the (N_1+N_2) places could be filled would be the total number of permutations of (N_1+N_2) objects taken all together, which is $(N_1+N_2)!$ But since the N_1 molecules of constituent 1 are indistinguishable, we must divide this by the number of permutations of these molecules with each other, namely $N_1!$; and similarly for constituent 2 we must divide by $N_2!$ Thus for the number of arrangements we find the value

$$(N_1+N_2)!/N_1!\,N_2! \tag{26}$$

This is the factor by which W is increased on mixing. Since $S = k\ln W$ (p. 145), $\Delta S = k\Delta \ln W$, and so on mixing the entropy increase is

$$\Delta S_m = k\ln[(N_1+N_2)!/(N_1!\,N_2!)]. \tag{27}$$

Since N_1 and N_2 are large, we can use Stirling's approximation $(\ln x! = x\ln x - x)$, and obtain

$$\begin{aligned}
\Delta S_m &= k[(N_1+N_2)\ln(N_1+N_2) - N_1\ln N_1 - N_2\ln N_2]\\
&= -k[N_1\ln N_1/(N_1+N_2) + N_2\ln N_2/(N_1+N_2)]\\
&= -k(N_1\ln x_1 + N_2\ln x_2). \tag{28}
\end{aligned}$$

This refers to (N_1+N_2) molecules; hence for one mole, consisting of N^0 molecules, we find

$$\begin{aligned}
\Delta S_m &= -N^0 k(N_1\ln x_1 + N_2\ln x_2)/(N_1+N_2)\\
&= -R(x_1\ln x_1 + x_2\ln x_2). \tag{29}
\end{aligned}$$

This is identical with the ideal entropy of mixing.

Thus the quasi-crystalline model of a liquid suggests that ideal behaviour will be shown by a mixture of equally

[†] Guggenheim, *Mixtures* (Oxford, 1952), pp. 16, 24.
[‡] The argument is given by Butler, *Chemical Thermodynamics* (Macmillan, 1946), p. 370.

interacting particles provided that they mix randomly. The simplest condition for this is that they should be of the same size and shape. Actually, a less rigorous condition (along with the condition that an interchange of molecules 1 and 2 leaves the energy of the solution unchanged) leads to the same values for ΔH_m and ΔS_m,† namely that the molecules are sufficiently alike in size and shape to be able to pack in the same way when mixed as in the pure liquids; for spherical molecules this implies a ratio of molecular diameters between 1·26 and 1. This, then, is the statistical interpretation of the laws of ideal solutions. When liquids composed of such molecules are mixed, there is no change in heat content, and the extra sites available to each type of molecule lead to the correct increase in entropy; it follows that $a_1 = x_1$ (p. 368), from which may be deduced the experimental properties of ideal solutions, as in section 10.1.

The gas constant R in the theory of solutions. We can now see how it is that the constant R, which originated in the theory of gases (section 3.33, p. 91), continually appears in the theory of solutions. It enters the thermodynamics of solutions through the fundamental expressions for ideal behaviour, whether in terms of chemical potential (section 9.23, p. 315),

$$\mu_1 - \mu_1^0 = RT \ln x_1,$$

or in terms of thermodynamic functions for mixing (p. 368), such as

$$\Delta S_m^{id} = -R(x_1 \ln x_1 + x_2 \ln x_2).$$

The statistical interpretation of its presence in these equations is to be found fundamentally in the increased number of sites available to molecules of a given type upon mixing with molecules of a different type, when random distribution is set up. Equations 27 to 29 above show how R enters the equations.

Analogy between solutions and gases. An analogy was formerly drawn between solutions and gases, on the ground of the similarity of form of the perfect gas equation $PV = RT$ and the equation $\pi V^* = RT$ for the osmotic pressure of a dilute ideal solution. But, as we noted (p. 344), the formal analogy is

† Guggenheim, *Mixtures* (1952), chap. 3.

imperfect, since $\pi V^* = RT$ is only an approximation even for ideal solutions.† Moreover, similarity of mathematical form does not necessarily imply physical similarity, as the failure of the bombardment theory of osmotic pressure shows.

There is none the less a certain analogy between gases and solutions. The expressions for the entropy of mixing at constant pressure for perfect gas mixtures (p. 221) and for ideal solutions (p. 368) are identical: $\Delta S_m = -R \sum x_i \ln x_i$. To this relation (with $\Delta H_m = 0$) can be traced the important expressions for the chemical potential

$$\mu_1^{\text{gas}} - (\mu_1^0)^{\text{gas}} = RT \ln p_1 \quad \text{(p. 216)}$$

and $\qquad \mu_1^{\text{soln}} - (\mu_1^0)^{\text{solvent}} = RT \ln x_1 \quad \text{(p. 360)},$

and all their consequences. And for both systems the increase in entropy on mixing is due to the larger volume available to each constituent after mixing. There is, however, an important difference in the effect of this increase in volume. For solutions, it simply increases the number of available sites and hence the configurational entropy only; for gases, it leads in addition to changes of the energy-levels and so to a different energy-distribution of the molecules. The analogy to be drawn between solutions and gases is thus a partial one, but all the same it is illuminating.

† There is, however, a formal analogy between the statistical expression for the pressure of a real imperfect gas and that for the osmotic pressure of any solution; cf. Guggenheim, *Disc. Faraday Soc.* no. 15, 1953, 66.

NON-IDEAL SOLUTIONS (I):
NON-ELECTROLYTE SOLUTIONS

11.1. General classification of solutions

As we have seen, there are two equivalent sets of criteria for an ideal solution, both leading to the same experimental relations. One is in terms of activity or activity coefficients:

$$f_1 = 1, \qquad a_1 = x_1, \qquad \mu_1 - \mu_1^0 = RT \ln x_1; \qquad (1)$$

and the other is in terms of thermodynamic functions for mixing:

$$\Delta H_m = 0 \quad \text{together with} \quad \Delta S_m = -R \sum x_i \ln x_i. \qquad (2)$$

Non-ideal solutions likewise may be classified according to their deviations from each of these sets of criteria. In the following table are listed some important classes suggested by experimental investigations.

TABLE 45

Class	ΔH_m	ΔS_m	$\ln f_2$
Ideal solutions	0	ideal	(p. 319)
Regular solutions . . .	$\neq 0$	ideal	Bx_1^2
High-polymer solutions . .	$\simeq 0$	$\neq$ ideal	(p. 385)
Strong electrolytes in dilute aqueous solutions	$\neq 0$	$\neq$ ideal	$-\alpha I^{\frac{1}{2}}$

The behaviour of ideal solutions, as we have seen (p. 369), corresponds theoretically to zero interchange energy for the molecules of solvent and solute. If the interchange energy is not negligible, we may expect (i) a heat change on mixing, and (ii) a non-random distribution of molecules in the solution, leading to a non-ideal entropy of mixing. Solutions of many non-electrolytes in non-hydroxylic solvents approximate to Hildebrand's definition of a 'regular' solution, namely one which has a finite heat of mixing but a nearly ideal entropy of mixing. Such solutions correspond approximately to a theoretical class called 'strictly regular solutions' (p. 379), consisting of non-polar molecules of comparable size and simple shape exerting short-range forces on each other. For solutions of high polymers in such solvents as benzene (section 11.2) the heats of mixing are nearly zero, corresponding to the small intermolecular forces, but the entropies of mixing are far from ideal because the molecules are flexible. In solutions of strong electrolytes (Chapter XII), there are relatively large long-range forces between the ions, as well as short-range specific interactions; in terms of these the considerable deviations of both ΔH_m and ΔS_m from the ideal values can be interpreted.

11.2. Regular solutions

When non-polar or slightly polar substances, such as iodine, sulphur, phosphorus, or naphthalene, are dissolved in non-hydroxylic solvents such as CCl_4, CS_2, hexane, or benzene, the solutions often deviate from ideal behaviour in a simple way. Much of our information on these systems has been obtained from solubility measurements (p. 339).† The plots of $\ln s$ against $1/T$ for such a solute in a series of solvents form a family of curves, deviating from the ideal line calculated from the latent heat of fusion (fig. 61 a, 61 b, p. 340). The activity coefficients f_2 calculated from the ratio of the ideal to the actual solubility are often greater than 1, corresponding to positive deviations from Raoult's law and to an 'escaping tendency' greater than that of an ideal solution, that is to a tendency for the two constituents to draw apart. The relation between the activity coefficient and concentration is found to agree closely with the equation

$$RT \ln f_2 = Bx_1^2, \tag{3}$$

in which B is a constant independent of temperature. This implies that

$$RT \ln a_2 = \mu_2 - \mu_2^0 = RT \ln x_2 + Bx_1^2, \tag{4}$$

in which the term Bx_1^2 is added to the equation for ideal behaviour. The following are typical experimental data showing the constancy of B.‡

† Hildebrand and Scott, *Solubility of Non-electrolytes* (Reinhold, 1950), especially chaps. 13, 15–19, 23.

‡ Hildebrand, *Trans. Faraday Soc.*, 1937, **33**, 149.

TABLE 46

System	Temp. °C	Solubility moles %	$\dfrac{B}{2 \cdot 3R}$
Sulphur-CCl$_4$ . . .	0	0·203	529
	25	0·500	529
	35	0·697	528
	45	0·966	527
	54	1·212	528
Sulphur-toluene . .	0	0·324	474
	25	0·734	478
	35	0·995	483
	45	1·330	483
	54	1·797	480

The coefficient B depends on the solvent and solute, but is practically independent of the temperature. For systems showing positive deviations, B/RT lies between 0 and 2 (cf. below) so that f_2 at a mole fraction of 0·5 lies between 1 and about 1·6. By applying the Gibbs–Duhem relation, it is easy to show that, corresponding to equations 3 and 4, the following relations must also be true:

$$RT \ln f_1 = Bx_2^2, \tag{5}$$

$$RT \ln a_1 = \mu_1 - \mu_1^0 = RT \ln x_1 + Bx_2^2. \tag{6}$$

Many other systems besides those mentioned above follow these relations: for instance, solutions of water in hydrocarbons, solutions of hydrogen and other gases in organic solvents, and various alloy systems.†

It is found empirically that B for many solvent-solute pairs can be expressed in terms of parameters characteristic of the substances concerned, commonly written δ_1 and δ_2. It is also found that δ_1 and δ_2 can be related empirically to the energies of vaporization of the solvent and solute. If we call these $(\Delta E_e)_1$ and $(\Delta E_e)_2$ and write

$$[(\Delta E_e)_1 / V_1^0]^{\frac{1}{2}} = \delta_1 \quad \text{and} \quad [(\Delta E_e)_2 / V_2^0]^{\frac{1}{2}} = \delta_2,$$

then the following expression gives fair agreement with the experimental values of B:

$$B = (V_2 \phi_1^2 / x_1^2)(\delta_1 - \delta_2)^2, \tag{7}$$

† See note † on p. 374.

where ϕ_1 is the volume fraction of solvent. In dilute solution, this takes the form

$$B = V_2(\delta_1 - \delta_2)^2.$$

In Table 47 the values of $(\delta_1 - \delta_2)$ calculated in this way from the energies of evaporation are compared with those calculated by equation 5 from the values of B derived experimentally from solubilities.

TABLE 47†

System	$\delta_1 - \delta_2$ calc.	$\delta_1 - \delta_2$ experimental
Benzene-butane . .	2·4	2·6
Benzene-cyclohexane .	1·0	1·5
Benzene-CS$_2$.	1·0	1·8
CCl$_4$-bromine .	3·1	2·8
CCl$_4$-SiCl$_4$ . .	1·0	1·1
CCl$_4$-benzene .	0·6	1·0
CCl$_4$-n-heptane . .	1·1	1·5
SiCl$_4$-SnI$_4$ . .	1·8	3·7
Benzene-phosphorus .	5·0	5·7
SiCl$_4$-iodine .	6·0	6·1

The function $(\Delta E_e/V^0)$ may be taken as an approximation to $(\partial E/\partial V)_T$. For liquids, as for gases (section 3.2), this is a measure of the intermolecular forces. It has also been called by Hildebrand the 'internal pressure'. It has the dimensions of pressure, as may be seen from the general equation (p. 179):

$$(\partial E/\partial V)_T = T(\partial P/\partial T)_V - P. \tag{8}$$

Since for liquids the external pressure P is negligible in this equation, $(\partial E/\partial V)_T$ may be determined by finding $(\partial P/\partial T)_V$, which may be obtained as the ratio of the coefficient of expansion to the compressibility.

Vapour pressures. From equations 3 to 6 we could derive expressions for the vapour-pressure depression, boiling-point elevation, and other properties of regular solutions, by applying the relations of section 9.3. For the partial vapour pressures, in particular, we obtain

$$p_1/p_1^0 = x_1 \, e^{Bx_2^2/RT}, \tag{9}$$

$$p_2/p_2^0 = x_2 \, e^{Bx_1^2/RT}. \tag{10}$$

† Hildebrand, *Trans. Faraday Soc.*, 1937, **33**, 149.

For $B > 0$, the partial vapour pressures are larger than the ideal values. Vapour-pressure curves for a fixed temperature, calculated from equations 9 and 10 by taking $B/RT = 1$, are shown in fig. 71. They are similar to those found experimentally for mixtures of acetone and carbon disulphide, shown in fig. 53 (p. 324). In dilute solution, that is when x_2 is small, the curve

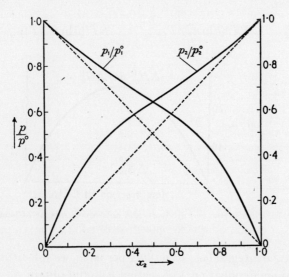

FIG. 71. Partial vapour-pressure curves for regular solutions with $B/RT = 1$.

for p_1 approximates to Raoult's law, as inspection of equation 9 will confirm; the curve for p_2 approaches linearity, as for an ideal solution, but the slope differs from that for solutions ideal over the whole range (p. 362). In dilute solution, equation 10 may be approximated to

$$p_2 = x_2[p_2^0 e^{B/RT}] = x_2/k, \tag{11}$$

where k is some constant. This is Henry's law, with the constant k differing from the value $1/p_2^0$ (which applies to solutions ideal over the whole range).

The larger the deviations from ideal behaviour, the larger the value of B. The value $B/RT = 2$ corresponds theoretically to the temperature of critical mixing; with higher values mixing is incomplete.†

Heats, entropies, and free energies of mixing. These can be expressed in terms of B, using equations 3 and 5. For the partial heats of dilution we obtain, using equation 12 of section 9.23:

$$H_1 - H_1^0 = -RT^2(\partial \ln a_1/\partial T)_{P,x_1} = -RT^2(\partial \ln f_1/\partial T)_{P,x_1} = Bx_2^2, \tag{12}$$

$$H_2 - H_2^0 = -RT^2(\partial \ln a_2/\partial T)_{P,x_1} = -RT^2(\partial \ln f_2/\partial T)_{P,x_1} = Bx_1^2. \tag{13}$$

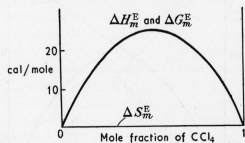

FIG. 72. Excess free energy, heat, and entropy of mixing of benzene and carbon tetrachloride.‡

To find the integral heat of mixing per mole, we substitute these expressions in equation 4 of section 9.4, and obtain

$$\Delta H_m = x_1(H_1 - H_1^0) + x_2(H_2 - H_0^2)$$
$$= Bx_1 x_2 = Bx_1(1 - x_1). \tag{14}$$

The plot of ΔH_m against x_1 should thus be parabolic, if our assumptions about B are correct.

The entropy of mixing per mole is given by equation 12 of section 9.4:

$$-\Delta S_m/R = x_1 \ln a_1 + x_2 \ln a_2 + x_1(H_1^0 - H_1)/RT + x_2(H_2^0 - H_2)/RT.$$

Using equations 4, 6, 12, and 13, this gives

$$-\Delta S_m/R = x_1 \ln x_1 + x_2 \ln x_2. \tag{15}$$

This is the same value of ΔS_m as for ideal solutions. Thus the

† Cf. Guggenheim, *Mixtures* (Oxford, 1952), chap. 4.
‡ From Scatchard, *Chem. Rev.*, 1931, **8**, 321.

excess entropy of mixing ΔS_m^E is zero. Since $\Delta G = \Delta H - T\Delta S$, the excess free energy of mixing ΔG_m^E is therefore equal to ΔH_m.

Smoothed curves for the excess functions for mixtures of benzene and carbon tetrachloride are plotted in fig. 72 and are seen to follow the relations just given. More often, however, the curves are unsymmetrical.

Statistical interpretation. Considerable progress has been made in the statistical theory of regular solutions,[†] but the problem is much more complex than that of ideal solutions. Briefly it may be said that 'statistical theory predicts that any mixture of two kinds of non-polar molecules of similar simple shape should obey certain laws, called the laws of *strictly regular solutions*, to which the formulae for regular solutions are a useful approximation'.[‡] One difference between the two is that the statistical theory, except in its crudest approximation, necessarily leads to deviations from random mixing, and so to an entropy of mixing slightly different from the ideal value. Also it has to envisage a slight temperature-dependence of B. The interpretation of B is that B/N^0 is the average increase of free energy when a solvent-solvent pair and a solute-solute pair are converted into two solute-solvent pairs.

11.3. High-polymer solutions

Solutions of high polymers, particularly those in non-aqueous solvents, have been much investigated in recent years,[§] especially by means of measurements of vapour pressure (section 9.31) and of osmotic pressure (section 9.36). The deviation from ideality here, in contrast with that shown by regular solutions, is mainly in the entropy of mixing:

$$\Delta H_m \simeq 0, \qquad \Delta S_m \neq \text{ideal.}$$

† Guggenheim, *Mixtures* (Oxford, 1952), chap. 4; Rushbrooke, *Statistical Mechanics* (Oxford, 1949), chap. 18.

‡ Guggenheim, *Thermodynamics* (1949), pp. 208–9. In the third edition (1957) Guggenheim proposes the name 'simple mixture'.

§ For reviews see P. J. Flory, *Principles of Polymer Chemistry* (Cornell U.P., 1953), chap. 12; Hildebrand and Scott, *Solubility of Non-electrolytes* (1950), chap. 20; Guggenheim, *Mixtures* (1950), chaps. 10, 11, 12; Tompa, *Polymer Solutions* (Butterworth, 1956).

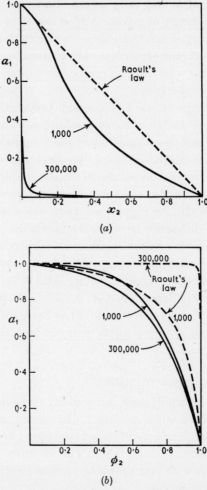

FIG. 73. Vapour pressure for rubber-benzene solutions plotted against
(a) mole fraction, (b) volume fraction, of rubber, with M.W. 1,000 and 300,000.

The experimental evidence from vapour pressures may be
exemplified by fig. 73, which shows p_1/p_1^0 (which is equal to a_1)
for mixtures of rubber and benzene over the whole range of
composition.† From fig. 73 a it is clear that there are large

† Data of Gee and Treloar, *Trans. Faraday Soc.*, 1942, **38**, 147 (cf. *Ann.
Rep. Chem. Soc.*, 1942, p. 1); diagrams from Huggins, *Industr. Engng. Chem.*,
1943, **35**, 219, by courtesy of *Industrial and Engineering Chemistry*.

deviations from Raoult's law. In fig. 73 *b* the vapour pressures are replotted against the volume fraction ϕ_2, instead of mole fraction x_2, to facilitate comparison with theory (see below). The values of x_2 and ϕ_2 differ greatly because the molecular

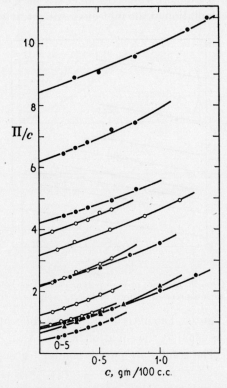

FIG. 74 *a*. Osmotic pressure of high-polymer solutions: plot of π/c against *c* for polystyrene of various molecular weights at 30° in toluene.†

weights of solvent and solute are widely different; in dilute solution, ϕ_2 is nearly equal to $x_2 r$, where *r* is the ratio of the molar volumes.

The experimental evidence from osmotic pressures is exemplified by fig. 74 *a*, which shows plots of π/c against *c* (here *c* is the concentration in grammes per 100 c.c. of solution) for various

† Figure from Krigbaum and Flory, *J. Amer. Chem. Soc.*, 1953, **75**, 1775.

specimens of polystyrene in toluene; and by fig. 74 b, which shows similar plots for neoprene in toluene. An ideal dilute solution would give a horizontal straight line (equation 16, p. 366). The polymer solutions give lines with a positive slope. Extrapolation to zero concentration, at which the ideal law may be assumed to hold, allows calculation of the molecular weight, with the results

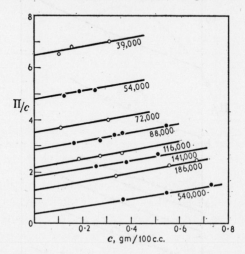

FIG. 74 b. Osmotic pressure of high-polymer solutions: plot of π/c against c for neoprene of various molecular weights in toluene.†

shown in the figure. The activity a_1 at any concentration may be calculated as usual by the equation $\ln a_1 = -\pi V_1/RT$ (section 9.36, p. 346). The results are curves similar to those shown in fig. 73.

The freezing-point method can be applied only to polymers of relatively low molecular weight; it then gives linear plots of $\Delta T/c$ against c, similar to those for osmotic pressure.‡

For high-polymer solutions, the determination of heats of mixing by direct calorimetry presents considerable difficulties. Heats and entropies of mixing can, however, be calculated if we have values for the activity at more than one temperature (section 9.4, p. 353). Calculations from such data as those cited

† Figure from Scott, Carter, and Magat; see Hildebrand and Scott, *Solubility of Non-electrolytes* (1950), pp. 356–7.

‡ Kemp and Peters, *Industr. Engng. Chem.*, 1942, **34**, 1192.

show that ΔH_m is small, while ΔS_m is considerably larger than that for ideal solutions. The excess functions are related to the volume fraction of polymer (not its mole fraction) more or less according to the scheme shown in fig. 75.

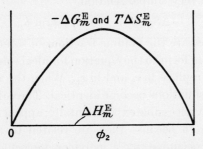

FIG. 75. Excess free energy, heat, and entropy of mixing for high-polymer solutions plotted against volume fraction of polymer (diagrammatic).

Statistical interpretation. The low heats of mixing of these solutions are easily understood, since the high-polymer molecules consist mainly of hydrocarbon chains and are usually dissolved in 'inert' solvents such as benzene. The excess entropy of mixing has been interpreted with considerable success as due to the presence of long flexible chains. It can be seen qualitatively that a flexible hydrocarbon chain can take up many configurations without appreciable change in energy, and this is found to lead to an excess entropy of the right order.

In the detailed calculations,† such as those of Flory, the solvent and solute molecules have usually been considered as arranged on a lattice, on which a site may be occupied either by a solvent molecule or by a unit of the long-chain solute. But this 'quasi-crystalline lattice' model is not essential; similar results have been derived without it.‡ We give the results of Flory's early approximate calculation; subsequent improvements have not improved the agreement as regards order of magnitude. The polymer molecule is regarded as made up of many spherical units, flexibly joined, and each equal in volume to a single spherical

† For a review see Guggenheim, *Mixtures* (1952), chaps. 10, 11, 12.
‡ Longuet-Higgins, *Disc. Faraday Soc.*, no. 15, 1953, 73.

solvent molecule. The number of ways in which a long flexible chain can be arranged on a lattice is computed, taking into account the fact that successive units must occupy adjacent sites. The final result for the entropy of mixing per mole of solution is the very simple relation

$$-\Delta S_m/R = x_1 \ln \phi_1 + x_2 \ln \phi_2, \tag{16}$$

where ϕ_2 and ϕ_1 are the volume fractions of solute and solvent. This is similar in form to the equation for ideal solutions (p. 368); $\ln \phi_2$ and $\ln \phi_1$ replace $\ln x_2$ and $\ln x_1$. When the molar volumes are equal, the equations become identical. The volume fractions, which are easily accessible experimentally, appear in the theoretical expression 16 because they are related to the number of lattice-points occupied by a polymer molecule, that is, the number of flexibly joined units or segments in a molecule. This number is equal to the ratio of the molar volumes of solute and solvent, r; it follows from the geometry of the system that

$$\phi_2 = r x_2/(1 - x_2 + r x_2).$$

We can most simply compare equation 16 with experiment by deducing from it theoretical values of the activity and hence of the vapour pressure or osmotic pressure. The entropy of mixing of n_1 moles of solvent with n_2 moles of solute will be given according to equation 16 by

$$-\Delta S_m/R = n_1 \ln \phi_1 + n_2 \ln \phi_2. \tag{17}$$

The partial molar entropy of dilution will be

$$\Delta S_1 = S_1 - S_1^0 = (\partial \Delta S_m/\partial n_1)_{T,P,n_2},$$

which comes out to be

$$\Delta S_1 = -R[\ln \phi_1 + (1 - 1/r)\phi_2]. \tag{18}$$

The heat of dilution is known to be small but it is not necessarily negligible. Theory suggests that as a first approximation we may put

$$\Delta H_1 = k\phi_2^2, \tag{19}$$

where k is some constant. Then the partial molar free energy of dilution is

$$\Delta G_1 = G_1 - G_1^0 = \Delta H_1 - T\Delta S_1 = k\phi_2^2 + RT[\ln \phi_1 + (1 - 1/r)\phi_2]. \tag{20}$$

Hence the activity a_1 and the vapour pressure are given by

$$\ln(p_1/p_1^0) = \ln a_1 = (\mu_1 - \mu_1^0)/RT = (G_1 - G_1^0)/RT$$
$$= \ln \phi_1 + (1 - 1/r)\phi_2 + k'\phi_2^2. \qquad (21)$$

This may be rearranged to give

$$(\ln a_1 - \ln \phi_1)/\phi_2 = k'\phi_2 - 1/r + 1. \qquad (22)$$

If the treatment is correct, the experimental results on the relation between a_1 and the volume fractions ϕ_1 and ϕ_2 should agree with equation 22; that is, plots of $(\ln a_1 - \ln \phi_1)/\phi_2$ against ϕ_2 should be linear. Their slope will give a measure of k, and their intercept a value of r, which may be compared with the size of the polymer molecules if this is independently known. In practice it is found that good linear plots are obtained. Unfortunately there are very few direct calorimetric experiments for comparison with the derived values of k.

We can also test the expression for the activity given in equation 21 by deriving from it an expression for the osmotic pressure, using the expression $\pi = -(RT/V_1)\ln a_1$, and comparing with the experimental results. In dilute solution, we can express $\ln \phi_1$ by expanding it as follows:

$$\ln \phi_1 = \ln(1 - \phi_2) \simeq -\phi_2 - \frac{\phi_2^2}{2}, \qquad (22\,\text{a})$$

neglecting higher terms of the expansion. We then find from equation 21:

$$\pi = (RT/V_1)[\phi_2/r + (\tfrac{1}{2} - k')\phi_2^2]. \qquad (23)$$

A plot of π/ϕ_2 against ϕ_2 would therefore be linear in dilute solution, with an intercept depending on r, and hence on the molecular weight. Since ϕ_2 is proportional to concentration in dilute solution, a plot of π/c against c would have the same form. This agrees with experiment in some cases (fig. 74 b). Curvature of the plots (fig. 74 a) may be due to the higher terms neglected in equation 23.

Broadly speaking, then, the statistical picture of high polymers in terms of flexible molecules accounts for the main thermodynamic facts about them; but there is still plenty of room both for improvement of the theory and for experimental work.

NON-IDEAL SOLUTIONS (II): ELECTROLYTE SOLUTIONS

12.1. Strong and weak electrolytes

SOLUTIONS of electrolytes have several unique features. They always contain, besides the solvent, at least two solute species—the anions and cations. These are present in equal concentrations, since the forces between ions are very large and the solution is electrically neutral when in equilibrium with its surroundings. The interionic forces are not only large but long-range, since they fall off with the square of the distance, compared with the seventh power of the distance for dispersion forces. To compare them with the thermal energy of the molecules, we may note that the potential energy due to the attractive forces between a monovalent and a divalent ion in water at 25° C is about equal to kT at the relatively large distance of 11 angstroms. Because the interactions are long-range and the law of interaction is relatively simple, a theoretical account of strong electrolyte solutions was given comparatively early, in 1923, by Debye and Hückel; but the simple theory applies only as a limiting law in dilute solution. Lastly, the presence of ions makes it possible to investigate electrolyte solutions by a method not available for other solutions, namely measurements of conductivity, from which are derived values of ionic mobilities and transport numbers. These, however, are kinetic, not thermodynamic, phenomena, and we shall not deal with them in detail, but refer the reader to monographs on electrochemistry.†

In the early development of the ionic theory, which was due largely to Arrhenius and Ostwald in the 1880's, the evidence

† Among the best are: MacInnes, *Principles of Electrochemistry* (Reinhold, 1939); Dole, *Experimental and Theoretical Electrochemistry* (McGraw-Hill, 1935); McKenna, *Theoretical Electrochemistry* (Macmillan, 1939); Robinson and Stokes, *Electrolyte Solutions* (Butterworth, 1955); Harned and Owen, *The Physical Chemistry of Electrolytic Solutions* (Reinhold, 2nd edn. 1950).

from conductivities, catalytic effects, and freezing-point depressions was used to classify electrolyte solutions into two broad classes: solutions of weak electrolytes, such as weak acids and bases, which are dissociated to the extent of a few per cent. in water, and solutions of strong electrolytes, such as alkali halides, which appeared to be dissociated to the extent of somewhere between 70 and 100 per cent. in water. Much of the early work on weak-electrolyte solutions still stands, with minor modifications. But the behaviour of many strong electrolytes in water is seen, in the light of later work, to be better interpreted in terms of complete dissociation into ions.† The apparent degrees of dissociation of a strong electrolyte in water calculated from conductivities and freezing-points were of the same order of magnitude, but did not correlate really satisfactorily, especially for salts containing multiply-charged ions. Other properties of these solutions have been found to vary much less with concentration than would be expected from these apparent degrees of dissociation. For instance, the refractive index, the optical density of coloured solutions, and the optical rotation, among other properties, are nearly proportional to the concentration; dilution produces relatively small volume changes and thermal effects; and the heat of neutralization of strong acids and bases is nearly independent of concentration as well as of the acid and base. This evidence can all be reconciled with complete dissociation into ions, when the strong interaction between the ions is taken into account. In solvents of lower dielectric constant, however, association of ions takes place; this also occurs in water with some electrolytes, giving complex ions or ion-pairs such as $[CaOH]^+$, $[PbCl]^+$, and $[BaIO_3]^+$.‡

In this book we shall give a brief introduction to the simplest systems, namely solutions in which the ions are completely dissociated. For fuller reviews of the voluminous literature on electrolyte solutions the reader is referred elsewhere.§

† For a short review see R. P. Bell, *Sch. Sci. Rev.*, 1949, no. 113, p. 13.

‡ See note †, p. 386, especially Robinson and Stokes, *Electrolyte Solutions*, chap. 14; and for aqueous solutions, Bell and George, *Trans. Faraday Soc.*, 1953, **49**, 619; also *Discuss. Faraday Soc.*, 1957, 'Interactions in Ionic Solutions'.

§ See note † on p. 386.

12.2. Activities in solutions of strong electrolytes

12.21. *The activity of the solute*

A special definition of the activity of the solute is convenient, because the solution contains at least two ionic species, whose relative amounts must satisfy the condition of electrical neutrality. We will consider first a uni-univalent electrolyte, giving two singly-charged ions. For the positive and negative ions of a given electrolyte, we can formally define activities a_+ and a_- by the equations

$$\mu_+ = \mu_+^{0\prime} + RT \ln a_+, \tag{1}$$

$$\mu_- = \mu_-^{0\prime} + RT \ln a_-. \tag{2}$$

The scale of activity is chosen so that the activity approaches the concentration as the solution is diluted, and becomes equal to it in a solution dilute enough to be ideal, as for convention II of section 9.24. In dealing with electrolyte solutions, concentrations have generally been expressed in molalities (m, gramme-ions per kilogram of solvent), or in molarities (c, gramme-ions per litre of solution), though there is no theoretical reason for preferring these to mole fractions. Using molal concentrations, a_+ becomes equal to m_+ and a_- to m_- in a solution dilute enough to be ideal. Activity coefficients for the ions are correspondingly defined as $\gamma_+ = a_+/m_+$ and $\gamma_- = a_-/m_-$, or sometimes as a_+/c_+ and a_-/c_- (in the most precise work the difference may be appreciable). These definitions have been called 'practical' to distinguish them from the 'rational' definitions in terms of mole fractions.

Such ionic activities cannot be measured, however. The activity of a species i in a solution is a measure of the free energy change $(\mu_i - \mu_i^{0\prime})$ that occurs when one mole of the species is transferred to the solution from the standard state (p. 318). But a positive or negative ion cannot be transferred alone; an equivalent amount of ions of the opposite sign must be transferred at the same time, to maintain electrical neutrality. It is therefore convenient to define a quantity called the *mean activity of the electrolyte*, $a_\pm$. For a *uni-univalent* electrolyte, this is given by

$$\mu_\pm = \mu_\pm^{0\prime} + 2RT \ln a_\pm, \tag{3}$$

where
$$\mu_\pm = \mu_+ + \mu_-, \tag{4}$$

$$\mu_\pm^{0'} = \mu_+^{0'} + \mu_-^{0'}, \tag{5}$$

and
$$a_\pm = (a_+ a_-)^{\frac{1}{2}}.$$

It is this mean activity $a_\pm$, not a_+ nor a_-, which can be experimentally determined, as will appear in section 12.24. We define also the *mean molality* as

$$m_\pm = (m_+ m_-)^{\frac{1}{2}}. \tag{6}$$

It is evident that for a solution containing no other electrolyte with a common ion, the mean molality $(m_+ m_-)^{\frac{1}{2}}$ is equal to m, the molal concentration of the electrolyte.

The corresponding mean activity coefficient, written $\gamma_\pm$ to distinguish it from those defined in terms of mole fractions, is defined as

$$\gamma_\pm = a_\pm / m_\pm. \tag{7}$$

A similar definition in terms of the mean molar concentration $c_\pm$ is also used.

For the general case of an electrolyte giving ν_+ cations and ν_- anions per molecule $(A_{\nu_+} B_{\nu_-} \to \nu_+ A^+ + \nu_- B^-)$, the corresponding definitions of the mean activities and related quantities are

$$\mu_\pm = \mu_\pm^{0'} + (\nu_+ + \nu_-) RT \ln a_\pm, \tag{8}$$

$$a_\pm = [a_+^{\nu_+} a_-^{\nu_-}]^{1/(\nu_+ + \nu_-)}, \tag{9}$$

$$m_\pm = [m_+^{\nu_+} m_-^{\nu_-}]^{1/(\nu_+ + \nu_-)}, \tag{10}$$

$$\gamma_\pm = a_\pm / m_\pm, \tag{11}$$

whence
$$\ln \gamma_\pm = (\nu_+ \ln \gamma_+ + \nu_- \ln \gamma_-)/(\nu_+ + \nu_-). \tag{11a}$$

12.22. *The activity of the solvent; the osmotic coefficient*

The activity a_1 and activity coefficient f_1 of the solvent species in an electrolyte solution are related to those of the solute by the usual general relations (section 9.25, p. 318). Numerically, it turns out that whereas the activity coefficient of the solute $\gamma_\pm$ differs from unity by 10 per cent. or more in a 0.01 N solution, the activity coefficient of the solvent f_1 in the same solution differs from unity by only about 1 in 10^4.

For this reason f_1 is a less convenient function than $\gamma_\pm$ for measuring deviations from ideal behaviour and so for testing theoretical models. There is, however, a function related to f_1 which is numerically as convenient as $\gamma_\pm$, namely the *osmotic coefficient*, g. The 'rational' osmotic coefficient is defined by

$$\mu_1 - \mu_1^0 = gRT \ln x_1. \tag{12}$$

Comparison with the equations defining f_1 and a_1, namely

$$\mu_1 - \mu_1^0 = RT \ln f_1 x_1 = RT \ln a_1,$$

shows that the osmotic coefficient is related to the activity and activity coefficient by the equations

$$\ln f_1 = (g-1)\ln x_1 \tag{13}$$

and $$\ln a_1 = g \ln x_1. \tag{14}$$

The origin of the name 'osmotic coefficient' may be seen as follows. For the osmotic pressure, we have equation 61 of section 9.36 (p. 346):

$$\ln a_1 = -\pi V_1 / RT.$$

Hence, by equation 14 above,

$$\pi = -(RT/V_1)g \ln x_1. \tag{15}$$

In ideal solutions, $g = 1$, and so

$$\pi^{\mathrm{id}} = -(RT/V_1)\ln x_1. \tag{16}$$

On dividing equation 15 by 16, we obtain

$$\pi/\pi^{\mathrm{id}} = g. \tag{17}$$

Thus g is equal to the ratio of the observed to the ideal osmotic pressure. Similar reasoning using equation 45 of section 9.34 shows that g is approximately equal to the ratio of the actual to the ideal value of the freezing-point.

12.23. *The determination of activities in electrolyte solutions from their colligative properties*

The experimental methods, apart from e.m.f. methods which we deal with separately, have already been outlined in section 9.3, and we shall merely summarize the work that has been done. The equations are modified only in so far as we use molalities in place of mole fractions.

Vapour pressure of solvent (section 9.31). Much work has been done on relatively strong solutions, especially by the isopiestic technique.† Very dilute solutions cannot be accurately investigated.

Vapour pressure of solute (section 9.32). This method is available only for the few volatile solutes such as HCl.‡

Boiling-point elevation (section 9.33). This can be made fairly accurate but has seldom been used.§

Freezing-point depression (section 9.34). The accuracy of this method is high, and is comparable with that of the e.m.f. methods discussed later. It has been much used.‖

Solubility (section 9.35). The method has been considerably used for determining the effect of added salts on the activity coefficient of a given salt (pp. 341–2). Investigations have been made, for instance, on aqueous solutions of thallous chloride, barium iodate,†† calcium iodate,‡‡ silver chloride,§§ and various cobaltammines.‖‖

Osmotic pressure (section 9.36). As no suitable semi-permeable membrane has been found, this method cannot generally be applied to electrolyte solutions.

12.24. *Activities from e.m.f.s of concentration cells without liquid junction*

A typical cell 'without liquid junction' is that formed by a hydrogen electrode and a silver–silver chloride electrode dipping

---

† Robinson and Sinclair, *J. Amer. Chem. Soc.*, 1934, **56**, 1830, and later papers by Robinson *et al.*; also Robinson and Stokes, *Electrolyte Solutions* (1955); Lovelace, Frazer, and Sease, *J. Amer. Chem. Soc.*, 1921, **43**, 102 (Rayleigh manometer); Brown and Delaney, *J. Phys. Chem.*, 1954, **58**, 255 (differential bellows manometer).

‡ Bates and Kirschman, *J. Amer. Chem. Soc.*, 1919, **41**, 1991 (HCl aq.).

§ Saxton and Smith, ibid., 1932, **54**, 2626 (KCl aq.); Smith, ibid., 1939, **61**, 497, 500, 1123 (NaCl aq.).

‖ Cf. Lewis and Randall, *Thermodynamics* (McGraw-Hill, 1923), chap. 27; Harned and Owen, *The Physical Chemistry of Electrolytic Solutions* (2nd edn. 1950), chap. 9; tables, p. 543.

†† Macdougall and Davies, *J. Chem. Soc.*, 1935, 1416.

‡‡ Davies, ibid., 1938, 277.

§§ Popoff and Neumann, *J. Phys. Chem.*, 1930, **34**, 1853.

‖‖ Brønsted and LaMer, *J. Amer. Chem. Soc.*, 1924, **46**, 555.

in aqueous hydrochloric acid of concentration m:

$$(Pt)H_2(1 \text{ atm}), \text{ HCl aq.}(m), \text{ AgCl; Ag.}$$

If we write down the electrode reactions and sum them, as in section 6.23, we find that the cell reaction is

$$AgCl + \tfrac{1}{2}H_2 = Ag + H^+ + Cl^-. \tag{18}$$

Thus when one faraday of electricity passes through the cell, the only change in the solution is that one mole of HCl (or strictly one gramme-ion each of hydrogen and chloride ions) is lost, or gained, according to the direction of the current. Suppose now that we have two such cells, A and B, connected 'back to back':

$$(Pt)H_2, \text{ HCl}(m_A), \text{ AgCl; Ag–Ag; AgCl, HCl}(m_B), H_2(Pt).$$

The composite cell is called a 'concentration cell without liquid junction', or 'without transference'. When current passes, HCl disappears from cell A and appears in cell B, and the net reaction is the *transfer* of HCl from A to B (or vice versa), while the changes in the amounts of Ag, AgCl, and H_2 balance exactly. One mole of HCl is transferred per faraday of electricity. The spontaneous direction of transfer must be that which tends to bring about equilibrium by equalizing the concentrations; this tendency is the source of the e.m.f. Consequently HCl will disappear from the stronger solution, which we may suppose to be A, and appear in the weaker; then referring to equation 18 we see that in the half-cell A the silver will act as anode and the hydrogen electrode in this half-cell will therefore be the negative pole of the complete cell.

Suppose that dn faradays pass in this direction, and that all the changes are effectively reversible, i.e. that the e.m.f. is very nearly balanced. The amount of HCl transferred will be dn moles; the other changes in the solution will be negligible. The change in free energy, which is equal to the negative of the electrical work done (section 6.22), can therefore be identified with the change in the free energy of H^+ and Cl^- ions on passing from solution A to solution B. If the e.m.f. is $\mathbf{E}'$, the electrical work per faraday is $\mathbf{E}'F$. Hence

$$dn[\mathbf{E}'F] = dn[(\mu_+)_B-(\mu_+)_A+(\mu_-)_B-(\mu_-)_A], \qquad (19)$$

whence, by equation 4 (p. 389),

$$\mathbf{E}'F = (\mu_\pm)_B-(\mu_\pm)_A.$$

Expressing the chemical potentials in terms of mean activities by equation 3,

$$\mathbf{E}'F = 2RT\ln(a_\pm)_B/(a_\pm)_A. \qquad (20)$$

The reason why the factor 2 enters here may be traced to the fact that passage of one faraday of electricity leads to the transfer of two gramme-ions of solute, one of H^+ and one of Cl^-. For salts containing multivalent ions, the appropriate factor must be used instead of 2.

Measurements of the e.m.f. thus allow us to determine the ratio of the mean activities in the two halves of the concentration cell. If it were possible to use in one half, say B, a solution so dilute that $(\gamma_\pm)_B = 1$ and $(a_\pm)_B = (m_\pm)_B$, we could at once find the activity in A, from the measured values of $\mathbf{E}'$ and $(m_\pm)_B$, using equation 20. In practice it is impossible to use solutions dilute enough for this, and an extrapolation to zero concentration is necessary. This can be done as follows.

Let the e.m.f. of the half-cell A be $\mathbf{E}_A$, and that of B be $\mathbf{E}_B$. Then

$$\mathbf{E}' = \mathbf{E}_A-\mathbf{E}_B = (2RT/F)\ln(a_\pm)_B/(a_\pm)_A. \qquad (21)$$

Rearranging,

$$\mathbf{E}_A+(2RT/F)\ln(a_\pm)_A = \mathbf{E}_B+(2RT/F)\ln(a_\pm)_B. \qquad (22)$$

The left-hand side is entirely determined by the conditions in cell A, and the right-hand side by conditions in cell B; and the conditions in the two cells can be varied independently. Suppose that when the solution in cell B is of such a concentration that $(a_\pm)_B = 1$, so that the last term in equation 22 becomes zero, the e.m.f. $\mathbf{E}_B$ takes up a certain value $\mathbf{E}^0$. Then equation 22 gives for the e.m.f. of the cell A:

$$\mathbf{E}_A = \mathbf{E}^0-(2RT/F)\ln(a_\pm)_A. \qquad (23)$$

Omitting the subscript A, and rearranging after putting $a_{\pm} = m_{\pm}\gamma_{\pm}$, we obtain for any cell such as A the following relation:

$$\mathbf{E}+(2RT/F)\ln m_{\pm} = \mathbf{E}^0-(2RT/F)\ln\gamma_{\pm}. \qquad (24)$$

The quantities on the left of this equation can all be measured. In a solution dilute enough to be ideal $\gamma_{\pm} = 1$ and the last term on the right vanishes, so that the left-hand side then becomes equal to $\mathbf{E}^0$. Thus $\mathbf{E}^0$ may be determined by measuring $\mathbf{E}$ at various values of $m_{\pm}$ and extrapolating the values of

$$[\mathbf{E}+(2RT/F)\ln m_{\pm}]$$

to zero concentration; this is conveniently done by plotting against $m_{\pm}^{\frac{1}{2}}$. Measurements at low concentrations are desirable, if the behaviour of the electrodes allows them. Once $\mathbf{E}^0$ has been determined, the activity coefficient $\gamma_{\pm}$ can be found at any concentration by measuring the e.m.f. $\mathbf{E}$ and using equation 24.

In practice the number of solutes to which this method can be applied is severely limited by the necessity for two electrodes, one reversible to the anion and one to the cation. Much work has been done on the cell that we have been discussing,[†] since very accurate measurements can be made on it, and the cell can also be applied to measure the dissociation constants of acids (see below). Amalgam electrodes, reversible to alkali metals, have been used to measure the activities of alkali-metal halides (MCl) using the cell[‡]

Ag; AgCl, MCl aq.; M(Hg),

and of sodium hydroxide solutions using the cell[§]

(Hg)Na; NaOH aq.; H_2(Pt).

Dissociation constants of acids. An important application of measurements of the e.m.f. of the cell combining the hydrogen

---

[†] e.g. Harned and Ehlers, *J. Amer. Chem. Soc.*, 1932, **54**, 1350.

[‡] Harned, ibid., 1929, **51**, 416.

[§] Idem, ibid., 1925, **47**, 676.

and silver–silver chloride electrodes is to determine the dissociation constants of weak acids.† For the e.m.f. of the cell

$$(Pt)H_2; \text{ HCl aq.}; \text{ AgCl}; \text{ Ag}$$

we have, using equation 23 or 24,

$$E = E^0 - (2RT/F)\ln a_{\pm}$$

$$= E^0 - (RT/F)\ln a_{H^+} a_{Cl^-} \tag{25}$$

$$= E^0 - (RT/F)\ln(m_{H^+} \gamma_{H^+} m_{Cl^-} \gamma_{Cl^-}). \tag{26}$$

This shows that the e.m.f. depends on a_{H^+} (equation 25). If instead of HCl aq. we use a buffer solution containing a weak acid, the e.m.f. will still depend on a_{H^+}, which now depends on the strength of the acid. The solution must of course contain chloride, since this is the ion to which the silver–silver chloride electrode is reversible. Suppose then that in place of HCl aq. we have a solution made up from NaCl, the weak acid HA, and its sodium salt NaA. Let the amounts taken in moles per 1,000 g of solvent be M_{NaCl}, M_{HA}, and M_{NaA}. The electrode reactions and hence the cell reaction remain unchanged, and equation 25 still holds good for the e.m.f. The dissociation constant K of the acid is given by (section 6.1, p. 254)

$$K = a_{H^+} a_{A^-}/a_{HA}$$

$$= m_{H^+} m_{A^-} \gamma_{H^+} \gamma_{A^-}/m_{HA} \gamma_{HA}. \tag{27}$$

Substituting this in equation 26, and collecting all concentration terms on the left with the e.m.f.s, we obtain

$$E - E^0 + (RT/F)\ln(m_{Cl^-} m_{HA}/m_A)$$

$$= -(RT/F)\ln K - (RT/F)\ln(\gamma_{Cl^-} \gamma_{HA}/\gamma_{A^-}). \tag{28}$$

In solutions dilute enough to be ideal, the last term on the right becomes zero, and the left-hand side is then equal to $-(RT/F)\ln K$. If, therefore, we make successive dilutions of the solution and determine E and the concentrations, extra-

† Harned and Ehlers, *J. Amer. Chem. Soc.*, 1932, **54**, 1350; 1933, **55**, 652, 2179.

polation of the left-hand side to zero concentration will give K. The concentrations at equilibrium are given by

$$m_{Cl^-} = M_{NaCl},$$
$$m_{HA} = M_{HA} - m_{H^+},$$
$$m_{A^-} = M_{NaA} + m_{H^+}.$$

Since m_{H^+} appears only as a small correction, it may be calculated from a rough value of K, determined for instance by potentiometric titration or by Ostwald's conductimetric method; successive approximations can be used if necessary. The result for acetic acid is in good agreement with that from an accurate conductimetric method.[†]

12.25. *Activities from e.m.f.s of concentration cells with liquid junction*

A typical concentration cell with liquid junction consists of two hydrogen electrodes, in separate compartments containing hydrochloric acid solution, connected by a bridge tube:

$$(Pt)H_2, \; HCl \; aq.(m_A), \; HCl \; aq.(m_B), \; H_2(Pt).$$

Such cells have the practical advantage that only one type of reversible electrode is required. Here the electrode in each compartment is reversible to the cation, the electrode reaction being $H^+ + e \rightleftharpoons \frac{1}{2}H_2$.

Suppose one faraday of electricity passes through the cell, discharging one gramme-ion of hydrogen ions in compartment A and producing the same amount in B. (We will suppose at first that the amount of solution is so large that the concentrations are not appreciably altered.) Electro-neutrality in A and B is maintained not by discharge of anions at another electrode, as in cells without liquid junction, but by *migration* of ions between A and B. Hydrogen ions migrate from B into A, and chloride ions from A into B; the algebraic sum of the charge changes in each compartment from migration and electrode reactions must be zero.

---

   † The values from cells and from conductivities, both in concentration units, are $1{\cdot}749 \times 10^{-5}$ and $1{\cdot}753 \times 10^{-5}$ respectively; cf. MacInnes, *Principles of Electrochemistry* (1939), p. 347.

The amounts of hydrogen ion migrating into A, and of chloride ion migrating out of A, will clearly be in the ratio of the velocities of the ions, under the given potential gradient and the conditions of concentration and temperature. Let these velocities be v_+ and v_-, and suppose that kv_+ moles of hydrogen ion and kv_- moles of chloride ion migrate. The condition of neutrality applied to compartment A tells us that the decrease of positive charge due to discharge of hydrogen ions by one faraday of electricity must be equal to the increase of positive charge due to hydrogen ions migrating in, less the decrease of negative charge due to chloride ions migrating out. Thus

$$1 = kv_+ + kv_-.$$

Hence $k = 1/(v_+ + v_-)$. Substituting this value of k, the amounts of the cation and anion which migrate per faraday are respectively

$$kv_+ = v_+/(v_+ + v_-) = t_+ \quad \text{and} \quad kv_- = v_-/(v_+ + v_-) = t_-.$$
$$(29)$$

These quantities t_+ and t_- are the *transport numbers* or *transference numbers* of the cation and anion; they depend on the temperature and concentration as well as on the ions. It is evident that $t_+ + t_- = 1$. The changes in the contents of A may now be expressed in gramme-ions as

	Loss by discharge	Loss by migration	Net loss
Hydrogen ion	1	$-t_+$	$1 - t_+ = t_-$
Chloride ion	0	t_-	t_-

The change in the solution in A is thus the loss of t_- gramme-ions each of H^+ and Cl^-, or t_- moles of hydrochloric acid. Similar treatment shows that this amount is gained by the solution in B. Thus the passage of one faraday of electricity leads to the transfer of t_- moles of HCl from one solution to the other. This is to be compared with 1 mole for the cell without liquid junction (p. 392). Equating the electrical work to the negative of the free energy of transfer, as before, we obtain the following expression, which may be compared with equation 21 (p. 393):

$$\mathbf{E} = (2t_- RT/F)\ln(a_{\pm})_\mathrm{B}/(a_{\pm})_\mathrm{A} \tag{30}$$

$$= (2t_- RT/F)[\ln(\gamma_{\pm})_\mathrm{B}/(\gamma_{\pm})_\mathrm{A} + \ln(m_{\pm})_\mathrm{B}/(m_{\pm})_\mathrm{A}]. \tag{31}$$

To find $\gamma_{\pm}$, we can now apply an extrapolation procedure similar to that of section 12.24 if we assume as a first approximation that t_- is independent of concentration. We need to know the value of t_-. This has been determined for many ions, either by the Hittorf method[†] or the moving-boundary method.[‡] The need for independent determination of transport numbers somewhat counterbalances the advantage that only one type of electrode is required in a concentration cell of this type.

In accurate work we must take into account the variation of the transport number with concentration. Suppose the liquid–liquid junction to be relatively long, and the molality of HCl, which is m_A and m_B at the ends of the junction, to be m at some intermediate point. If we consider the transport of electrolyte across a distance corresponding to an infinitesimal concentration change, we obtain the differential of equation 30,

$$d\mathbf{E} = (2t_- RT/F)d\ln a_{\pm}. \tag{32}$$

On integration, we obtain

$$\mathbf{E} = (2RT/F) \int_\mathrm{A}^\mathrm{B} t_- d\ln a_{\pm}. \tag{33}$$

Thus $a_{\pm}$ is related to $\mathbf{E}$ and t_-. The computations needed to determine $a_{\pm}$ and $\gamma_{\pm}$ may be done by graphical integration.

The activity coefficient of silver nitrate in aqueous solution has been determined in this way,[§] using values of t_- from moving-boundary experiments, and e.m.f. measurements on the cell:

$$\text{Ag; AgNO}_3(m_\mathrm{A}), \text{ AgNO}_3(m_\mathrm{B}), \text{ Ag.}$$

† MacInnes and Dole, *J. Amer. Chem. Soc.*, 1931, **53**, 1357.
‡ MacInnes and Longsworth, *Chem. Rev.*, 1932, **11**, 172.
§ MacInnes and Brown, ibid., 1936, **18**, 335 (results); *J. Amer. Chem. Soc.* 1935, **57**, 1356 (computation); MacInnes, *Principles of Electrochemistry* (1939), chap. 8.

For a cell with electrodes reversible to the *anion*, we obtain an equation similar to 33 or 31 but containing t_+, the transport number of the cation. Such a cell is

$$\text{Ag; AgCl, HCl}(m_A), \text{ HCl}(m_B), \text{ AgCl; Ag}$$

from which activity coefficients of hydrochloric acid can be obtained.† Good agreement with the results from cells without liquid junction is found.‡ §

12.26. *The relations between activity and concentration for strong electrolytes in water*

(i) *Very dilute solutions.* Solutions containing a single electrolyte give, when dilute enough, nearly linear plots of $\log \gamma_\pm$ against $m^{\frac{1}{2}}$. This behaviour is shown at concentrations below about 0·01 molar for uni-univalent (1–1) electrolytes, and at lower concentrations for higher charge-types. The slope of the plot depends primarily on the charge-type. Fig. 76 shows some results derived from e.m.f.s of cells with liquid junction; ‖ † similar results have been obtained from freezing-point measurements.†† Some values of the activity coefficient are given in Table 48.‡‡

If the activity coefficient of an electrolyte is measured in the presence of other electrolytes, in sufficiently dilute solutions we obtain nearly linear plots of $\log \gamma_\pm$ against $I^{\frac{1}{2}}$, where I is the 'ionic strength' of the solution. This may be defined as $I = \frac{1}{2} \sum c_i z_i^2$, where z_i is the charge on an ion and c_i its molarity, and the summation extends over all the ions. (Some authors use molal concentrations instead of molarities, and define the ionic strength as $\frac{1}{2} \sum m_i z_i^2$; in dilute solution the difference is small.) Some results from solubility measure-

---

† Shedlovsky and MacInnes, *J. Amer. Chem. Soc.*, 1936, **58**, 1970.

‡ MacInnes, *Principles of Electrochemistry* (1939), pp. 162–3.

§ For application of concentration cells to general chemical problems, such as the investigation of solubilities and of complex ions, the reader is referred to textbooks of general inorganic and physical chemistry.

‖ See note § on p. 398.

†† Hovorka and Rodebush, *J. Amer. Chem. Soc.*, 1925, **47**, 1614; Prentiss and Scatchard, *Chem. Rev.*, 1933, **13**, 139.

‡‡ From MacInnes, *Principles of Electrochemistry* (1939), p. 167.

TABLE 48

Activity coefficients $\gamma_{\pm}$ at 25° C in water

Concentrations (m) in moles per 1,000 grammes of water.

	Electrolyte								
m	NaCl	KCl	HCl	NaOH	CaCl$_2$	ZnCl$_2$	H$_2$SO$_4$	ZnSO$_4$	CdSO$_4$
0·005	0·928	0·927	0·930	..	0·789	0·767	0·643	0·477	0·476
0·01	0·903	0·902	0·906	0·89$_9$	0·732	0·708	0·545	0·387	0·383
0·02	0·872	0·869	0·878	0·86$_0$	0·669	0·642	0·455	0·298	..
0·05	0·821	0·817	0·833	0·80$_5$	0·584	0·556	0·341	0·202	0·199
0·10	0·778	0·770	0·798	0·75$_9$	0·524	0·502	0·266	0·148	0·137
0·20	0·732	0·719	0·768	0·71$_9$	0·491	0·448	0·210	0·104	..
0·50	0·680	0·652	0·769	0·68$_1$	0·510	0·376	0·155	0·063	0·061
1·00	0·656	0·607	0·811	0·66$_7$	0·725	0·325	0·131	0·044	0·042
1·50	0·655	0·587	0·898	0·67$_1$	..	0·290	..	0·037	0·039
2·00	0·670	0·578	1·011	0·68$_5$	1·554	..	0·125	0·035	0·030
3·00	0·719	0·574	1·31	..	3·384	..	0·142	0·041	0·026

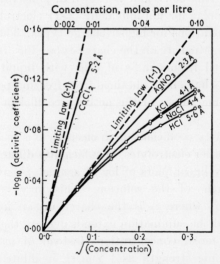

FIG. 76. Activity coefficients of salts in dilute solution.

ments (section 9.35) on various cobaltammines are shown in fig. 77.† Good linear plots are also obtained for silver chloride;‡ and for barium iodate the plots approach the same limiting law (fig. 62, p. 342).

These results are in good agreement with the equation first

† See note ‖‖ on p. 391.   ‡ See note §§ on p. 391.

proposed by Debye and Hückel as the theoretical law to be expected in the limit at low concentrations:

$$\log_{10}\gamma_{\pm} = -\alpha I^{\frac{1}{2}}, \tag{34}$$

where α is a constant. For single 1–1 electrolytes this becomes

$$\log_{10}\gamma_{\pm} = -\alpha c^{\frac{1}{2}}. \tag{35}$$

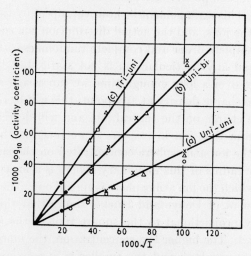

Fig. 77. Activity coefficients of complex salts in dilute solution in presence of added salts.

(a) $[Co(NH_3)_4NO_2CNS]^+[Co(NH_3)_2(NO_2)_2C_2O_4]^-$.
(b) $[Co(NH_3)_4C_2O_4]_2^+[S_2O_6]^{--}$.
(c) $[Co(NH_3)_6]^{+++}[Co(NH_3)_2(NO_2)_2C_2O_4]_3^-$.

Added salts:

○ NaCl,   △ KNO₃,   × K₃Co(CN)₆,   □ BaCl₂,   ● None.

(Reproduced from Butler, *Chemical Thermodynamics* (Macmillan).
After Brønsted and LaMer.)

The constant α is equal to

$$\alpha = z_+ z_- \left(\frac{e^2}{2DkT}\right)\left(\frac{4\pi e^2}{DkT}\frac{N^0}{1000}\right)^{\frac{1}{2}}, \tag{36}$$

where D is the dielectric constant of the solution and e the electronic charge. For a 1–1 electrolyte in water, α has the value 0·50 at 18° C; it is 1·00 for a 1–2 or 2–1 electrolyte. The same equations will naturally apply to the ions formed by partial dissociation of a weak electrolyte.

The physical picture which leads to this result is that of the *ion atmosphere.*† Because the electrostatic forces between ions are large and long-range, the distribution of ions in solution is not random. If these electrostatic forces were the only determining factor, the ions would arrange themselves in a regular lattice, with each positive ion surrounded by negative ions, and vice versa. This arrangement is, however, upset by the thermal motion of the ions, and the actual distribution is a compromise between complete order and complete randomness. The distribution round any particular ion is not static, but if we take the average over a long enough time we can assign a value to the average charge density at any point; this will be of opposite sign to the charge on the central ion, and will decrease as the distance from that ion increases. If we imagine the average charge of the ion atmosphere concentrated on the surface of a sphere, the radius of this imaginary sphere is a measure of the extent to which the ion atmosphere is spread out. The quantitative treatment of Debye and Hückel shows that this radius r is inversely proportional to the square root of the concentration: $r \propto c^{-\frac{1}{2}}$. The higher the concentration, the more compact is the ion-atmosphere and the smaller is r; conversely, when the concentration becomes very small, r becomes large, since the interionic forces become very small and the ionic atmosphere disperses. When the solution is diluted, therefore, the ionic atmosphere expands, and in consequence work must be done to separate the ions. The work required to transfer one mole of the solute from the solution to an infinitely dilute solution— which is the negative of the free energy of transfer, and is therefore $-RT \ln a_2$ (p. 318)—is therefore more than it would be for an ideal solution, namely $-RT \ln x_2$. This implies (since a_2 and x_2 are both less than unity, and their logarithms are therefore negative quantities), that $a_2 < x_2$. Consequently the activity

† The detailed calculation will not be given here; readers are referred to monographs on electro-chemistry (note †, p. 386), or to Butler, *Chemical Thermodynamics* (1946), pp. 414–19. The assumptions of the calculations are very carefully considered by Fowler and Guggenheim, *Statistical Thermodynamics* (Cambridge, 1939), chap. 9. For an excellent non-mathematical account see R. P. Bell, *The Modern Theory of Electrolytes*, in *Sch. Sci. Rev.*, 1949, no. 113, pp. 22 seq.

coefficient of the solute will be less than unity. Equation 35 expresses this, and also the characteristic dependence on $c^{\frac{1}{2}}$.

(ii) *Solutions of concentrations up to* 0·1 M. The Debye–Hückel limiting law rests on assumptions which are true only in the limit at low concentrations. An extension of the theory, in which the size of the ions was taken into account, led to the 'second-approximation' equation

$$\log_{10}\gamma_{\pm} = \frac{-\alpha I^{\frac{1}{2}}}{1+ab I^{\frac{1}{2}}}. \tag{37}$$

Here b is a constant, while a, which varies from one electrolyte to another, has the dimensions of distance and has been called the 'ionic diameter'. Equation 37 gives agreement with the observed curvature of the plots of $\log_{10}\gamma_{\pm}$ against $I^{\frac{1}{2}}$ (fig. 76) if a is suitably chosen. For some electrolytes the values of a required are reasonable in the light of the known diameters of the ions in crystals; but Brønsted and LaMer's results required $a = 0$ for many large complex ions, and 'it must be reluctantly admitted that the parameter a is not a real mean ionic diameter, but rather a parameter correcting for a whole variety of theoretical imperfections'.[†] Attempts at obtaining a further approximation of the Debye–Hückel treatment have not proved to be self-consistent.[‡]

A complete solution of the problem would be extremely complex, because short-range (dipole and dispersion) forces are involved as well as the inter-ionic forces. Short-range forces will be especially important between ions of unlike sign, which will approach more closely than ions of like sign. These *specific* interactions of ions will make each electrolyte a different problem. The effects of the short-range forces can, however, be treated statistically by methods similar to those worked out for imperfect gases (p. 104). The treatment has been carried through by Guggenheim,[§] whose final equation contains a single

† Fowler and Guggenheim, *Statistical Thermodynamics* (1939), p. 403.
‡ Idem, ibid., p. 409.
§ Idem, ibid., pp. 415–20; Guggenheim, *Phil. Mag.*, 1935, **19**, 588; 1936, **22**, 322; Guggenheim and Turgeon, *Trans. Faraday Soc.*, 1955, **51**, 747.

additional constant β', which is characteristic of the electrolyte and must be chosen so as to fit the experimental data:

$$\log_{10}\gamma_\pm = -\frac{\alpha I^{\frac{1}{2}}}{1+I^{\frac{1}{2}}}+\beta'm. \tag{38}$$

Comparison with experiment shows that the constant β' can be so chosen as to give excellent agreement with the observations up to 0·1 molar.

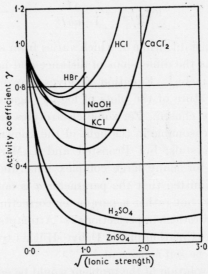

FIG. 78. Activity coefficients of salts at higher concentrations.

(iii) *Concentrated solutions*. At higher concentrations the activity coefficient may pass through a minimum, each electrolyte showing different behaviour (fig. 78). An equation with a linear concentration term, similar in form to 38, will reproduce such behaviour, but its interpretation must be regarded as speculative.

12.27. *Heats of dilution of strong electrolyte solutions*†

Dilution of an ideal solution produces no heat change (p. 368), and the heats of dilution of electrolyte solutions are due to ionic

† For reviews see Lange and Robinson, *Chem. Rev.*, 1931, **9**, 89; Harned and Owen, *Physical Chemistry of Electrolytic Solutions* (1950), chap. 8; McKenna, *Theoretical Electrochemistry* (Macmillan, 1939), pp. 211–20.

interaction. At concentrations in the range above 0·1 molar, the heats of dilution are highly specific and may be positive or negative, depending on the electrolyte.† Differentiation of the Debye–Hückel limiting law indicates, however, that at low concentrations the heats of dilution should be positive and should vary with the square root of the concentration, the limiting slope of the plots against $c^{\frac{1}{2}}$ depending on the charge-

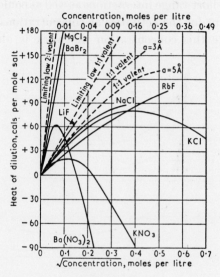

FIG. 79. Integral heats of dilution of strong electrolytes at low concentrations.

type. Experiments using very sensitive differential calorimeters have confirmed most of the predictions (fig. 79).‡ The only point which has not been covered is the limiting slope of the plots; this is experimentally very difficult to determine because of the low concentrations, and cannot theoretically be predicted with high accuracy, since it involves the temperature-coefficient of the dielectric constant.

Concluding remarks on strong electrolyte solutions in water. We may conclude this brief treatment of the immense bulk of

† Richards and Rowe, *J. Amer. Chem. Soc.*, 1921, **43**, 770.
‡ From Lange and Robinson, *Chem. Rev.*, 1931, **9**, 80.

work on strong electrolyte solutions in water with the following summary. There are powerful experimental methods for determining the thermodynamic properties of these solutions, which have been measured systematically over a wide range of concentration. The Debye–Hückel limiting law provides an understanding of the results at the lowest concentrations, in terms of coulombic interaction. By taking into account, in a general way, specific short-range interactions as well as coulombic forces, we can account for the activities at concentrations up to about 0·1 M. Above this concentration the work is almost purely empirical.

APPENDIX

(a) Variation of a quantity related to two independent variables

SUPPOSE a quantity X depends on two variables only, x and y, which can be independently varied. The dependence of X on x and y can be generally expressed as $X = f(x, y)$.

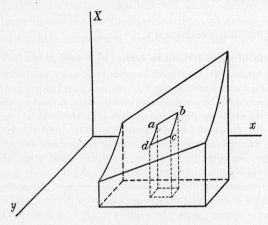

FIG. 80.

If only one of the variables (x) changes, the other (y) being held constant, the rate of change of X with x is equal to the partial differential coefficient $(\partial X/\partial x)_y$, and for an infinitesimal change dx in x the corresponding change in X is evidently

$$dX = (\partial X/\partial x)_y \, dx. \tag{1}$$

If both the variables x and y change simultaneously, the corresponding change in X turns out to be the sum of two terms such as that on the right-hand side of equation 1:

$$dX = (\partial X/\partial x)_y \, dx + (\partial X/\partial y)_x \, dy. \tag{2}$$

To prove equation 2, which is quoted on p. 33 and used throughout the book, consider fig. 80, in which the variation of some function X with x and y is represented in a three-dimensional diagram.† The value of X for a given pair of values of x and y is given by the corresponding point on the curved surface of which a part is shown. Suppose a and c

---

† The figure is taken by permission from *Thermodynamics* by Lewis and Randall. Copyright, 1923, McGraw-Hill Book Company, Inc. The treatment also is that of Lewis and Randall.

are two points on this X–x–y surface, at an infinitesimal distance apart, and that *abcd* is an infinitesimal element of the X–x–y surface, cut off by planes parallel to the X–x and X–y planes. Then

$$dX = X_c - X_a = (X_b - X_a) + (X_c - X_b). \qquad (3)$$

Now $\qquad (X_b - X_a) = dx \times (\text{slope of line } ab) = (\partial X / \partial x)_y \, dx$

and $\qquad (X_c - X_b) = dy \times (\text{slope of line } bc) = (\partial X / \partial y)_x \, dy.$

Inserting in equation 3, we obtain

$$dX = (\partial X / \partial x)_y \, dx + (\partial X / \partial y)_x \, dy,$$

which is identical with equation 2.

(b) Criteria of equilibrium in terms of E and H (p. 148)

Suppose that a given closed system in some equilibrium state is characterized by internal energy E_1, volume V_1, and entropy S_1. Then in any non-equilibrium state with the same values E_1 and V_1, the entropy S_2 will be less than S_1; for if the system is in this state, it will tend to change in the direction of the equilibrium state, and the condition of observable change at constant E and V (equation 18, p. 147) will require the entropy to increase. Suppose now that there is a second equilibrium state characterized by E_2, V_1, and S_2; compared with the original equilibrium state, the volume is unaltered, but $S_2 < S_1$. Now S and E always change in the same direction in a change at constant volume, since the equation $dE = T \, dS - P \, dV$ (p. 149) gives $(\partial E / \partial S)_V = T$, which is always positive. Hence in the second equilibrium state, the internal energy $E_2 < E_1$. Comparing this second equilibrium state with the non-equilibrium state mentioned above, we see that each is characterized by the same entropy S_2 and volume V_1, but $E_2 < E_1$. Thus, when S and V are constant, the internal energy is a *minimum* for the equilibrium state. The direction of observable change will be towards this equilibrium state and so will require decrease of E. Thus we obtain the criteria in terms of E given in equations 21 and 21 a (p. 148). Similar arguments applied to the criterion at constant heat content and pressure (equation 20) lead to the criteria in terms of H given in equations 22 and 22 a.

SUBJECT INDEX

PRINTED IN GREAT BRITAIN
AT THE UNIVERSITY PRESS, OXFORD
BY CHARLES BATEY, PRINTER TO THE UNIVERSITY